P9-DTM-465

GENESIS ON PLANET EARTH

GENESIS ON PLANET EARTH

Published by
The House of Talos Publishers
125 Loree Drive
East Lansing, Michigan 48823

Library of Congress Catalog Number: 79-84191

ISBN 0-935970-00-2

Current Printing (last digit):
10 9 8 7 6 5 4 3 2

PRINTED IN THE UNITED STATES OF AMERICA

Genesis on Planet Earth

The Search for Life's Beginning

William Day

1979

The House of Talos Publishers
125 Loree Drive
East Lansing, Michigan

"Nature set herself the task to catch in flight the light streaming towards the earth, and to store this, the most evasive of all forces, by concerting it into an immobile form. To achieve this, she has covered the earth's crust with organisms which while living take up the sunlight and use its force to add continuously to a sum of chemical difference."

Julius Robert von Mayer
Die Organisch Bewegung In Ihren Zusammenhange Mit Den Stoffwechsel, 1845

Preface

Until twenty-five years ago any meaningful study of how life could have begun on primordial earth seemed beyond the pale of scientific inquiry. Even the simplest microorganism consisted of extremely large and complex molecules called proteins, much too intricate for precise analysis. The key to life's reproduction were the genes, and production of proteins was hypothesized to take place on some type of template. Since the constituents of proteins — amino acids — occur only as products of biological systems, how then could the first cell have ever formed?

Then in 1953, all within the same year, Frederick Sanger announced that he and his coworkers had determined the primary structure of a protein molecule, James Watson and Francis Crick unraveled the chemical basis of life and found it to be a double-helical nucleic acid, and Stanley Miller discovered how matter and energy could create the building blocks of life without a pre-existing living cell.

Unleashed from the paralysis and spurred by the Space Age, research on the origin of life was launched by these three momentous scientific achievements into an era of discovery and revelation. Old impressions were rapidly supplanted by new concepts as experiments changed the image of primordial earth — and the new scenario gave clues to life's beginning.

Today a reconstruction of the manner in which life first appeared on earth is within scientific definition. It is a fascinating story, both in the search and conclusion. Although the origin of life is a chemistry problem, one need not be a chemist to appreciate and enjoy the findings that have led to its solution. It does, however, require an understanding of the prevailing circumstances that led to its formation and some knowledge of the basic chemistry of biological systems. For this reason, parts of this book may appear too technical for readers without a familiarity with chemical symbolism, but these were included for completeness. All readers, however, who have an interest in the scientific explanation of how life began, should find this volume comprehensive and written in a manner easy to read.

A Note of Thanks

Ideas may emerge from experience and imagination, but it is the churning of discussion that gives them polish. I owe a debt of gratitude to William Stillwell, Frank Dénes and others for their stimulating conversations while we were at the Institute for Molecular and Cellular Evolution in Miami. When this book was being written, it was the invaluable critiques and proofreading by William Stillwell that made it all possible.

The text was read and improved upon by George Hildenbrandt, Dennis O'Callaghan, James Corbin, and Ben and Sandy Van Osdol. John Basford gathered some material in Great Britain, and Terry Stemle found the cartoon strip and gave ideas for the cover and compostition. Kevin O'Boyle offered valuable suggestions in editing the organization of the final form.

A note of appreciation also goes to Stanley Miller, J. William Schopf, Preston Cloud, David Deamer and Will Hargreaves for correcting particular chapters and for their assistance. These and others who contributed material for the book are credited in this volume.

The acknowledgement, finally, is not complete until I express my gratitude to the ladies of the East Lansing Public Library for their assistance, their patience, their interest and their encouragement while this book was becoming a reality.

East Lansing, Michigan
February, 1979

W. D.

Contents

EEK & MEEK
by Howie Schneider
DID YOU EVER STOP TO WONDER...
ABOUT WHERE IT ALL BEGAN?
ST. LOUIS
© 1978 by NEA, Inc., T.M. Reg. U.S. Pat. Off.
6-26

1
Building Blocks

An autumn afternoon in 1951, Harold Urey, physical chemist and discoverer of deuterium, a heavy form of hydrogen, began his lecture at the University of Chicago on a subject that was one of his life's studies, the origin of the solar system. In his latest book,[1] just recently completed, he postulated that because of the reduced conditions of the solar nebula that gave rise to the planets, the primordial atmosphere of the earth had not contained oxygen like today, but had actually consisted of methane, ammonia and hydrogen.

The gathering of students and faculty sat listening with interest. Theories regarding the origin of the sun, earth and planets have changed throughout the centuries. No longer is it believed that the planets were formed from molten globs of matter ejected from the sun during a close encounter with another star. In 1943, only eight years earlier, a German scientist had postulated that the planets were formed by the accretion of solid material in swirling eddies of an immense cloud of dust and gases.

And only since 1929 has it been realized that the universe is mostly hydrogen and that the free oxygen in the earth's atmosphere is a strange cosmic occurrence.

The professor continued on into another favorite subject of his: the origin of life. Scientists generally believe life must have begun on early earth billions of years ago in a manner that can be explained scientifically. But to demonstrate how it cound have happened has been extremely difficult. As a result, studies on the origin of life were in a state of paralysis. The life sciences have shown that all forms of life consist of certain chemical substances that are the building blocks: amino acids, sugars, lipids and two kinds of heterocyclic bases called purines and pyrimidines. The building blocks are linked together into large polymeric molecules; the amino acids forming proteins; the sugars, polysaccharides; and the bases, nucleic acids. It is then the assembly of these complex polymers into units bound by a lipid membrane that creates living cells. The difficulty that has stymied scientists for over one hundred and fifty years, however, is that the building blocks of life appear to be produced in nature only by living organisms. There, then, lies the paradox. If only living plants and animals can synthesize the amino acids and other building blocks necessary for their own creation, how then could life have ever begun on earth?

Some students jotted down notes; most allowed their thoughts to sweep over the problem, searching for ready answers to the question. The seminar was becoming more engrossing. Theories on matter, energy and the universe were fascinating and stimulating, but to speculate on the formation of life from lifeless, inanimate substances excited the imagination and sensed of the momentous.

Urey went on. There must have existed circumstances on primordial earth that no longer exist that permitted life to begin. The absense of free oxygen and the reduced atmosphere would have given a different chemical environment. In order for a living cell to develop, some organic compounds must have preceded the origin of life. But it was only a hypothesis. There was no experimental proof that organic substances necessary for the assembly of life could ever have formed on prebiological earth. Nevertheless, logic dictates that organic compounds must have been created on earth in some way before life could form.

As Urey continued to lecture on the paradox of life's beginning, one of the first year graduate students, a young Californian by the name of Stanley Miller, listened intently. Miller, twenty-one at the time, had come to Chicago in September from Berkeley and was still probing around for a suitable research problem to work on for his dissertation. The point Professor Urey made seemed valid, but to prove how organic matter formed under primordial conditions probably would take a considerable amount of experimenting and a long time. He brushed the thought aside and resigned to his original intention of finding a more theoretical problem.

The seminar ended with the customary questioning period. Did not the Russian biochemist, Alexander Oparin, also discuss the possibility of organic compounds being produced in a reduced atmosphere before there was free oxygen? Urey answered in the affirmative, pointing out that no one had yet put the hypothesis to the test of experimental verification.

That winter the young graduate student from California consulted with the various chemistry professors, discussing with them their particular research interests and searching for an interesting project to work on for his thesis. Eventually, he made a choice and decided to study the manner in which elements are synthesized in extemely hot stars under Professor Teller, the discoverer of carbon 14 and an authority on atomic physics.

Six months later Teller announced he was leaving the University of Chicago to set up a laboratory in Livermore, California. Faced with the problem of finding a new mentor and topic for his dissertation, Miller's thoughts returned to Urey's seminar and the questions it had posed. Perhaps the experimental work would not be as messy as originally thought. The more he thought about it, the more the problem appealed to him and his enthusiasm mounted.

When he approached Urey with the proposition that he study how organic compounds could have formed on prebiotic earth, his enthusiasm was met with caution. The professor explained that the research could become a long and fruitless task. Perhaps he should consider studying the occurrence of thallium in meteorites. Only after realizing the student's determination did Urey consent that he could try the organic compound synthesis problem. If, however, nothing came of the study within six months, he should then switch to a more conventional research problem to assure success for his thesis.

The following weeks Miller studied Urey's paper on the subject[2] and read the book by Oparin.[3] The two then attempted to design a laboratory apparatus that would simulate the postulated atmospheric conditions of primordial earth. Something resembling a natural source of energy was needed to act on a mixture of gases to generate a chemical reaction. Since the atmosphere receives evaporation from the oceans which condenses again to return to the surface as rain, a supply of water would have to be included. A design was sketched and taken to the glassblower for construction.

A week later the drawing had been converted into a full scale model of connecting glass tubes and flasks. The completed apparatus consisted of a 5-liter glass chamber atop a glass tube with two tungsten electrodes protruding into it with their tips close enough to permit a spark gap. Joined below this a condenser connected to a U-tube that ran over to a reflux flask for water; a return tube extended from the flask back to the large chamber. It was a closed system in which water boiled in the flask would be carried as vapor past the electric spark, condensed, and returned to the flask. The apparatus was to be a model of the atmospheric conditions of primitive earth simulating the occurrence of thunderstorms in the primordial atmosphere.

Miller set up the apparatus and pondered its construction. He read the instructions for the Tesla coil that was to generate the electric spark and was astounded that it produced 60,000 volts. He hesitated and doubts began to cloud his thoughts on the feasibility of the experiment. Hydrogen and methane both form explosive mixtures with air; any leak could be disasterous. Even the thought of sparking 60,000 volts in water vapor seemed hazardous. And since it was an air tight system, heating the water to a reflux temperature would expand the gases and could create dangerous pressures. He took the apparatus back to the glassblower and had him interchange the positions of the condenser and the tube containing the spark gap.

With the construction now changed so that the spark came after the water vapor condensed, it seemed safer and he decided to put the experiment to the test. He added water to the flask, then pumped out the air from the system and replaced it with a mixture of ammonia, methane and hydrogen, being certain it was cleared completely of any traces of oxygen. He checked for leaks and found the apparatus to be tight. Cautiously, he plugged in the Tesla coil and slowly ran the discharge up to 60,000 volts. Flashing streaks of blue darted across the gap between the tungsten electrodes with a crackling cadence.

Nothing seemed to happen. He went to his desk and tried to study, walking over to the experiment periodically that afternoon to see if he could detect any change. When it came time to go home, he decided to let it run overnight. The next morning when he entered the lab and looked at the experiment, he saw a faint film of hydrocarbon floating on the surface of the water. There was nothing new there. This was the same result earlier researchers had observed when they exposed methane to an electric discharge. He allowed the experiment to continue for several days. The hydrocarbon film thickened, but an analysis of the water failed to show anything resembling the organic substances of a biological nature.

Perhaps the 60,000 volts was less dangerous than had appeared. Miller returned the apparatus to the glassblower and asked him to restore the condenser and the tube with the electrodes to their original arrangement. After a week he was ready for another attempt. The experiment was repeated. This time the water in the flask was warmed to a low heat with a heating coil. Again the experiment was allowed to run continuously. After two days he saw the hydrocarbon film was no longer present and the solution had become a pale yellow. Something was happening. The water was analyzed and the results were suggestive, but not conclusive.

The experiment was repeated. This time he turned up the heat so the water boiled vigorously. As he saw the drops of water dripping from the condenser, he knew the apparatus had withheld the pressure until a steady state was reached and the water was circulating through its cycle. The discharge sparkled and crackled across the gap as the boiling water drove its vapors with the gases past the electric discharge. He looked on with satisfaction at the experiment performing the way it was designed to in simulating the primordial atmosphere.

Nothing could be done now but wait. Hour after hour the sparking continued as the water vapors and gases circulated around and around, imitating the cycle of water evaporating from the oceans into the atmosphere where it mixes with the atmospheric gases and is exposed to thunderstorms, only to return again to the oceans as rain. For a long while there was no perceptible change. The experiment was left to run overnight. The next morning when Miller entered the lab he immediately noticed the water in the flask had become pink. Excitement seized him and he rushed over to look more closely. Then noticing the heating mantle had an exposed coil that glowed red through the water, his exuberance was quickly dampened with disappointment. Slowly he lowered the mantle and looked at the solution in the flask. It was still pink. A definite chemical reaction had been taking place after all. His thoughts raced. Porphyrins? They give red color to blood. Were porphyrins being produced in this simulation of the conditions of prebiotic earth?

He let the experiment run. Day followed day. The color deepened. After one week the water in the flask had become decidedly red.

The time had finally arrived to test the results. He stopped the experiment and allowed the apparatus to cool. Extracting a sample from the flask, he analyzed it by paper chromatography, a standard procedure for separating and detecting small amounts of material. After running the chromatogram, the strip of paper was sprayed with a mist of ninhydrin solution and warmed in an oven. Within minutes purple spots appeared indicating the components. The compounds were amino acids!

He analyzed his one-gram sample by anion and cation exchange chromatography; he fractionated the components, made chemical derivatives of the ones in greatest yield and compared the melting points to those of known amino acids: he sterilized the entire apparatus and repeated the experiment to be certain the results could not be due to bacterial contamination. There was no question of the results. They were amino acids, the very components that are used by plants and animals to construct their proteins.[4] No longer was there the dilemma of how organisms could have produced organic compounds before they themselves existed - the building blocks had already been there on primordial earth.

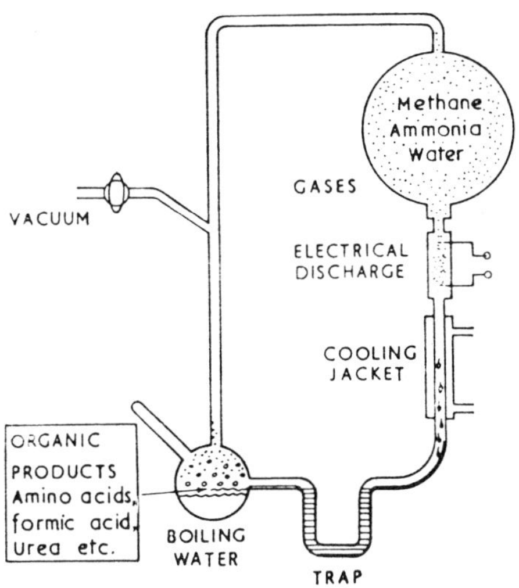

Apparatus used by Miller to simulate the prebiotic synthesis of amino acids and other organic compounds.

It was an experiment that broke the logjam. The simplicity of the experiment, the high yield of the products and the specific biological compounds in limited number produced by the reaction was enough to show that the first step in the origin of life was not a chance event, but one that had been inevitable. In effect, the experiment revealed that the basic components from which biological systems are constructed are energetically favored compounds. With the appropriate mixture of gases, any energy source that can cleave the chemical bonds will initiate a reaction resulting in the formation of life's building blocks.[5]

References

1. H. Urey, **The Planets**, Yale University Press, New Haven, Conn., 1952.
2. H. C. Urey, On the early chemical history of the earth and the origins of life, *Proc. Nat. Acad. Sci.* **38**, 351-363 (1952).
3. A. I. Oparin, **The Origin of Life**, Macmillan Co., New York, 1938.
4. S. L. Miller, A production of amino acids under possible primitive earth conditions, *Science* **117**, 528-529 (1953).
5. S.L. Miller, The first laboratory synthesis of organic compounds under primitive earth conditions,in **The Heritage of Copernicus: Theories Pleasing to the Mind**, J. Neyman, ed., The MIT Press, Cambridge, Mass., 1974, pp. 228-242.

2
Man and His World

One of life's greatest mysteries has always been its beginning. Mankind is like a child; within the deep recesses of the mind there are no remembrances of coming into being. Like the child, man did not question his origins until his mental faculties developed sufficiently for him to ponder his existence.

Our ancestors in prehistory were not substantially less intelligent that ourselves; we differ only by the accumulation of knowledge over the thousands of years. We share with our antecedents the same question: Who are we that we find ourselves with other creatures on the surface of the earth; and what has happened before us that led to our being?

These are natural questions that come from man's evolvement. A necessity of any higher form of life is to orient itself with its environment; and man's greater self-awareness demands his orientation in time and space. Deep in the remote past the sense of self-awareness began to weigh upon man's thoughts and the question cried out for answers.

The answers have been the stories of creation, expressed in symbolic and empirical comprehension of basic reality by culture. These myths of creation and life's beginning are as numerous and varied as human cultures, but they all served to define man's place in the world and give him orientation. In the Navaho creation, order emerged gradually in continuous stages; the Dogon peoples of West Africa believe creation proceeded from a small seed to form all beings in the universe; and in Polynesian myth, Ta-aroa developed the world out of himself and the shell in which he lived.

The time is lost when society formulated the early accounts of creation and the origin of man, for they are probably as ancient as language itself. They, nevertheless, would have evolved or have been altered with disconnecting migrations, intersocial contacts, or other circumstances that greatly affected the culture and its orientation. All myths of a beginning have not alluded to a transcendental creator as in Genesis of Judaism, Christianity and Islam. They do, however, share a common feature: all are based on the formation of order from the chaos of undifferentiated primordial matter.

As our culture has evolved a greater understanding of the world we live in, so too, has our orientation in time and space been greatly altered. The scientific explanation of creation and the emergence of man, like other accounts of creation, delineates order and man's relationship with the material world that is consistent with our comprehension of reality. In this respect, science has become the heir to man's earlier attempts to understand himself and his world.

It is curious that science began with the most distant objects, reaching a high level of achievement by the Chaldean astronomers of Babylonia around 600 B.C., and developed to the most intimate, the molecular biology of life's genetic structure. Science, too, had to evolve before it could realistically explain what life is and how it began.

The oldest systematic classification of living things we have is by Aristotle from the 4th century B.C. Since he considered psychology inseparable from biology, he arranged animals according to their behavior, as well as their manner of reproduction and component parts in which he analyzed the functions of organs, always keeping in mind the purpose of life and its reproductive creativity. Recognizing that life had to be made up of smaller units, he postulated that it must have passed from the inanimate with a development and evolution from lower to higher forms. After Aristotle, over two thousand years passed before taxonomy and the theory of evolution again became a part of biology.

The modern system of classifying plants and animals is based on **Systema Naturae**, a ten-volume compilation published in 1758 by the Swedish naturalist, Carolus Linneaus. In nature the distinguishing characteristics of plants and animals are generally not all inclusive. In the absence of a natural system, classification often had to be arbitrary in grouping them by physical features. Linneaus presented a systematic and comprehensive listing of plants and animals with a convenient binominal nomenclature in a framework into which new plants could be fitted. It was a timely invention. He lived at the height of the age of exploration, and as ships of Europe combed the globe in pursuit of discovery and exploitation, they returned with stories and specimens of strange lands. Nations and wealthy patrons vied with each other to own and stock botanical gardens. It was a craze that led to the voyage of *H.M.S. Beagle* and the publishing of **On the Origin of Species** by Charles Darwin one hundred years later.

Darwin realized that in order to convince anyone of his theory that species were not immutable, but evolved into other species, he had to give the mechanism for the evolution. It was common knowledge that man improved upon species of plants and animals by his careful selection of the parents. Darwin saw this as an explanation of how evolution was brought about in nature. In order for selection to operate in nature he recognized the variation in individuals within a species allowed for the best adapted to occupy an ecological niche to survive. When the environment changed or overpopulation of the niche pressured adaptation to new conditions, those individuals with traits most suitable for the change survived and passed their qualities on to their offspring. This is organic evolution of classical biology in which the function and shapes of organs, tissues and organelles that have changed through natural selection are used to reconstruct an orderly sequence of development of plants and animals.

Evolution is now a proven scientific fact. In the last two and a half decades, molecular biology has revealed the chemical basis of life, and molecular evolution has shown the fundamental chemistry of Darwinian evolution. The parameter that makes evolution the molding force of biological systems is time; and in Darwin's age, one of the principal questions of man evolving from a simple form of life was: Had there been enough time?

We measure the past by the sequence of passing events. The succession of generations clearly defines our relationship to the past, and it was by adding up the generations in the Old Testament that the Rev. James Ussher of Trinity College, Dublin, in 1654 concluded the biblical creation had taken place in 4004 B.C. But as there was an awakening of scientific inquiry in our culture, there arose a feeling that the earth must be considerably older than the account in Genesis, perhaps there had been forms of life even before mankind itself.

The story of the origin of life and its development is inseparably associated with the earth's own evolution, and the search for life's beginning has involved a pursuit of the geological past. Just as the earth's past is written in the arrangement and composition of its rocks, so too is the history of life sealed in rocks, and the only tangible and imperishable evidence of living things more remote than man's artifacts are fossils.

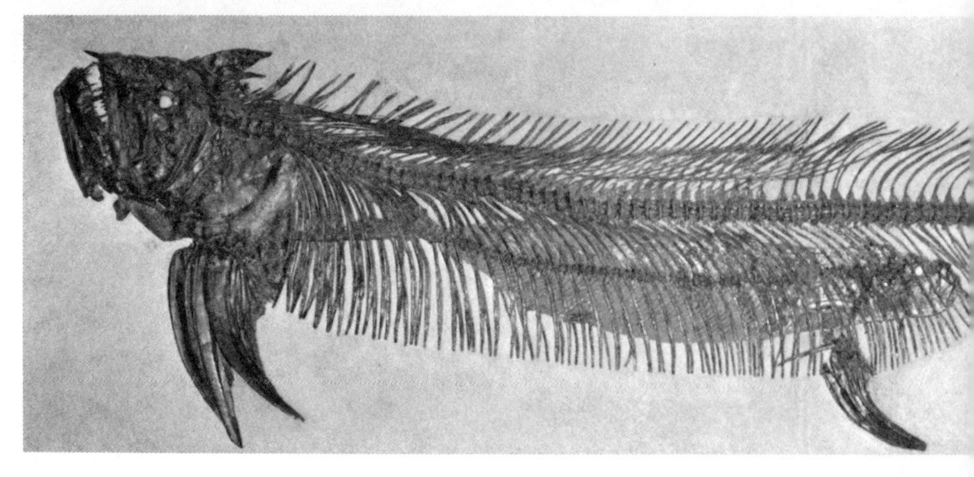

3
Of Fossils and Men

*Fossil of a 14-foot Cretaceous fish, **Xiphactinus molossus,** with a smaller 6-foot fish, **Gillicus arcuatus,** within its abdominal cavity. (Courtesy of the Sternberg Memorial Museum, Fort Hays Kansas State College, Hays)*

Long before fossils were recognized as the key to the history of the evolvement of life, they were looked upon as curious objects of nature. Herodotus of the 5th century B.C. saw the large foraminifers in the limestone of the Egyptian pyramids and thought they were petrified lentils that served as the food supply for the workers who labored in building the pyramids. During the Middle Ages the fossils were seen as those objects left over from the trial and error attempts before creation.

Only a few hundred years ago there was hazard in expressing views on such matters. The world of the 16th and 17th centuries saw geologic features as being caused by the Noachian Deluge, so when Bernard Palissay published a book in Paris in 1580 asserting that fossils were once living animals, he was burned at the stake for his heresy. And Giordano Bruno paid the same penalty in 1600 for denying the flood and stating that the sea and land often interchanged in the past. But remains of marine life entombed in sedimentary rocks and found far from the sea intrigued the curious and intensified the mystery. They were obvious clues to great things that had happened in the remote past.

The early geologists, seeing strata in folded sections of the earth's crust and fossils in compact layers, saw visions of widespread exterminations and looked upon the past as a time when the world was convulsed by enormous catastrophic events. So impressed were they that they divided geologic time into eras, periods and epochs. They realized the vast layers of sediment that gave rise to the sedimentary rocks must have taken an extremely long time to form — much longer than the thousands of years since the earliest civilizations. But how long? They could calculate only from rough estimates of the rates of deposition.

One of the earliest geologic maps was drawn around 1700 by John Strachey who studied and described the succession of strata in the coal district of southwestern England. A century later, William Smith, an ardent fossil collector, was a surveyor and engineer for a company building canals in Great Britain to carry that coal. Over the years Smith noticed that different rock layers he encountered in his work could be characterized by the fossils they contained. This meant the chronological succession of the rocks could be recognized by the fossils and the fossils could be used to measure the geologic age of the rock strata. In 1815, he consolidated his information into a geologic map of the outcroppings of England and Wales and established the scientific principles upon which the dating of rocks was based throughout the 19th century.

The work of constructing a standard stratigraphic and geologic chronology was vigorously pursued by geologists from the early part of the last century. As their science expanded, they learned unique fauna were associated with particular intervals in geologic time. By integrating the sedimentary rock throughout the world into an orderly sequence based on faunal succession, they were able to construct from fossils a geological column for the history of the earth.

Adam Sedgwick, an English geologist, was the first to use the name Paleozoic in a lecture in 1838 to designate the era of geologic history from the earliest fossils to and including the land plants, amphibians and the earliest reptiles. Soon Mesozoic was used for the era of dinosaurs, and marine and flying reptiles, and Cenozoic for the most recent era. The Paleozoic, Mesozoic and Cenozoic Eras were subdivided into periods, and the Cambrian Period, set at the first appearance of fossils 570 million years ago, was followed in succession by geologic periods characterized by their fossils.

The fossil record, though fragmentary in some instances, gives clear testimony to the principle of evolution. In many lines of descent, the sequence can be worked out in considerable detail. The most ancient fossils from the Cambrian include only invertebrates. Then primitive fish-like vertebrates appear and gradually blend in succession to true fishes. Fossils of amphibians and reptiles follow, and finally birds and mammals. The geologic column is clearly correlated with the simplest form of animals appearing in the oldest strata and evolving to greater complexity late in geologic history.

As we study the fossil record, we find the Cambrian fauna contain representatives of every important invertebrate animal phylum, but the only groups that are abundant and widespread are the trilobites and the brachiopods. Almost 75 percent of all fossils found in the Cambrian are trilobites. These arthropods that were distantly related to the modern horseshoe crab ranged in size from one-fourth inch to almost two feet and fed on microscopic organisms in the sea and on the bottom detritus. For the next 70 million years of the Cambrian Period from 570 to 500 million years ago, there is no record of any vertebrate fossils or any plants and animals on land or in fresh water.

The abrupt appearance of the Cambrian fauna constituted a major biological problem. The plants and animals found in the Cambrian are life forms with organs and characteristics as complex and developed as some found today. Furthermore, to compound the mystery, all the phyla (divisions based on a fundamental anatomical feature) known today are present in the Cambrian fossils. All, that is, except one — man's. The Chordata, the phylum of the vertebrates, is not there. The vertebrates were not to appear until about 450 million years ago. The phyla that are present appear quickly with no apparent origin. Moreover, the earliest Cambrian beds with skeletal remains contain several distantly related trilobite, brachiopod, mollusk and echinoderm groups and representatives of the other phyla that totaled about 20 distinct kinds of invertebrates, but there is no indication of convergence back towards a common ancestor. Where the Cambrian plants and animals came from

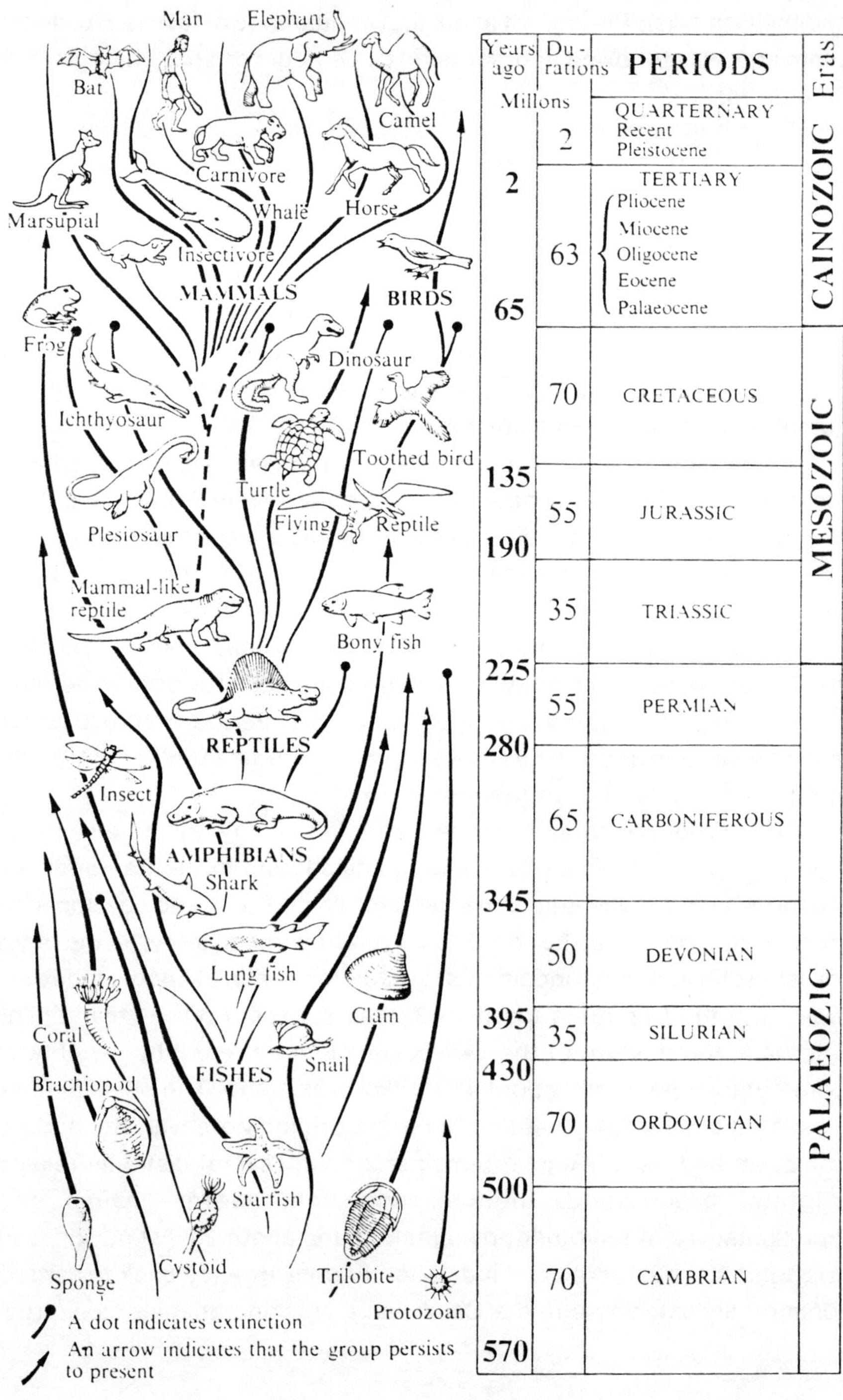
Man
Elephant
Bat
Camel
Carnivore
Marsupial
Whale
Horse
Insectivore
MAMMALS
BIRDS
Frog
Dinosaur
Ichthyosaur
Toothed bird
Turtle
Flying Reptile
Plesiosaur
Mammal-like reptile
Bony fish
REPTILES
Insect
AMPHIBIANS
Shark
Lung fish
Clam
Coral
Snail
Brachiopod
FISHES
Starfish
Sponge
Cystoid
Trilobite
Protozoan
A dot indicates extinction
An arrow indicates that the group persists to present
Years ago Millons
Du-rations
PERIODS
Eras
QUARTERNARY
Recent
Pleistocene
TERTIARY
Pliocene
Miocene
Oligocene
Eocene
Palaeocene
CAINOZOIC
CRETACEOUS
JURASSIC
TRIASSIC
MESOZOIC
PERMIAN
CARBONIFEROUS
DEVONIAN
SILURIAN
ORDOVICIAN
CAMBRIAN
PALAEOZOIC
2
2
63
65
70
135
55
190
35
225
55
280
65
345
50
395
35
430
70
500
70
570

remained a mystery.

Then in 1947, Reginald Sprigg, an Australian geologist, was exploring the Ediacara Hills, an abandoned mining area 380 miles north of Adelaide, when he discovered abundant fossil remains of jellyfish in upper strata of quartzites. At first he believed them to be of the Lower Cambrian, but further investigation established the rocks to be Late Precambrian. About 1,500 fossil specimens were collected from the beds. Two-thirds of these were fossils showing outlines of the characteristic swimming bell of a coelenterate medusa, around one-quarter were annelid worms, and the remainder, extinct invertebrate organisms.[1–3]

The composition of the fauna was that of a marine environment, and studies of the encasing sediment indicated their deposition in shallow water. The wormlike creatures probably lived in the shallow water where they tunneled in the mud or fed on the surface, whereas the *Medusa* may have drifted in from the open seas. There were no signs of predation, such as the tearing of large bodies.

Some of the members of the Ediacara fauna have been found elsewhere. *Charnia* were discovered by Trevor Ford in England in Precambrian rocks with an age of 680 million years. And a fossil closely resembling *Charnia* was found in the Olenck Highlands of northern Siberia in rocks dated at 675 million years.

The fossils of many of the animals of the Cambrian Period were invertebrates with mineralized skeletons. These organisms were absent in the Ediacara fossils which yielded impressions of soft-bodied animals or tracks and trails of invertebrates without hard parts. There appears to have been a period of possibly 100 million years when soft-bodied animals flourished in the sea, as many do today, before the evolutionary development of mineralized shells and skeletons.

The significance of the Ediacara fauna is that the animals belong to a

The geologic column based on the fossil record. (From **Chemical Evolution** *by Melvin Calvin, © Oxford University Press 1969. Reprinted by permission of the publishers)*

phylum that is on a simpler level of development than those found in the Cambrian. These animals are coelenterates, represented today by jellyfish, sea anemones and corals. The coelenterates are multicellular animals at the tissue level of construction, which means in general they lack organs.

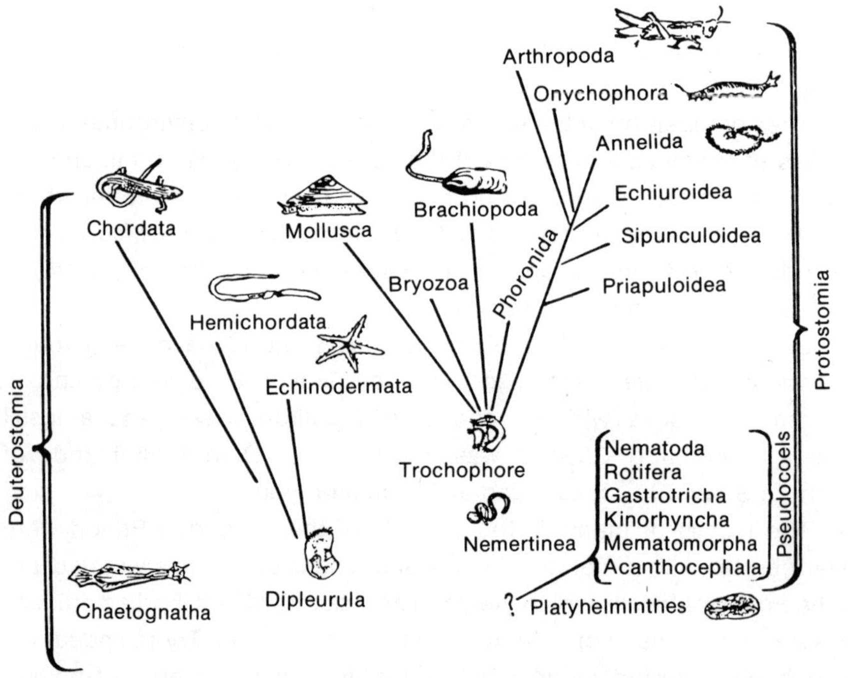

Main lines of invertebrate phylogeny from Cambrian fossils

The only multicellular animals more primitive than the coelenterates are the sponges. These primitive animals lack a well-defined organization of tissue and indicate similar ties with certain types of protozoan colonies, both lacking integrated parts, mouth and digestive systems, both having a type skeletal formation in which single elements are produced by a single cell or by a group of cells. Sponges are not well preserved as fossils, but specimens from the Cambrian have been found.

Measuring fossil-bearing strata carried the age of life back 570 million years to the base of the Cambrian, and the Ediacara fossils extended this to 680 million years. In no place on earth, however, are the strata all laid in one continuous succession. If the maximum strata for all the ages from the time of the earliest fossils were stacked vertically, the column would be nearly 400,000 feet (76 miles) thick.

Yet, it was apparent the fossil record seriously underestimated the age of the earth. Beneath the Cambrian lie the Precambrian formations — strata of volcanic and sedimentary rocks of immense thickness and covering a time span of over 3 billion years — 5 times the length of time since the earliest fossils. What happened in that incredibly long span of time representing nearly 85 percent of the earth's history before the Cambrian trilobites, sponges and jellyfish inhabited the earth?

The outstanding advances of physics, astronomy and geology have given us the means for establishing the time of creation and of reconstructing what took place in that vast interval that led up to the appearance of the Cambrian creatures embedded in rocks. It takes us back to the primordial earth with its environment so different from today which Professor Urey described and that Stanley Miller attempted to simulate in his experiment to show how life could have begun. And it shows not only the conditions of life's origin, but it shows also how and why it evolved in complexity to become the plants and animals that inhabit the earth today.

References

1. M. F. Glaessner, Pre-Cambrian animals, *Sci. Amer.* **204**, 72-76 (1961).
2. R. Goldring and C. N. Curnow, The stratigraphy and facies of the Late Precambrian at Ediacara, South Australia, *J. Geol. Soc. Aust.* **14**, 195-214 (1967).
3. M. Wade, Preservation of soft-bodied animals in Precambrian sandstones at Ediacara, South Australia, *Lethaia* **1**, 238-267 (1968).

4
In the beginning ...

Man stands near the midpoint between two worlds. Below is the Lilliputian realm of organisms in which size is on the molecular level and time is in seconds and minutes; above is the cosmos swirling through distances so immense they are measured in the years it takes light to traverse them, and time is recorded in eons. Finding himself between atoms and the stars, man's space-time concepts have had to be adjusted

The vestige of a cosmic explosion. In the year A.D. 1054 a star 3,600 light years away became a supernova with the explosive force of approximately 10^{24} hydrogen bombs, creating the Crab Nebula. The arrow points to a pulsar which is believed to be the remnant of the original star. Photographed in the red light of hydrogen. (Hale Observatories).

to understand either.

Time and space are relative to the size of the observer. When we peer into the microscopic world, we see continual movement and a rapid succession of change. Because of the difference in the time dimension, a microbe looking back would see us as some static feature of the universe on the other side of the glass. It is in this way we look out at the stars and galaxies that form the cosmos. We are seeing objects which change so slowly by our perspective that they appear frozen in time. They are systems that come into being, evolve and die in time periods measured in billions of years. Nonetheless, the variety is great, and by studying stars and other cosmic objects that are at different stages of development, a sequence of events in the birth and death of stellar systems can be pieced together.

As we look out at the universe, we see all the stars, star clusters and galaxies rushing away from us as though everything had been blown outward from a colossal cosmic explosion. It appears that at some time in the distant past all the celestial bodies were compacted into a dense configuration and burst in a primordial "fireball," sending matter out from a central point. The time when all matter was formed has swung as a tantalizing puzzle before the eyes of astronomers for centuries, and they have had a preoccupation for devising methods to learn the time of creation.

One means of calculating the age of the universe is to apply Hubble's constant.[1] Edwin Powell Hubble, an American astronomer during the first half of this century, established the principle that the velocity of recession of a galaxy is directly proportional to the distance from us. Since the velocities are known from the red shift in the spectrum of light from the galaxies, their distances can be used to compute back in time to when all galaxies began their simultaneous flight to the ends of the universe. In the simplest version of relativistic cosmology, the age of the universe is equal to two-thirds of the reciprocal of the Hubble constant. Recent calculations have placed the age of the universe at 16.6 billion years.

But the most common cosmological time-keeper is radioactive decay, a built-in clock whose mechanism was discovered 80 years ago. Most elements occur as mixtures of isotopes --- atoms of the same element but with slightly different masses because of variation in the number of neutrons in the nucleus. When an isotope is unstable, it degenerates to another element with the emission of radioactive radiation. The rate at which this reaction takes place is constant and unaffected by temperatures, pressures or other physical factors. And the rate, measured as the half-life, that is, the time for half of the sample to be converted, is extremely slow for some isotopes. The half-life for the decay of uranium 238 to lead 206 is 4.5 billion years, and for thorium 232 to lead 208, 14 billion years. By measuring the ratio of parent to daughter isotopes in a sample, the date of origin can be calculated.

In order to determine the time of origin for the universe, one calculates when nucleosynthesis of the elements took place. Hydrogen and helium are the primordial elements of creation, and the energy of the stars comes from the fusing of lighter elements to heavier ones, such as the fusion of hydrogen to helium. Because of the lesser electrostatic repulsion, lighter nuclei can react with one another at lower temperatures than heavier nuclei; nevertheless, elements up to the mass of iron are produced in the evolution of stars.

But it is the very heavy elements that are of interest in this method of dating the universe. Elements heavier than bismuth are produced only by the intense neutron flux and the enormous pressures and temperatures of cosmic explosions. By measuring the current abundance of thorium 232 and uranium isotopes, 235 and 238, Fowler and Hoyle[2] arrived at a chronology of supernova events, and hence the age of the universe. With this procedure their computed age of the universe was 14 billion years.

This radiometric method of dating the age of the universe, however, is fraught with uncertainty, some attributable to the half-lives of thorium and uranium being too short for the extreme age of the universe. In 1964, Donald Clayton[3] of Rice University suggested using the decay of rhenium 187 to osmium 187 with a half-life of 44 billion years as a more accurate procedure. Unfortunately, not only was osmium synthesized in the initial nucleosynthesis, but it is generated even today in the fires of stars by slow neutron capture. Without a precise value for the total production of osmium, the initial concentration could not be estimated and the rhenium-osmium method was not applicable.

It was only recently the final obstacle to using this procedure was hurdled. John Browne and Barry Berman[4] at the Lawrence Livermore Laboratory of the University of California succeeded in measuring the rate of nucleosynthesis of these isotopes of osmium in stellar reactions. With all the rates of formation of osmium 187 known, they were able to calculate the age of the original synthesis of all the elements. They found the formation of the galaxy occurred 17.6 billion years ago. Since it is estimated the galaxy was formed approximately 2 billion years after the creation of the universe, the time of creation was placed at nearly 20 billion years ago.

It was a moment so distant in the past that was the beginning of matter, space and time. Twenty eons later we look on the universe to study its character and to understand what occurred in its evolution. We see one striking feature about it --- nonuniformity. Matter is not evenly distributed throughout space; there is a hierarchy in the arrangement. There are clumps of matter in size units ranging from millions of light-years across to a few kilometers in diameter. Galaxies with hundreds of billions of stars are in clusters, multiple combinations or solitary. There are star clouds, star clusters, multiple stars and single stars. There are planets and satellites. The range of densities spans over a factor of 10^{28}; and the largest member of the hierarchy is 10^{14} times greater than the smallest. But despite this great diversity, all members are more or less self-gravitating systems. A feature they have in common is that the gravitational binding energy per unit mass is within a narrow range; from multiple galaxies to the solar system, it is 10^{12} to 10^{16} ergs per gram; for star clusters, it is 10^{10} to 10^{12} ergs per gram.

The English astrophysicist, Fred Hoyle,[6] recognized in this narrow range of binding energies a significance to account for the formation of hierarchy of masses in the universe. He calculated that a cloud of hydrogen contracting under its own gravitation would heat up from the adiabatic pressure until the contraction equilibrated with the compression at a temperature close to 10,000° K. That is, if it remained transparent to its own radiation. A cloud in equilibrium at this temperature would have a specific binding energy of about 10^{12} ergs per gram. It was at 10,000° K that equilibrium was attained because at this level any elevation of the temperature increased the radiation rapidly and balanced with the energy that was applied by gravity at that temperature.

But clouds initially in equilibrium at this temperature did not remain so when they began to contract. When they began collapsing, the temperature rose above that of equilibrium and the clouds fragmented into self-gravitating units small enough to be in equilibrium with the increased density of the cloud. And as the fragmentation occurred once, it occurred several times until fragments became so dense as to be no longer transparent. At this stage, the contraction of the opaque hydrogen cloud offset the radiation loss. The sequential fragmentation process resulted in a hierarchy of clusters, all with specific binding energies near 10^{12} ergs per gram.

As a vast cloud of hydrogen collapsed out of intergalactic space, it spawned a first generation of stars spherically distributed around the center of a new galaxy. The residual gas, because of its intrinsic angular momentum, settled into a thin disc along the rim characteristic of a spiral galaxy. Stars formed from the gas in the disc and clustered to form the spiral arms. The more massive stars formed, evolved quickly, and died in colossal explosions throwing out great masses of heavy elements to become interstellar dust. All elements with a mass greater than bismuth, and much of the material smaller, were synthesized by the tremendous pressures and temperatures generated in the cataclysmic bursts of these novae and supernovae.

As the galaxy rotated, the stars, the gas and the dust on the fringes flowed through the large spaces from one arm to another, enhancing the density of the matter in them. In one spiral arm, a cloud of high-density gas and dust accumulated. Gravitational forces compacted the cloud against the internal pressure, and at some time when gravity overcame the compression, the cloud began to collapse. As it became more dense, the outer dust particles shielded the center from outside stellar radiation and the temperature dropped, quickening the collapse. The cloud fragmented further and, as the separated sections completed their collapse, one formed the flattened disc of our primitive solar nebula.

This tenuous nebula slowly equilibrated to a dust cloud approximately four light-years across. Then between 5 and 5.5 billion years ago, a star in the vicinity became a supernova. The heavy elements generated by the immense pressures and temperatures billions of degrees were blown out into the surrounding space. Enriched by the heavy elements and buffeted by the shock waves of the cosmic explosion, the cloud reeled under the impact and began a general gravitational collapse.

This great cloud consisted of gaseous elements and dust of rock and ice. Only 0.44 percent of the matter was rocky material made up of iron oxide and the oxides and silicates of magnesium, aluminum, calcium and lesser amounts of the other metals. The ice was frozen ammonia, water and methane representing 1.4 percent of the total. Of the remaining 98.16 percent, about 87 percent was hydrogen, and the rest, helium and the inert gases.

While the flattened solar nebula was a large cloud with a density of about 1,000 hydrogen atoms per cubic centimeter and a temperature around 50° K, it rotated slowly with a weak magnetic field. [7] But the turbulances and gravitational instability began condensation that led to the general collapse. As the cloud contracted, the kinetic and potential gravitational energy converted to heat and the increased temperature and magnetic field caused fractionation to take place; with a rising temperature, dust and gases began to be distributed relative to their condensation temperatures. The dust of iron oxide, silicates and metallic particles gravitated toward the center faster than ammonia, water and methane which formed ices at lower temperatures. The outer fringe of the cloud where the temperature remained low was largely depleted of the dust and icy material and remained a concentration of hydrogen, helium and inert gases whose condensation temperatures are near absolute zero.[8]

What happened next has been constructed by astronomers on modifications of a hypothesis presented in 1943 by a young German physicist named Carl von Weizsäcker. As the primordial cloud rotated, the particles of dust continued to collide with each other and coalesce. When small particles flew into larger ones, they adhered to them and an accretion took place in which the aggregates became larger at the expense of the small dust particles. But the swarms of matter were not all moving in circular orbits; some were in long elliptical paths. So when the particles continued to collide, they reached a arrangement of least interference. The resulting configuration had the shape of traffic lanes of dust swirling in eddies like strings of beads in concentric circles.

Some fractionation, probably created by the magnetic field, caused varying degrees of separation of metal particles from silicate particles, so that the metal to silicate ratio differed in parts of the nebula. In the swirling eddies, the accretion process continued with the metallic particles aggregating at a faster rate as the protoplanets grew, and soon the constant bombardment pushed the temperature until the bodies became hot. But as soon as the growth exhausted the supply of dust, pebbles and large rocks, radiation from the bodies into space cooled the outer layer quickly.

This aggregation of dust in the solar nebula into a few large lumps to form the planets could have taken place within a period of 100 million years. At this rate the conversion of gravitational energy to heat was slow enough to allow the heat to be dissipated by radiation so that the inner planets were formed in an unmelted state at a mean temperature probably less than 1,000° C (1,800° F).

Most of the core of the earth must have segregated close to the time of accretion. The process of core segregation was a highly exothermic process which released an additional 600 calories per gram of gravitational potential energy. If this energy had been released after accretion was completed, it would have been enough heat to bring the entire earth to 2,000° C (3,600° F), but mounting evidence supports the hypothesis that the earth was never molten. For this reason, it is believed that during the early stages of accretion under relatively cool conditions, volatiles were trapped with oxidized iron deep in the interior. As the temperature rose during the later stages from compacting, carbon reacted with the oxidized iron to form the metal which segregated into large bodies and sank toward the center.

The hydrogen and helium of the original nebula at this stage must have formed heavy atmospheres around the protoplanets. According to the Dutch-born astronomer, Gerard Kuiper, the condensation of the matter in the planetary nebula surrounding the sun would have taken place faster than the completion of the sun itself. The planets then, rocky spheres of unmelted conglomerates encased in massive gaseous envelopes, were born in darkness and continued to circle through the hazy nebula around the center, awaiting the ignition of the fires of the sun.

And while the planets waited, more of the gaseous cloud was drawn toward the center of the system by the gravity of the ever-increasing mass of the developing sun. As the matter contracted under the intense gravity, it heated to extremely high temperatures. The ball glowed faintly as it became hotter and hotter. At this stage the mass of the sun, even now 333,400 times that of the earth, must have been enormous. The density to compress the ball to a temperature high enough would have been 100 times its present size.[9] When the center of the protosun reached 10,000,000° K (18,000,000° F), it passed the threshold temperature for fusing hydrogen to helium and the nuclear furnace blazed into action.

After its birth the youthful solar system was cluttered with vast amounts of residual gas and dust left over from its formation. The new sun burned vigorously in its beginning and entered what is called the *T. Tauri** stage. During this early period prodigious amounts of matter were ejected out from the sun at a rate that may have been as much as one solar mass every million years; and as the sun flooded space with intense radiation, its fierce *T. Tauri* winds swept the solar system clean of the remnant gases and dust. The wind cleared the young family of planets not only of the remains of the primordial nebula, it stripped the inner members of their primitive atmospheres of hydrogen and helium in long streamers like the tails of comets. Within a few hundred million years the solar system was cleaned of most of the debris and the sun settled down to a calm and uneventful long life.

It was an event like billions of others like it that took place in the past and continue to happen in the present. Astronomers have been observing a disc-shaped object --- designated MWC 349 --- since the 1930's in the constellation Cygnus which they believe may be at the stage of planet formation. The star, being studied by scientists at the University of Arizona and NASA's Ames Research Center, is 10 times the size and 30 times the mass of the sun surrounded by a glowing disc some 234 million kilometers (144 million miles) in diameter. Whereas the birth of some planetary systems may take millions of years, this star is believed to be only 10,000 years old and the disc is diminishing by around 1 percent per month. If it continues at this rate the process will be complete within 100

---

*Named after a star observed to be in this stage.

A spiral galaxy, NGC 5194, in Canis Venatici with a companion galaxy, NGC 5195. (Kitt Peak National Observatory).

years.

As one looks at the sun's position in the universe, he finds it is in a spiral arm 27,000 light-years from the center of a lens-shaped galaxy 80,000 to 100,000 light-years in diameter. The sun and its family of planets is circling the galaxy every 230 million years at a speed of 220 kilometers per second (136 miles per second). In order to maintain this velocity in orbit at that distance from the center of the galaxy, the gravitational pull on it must be from a mass 90 billion times that of the sun. If 90 percent of the galaxy is inward from the sun, there are then 100 billion stars in the galaxy. Only about 2 percent of the mass toward the center of the galaxy is interstellar gas; about 15 percent in the spiral arms. But as little as this may sound, it remains enough to make 2 to 3 billion additional stars.

As we stand on a clear moonless night and look up at the faint band of stellar light we call the Milky Way arching across the sky, we are looking toward the center of the galaxy. It is so distant that of the 100 billion stars there to balance the sun in its journey around the rim, only about 1,450 are visible to the unaided eye. Nor would our sun be visible to most others in the galaxy who would have our same visual acuity. If we were to travel toward the center of the galaxy, our sun would diminish in brightness as we became more distant. When we reached a distance of 65 light-years, the sun would have faded to a magnitude of 6.5 --- or barely visible. Beyond, it would pass from view. At this point we would have traveled only 1/400th of the journey of 27,000 light-years to the center of the galaxy.

Our home is out in one of the spiral arms, far too distant to be seen by most everyone else in the galaxy. We are among the last to evolve, and have probably been preceded by millions of planetary systems and forms of life that have developed, many having already passed into oblivion. But it was this place in our island universe, 4.6 billion years ago, the earth came into being.

References

1. A. Sandage and G. A. Tammann, Steps toward the Hubble constant VI. The Hubble constant determined from redshifts and magnitudes of remote Sc:I galaxies, *Astrophys. J.* **197**, 265-280 (1975).
2. William A. Fowler and F. Hoyle, Nuclear cosmochronology, *Ann. Phys.* **10**, 280-302 (1960).
3. D.D. Clayton, Cosmoradiogenic chronologies of nucleosynthesis, *Astrophys. J.* **139**, 637-663 (1964).
4. John Browne and Barry I. Berman, Neutron-capture cross sections for ^{186}Os and ^{187}Os and the age of the universe, *Nature* **262**, 197-199 (1976).

5. Virginia Trimble, The origin and abundances of the chemical elements, *Rev. mod. Phys.* **47**, 877-976 (1975).
6. F. Hoyle, On the fragmentation of gas clouds into galaxies and stars, *Astrophys. J.* **118**, 513-528 (1953).
7. Fred L. Whipple, The history of the solar system, *Proc. Nat. Acad. Sci.* **52**, 565-594 (1964).
8. H. Brown, On the composition and structure of planets, *Astrophys. J.* **111**, 641-653 (1950).
9. A.G.W. Cameron, The origin and evolution of the solar system, *Sci. Amer.* **233**, 33-41 (1975).

5
Hadean Earth

The *T. Tauri* stage could have lasted as long as 100 million years. When finally the fierce winds subsided, the primitive atmospheres of the four inner protoplanets, which may originally have been hundreds of times heavier than the planets themselves, had been blown away and out of the solar system, leaving behind the barren rocky spheres. The dense primal atmosphere of hydrogen, helium and the inert gases was reduced to a tenuous envelope in which the neon, argon, krypton and xenon today are 10^6 to 10^{10} times less abundant than their initial cosmic concentration. The ammonia, water and methane in the atmosphere, because they are of comparable molecular weights, would also have been lost in proportion to their masses.

It was a stark barren earth over which the sun rose quickly each morning, searing in a black sky in a blaze of intense ultraviolet radiation, rushing across the sky in a few hours to decend below the horizon just as quickly. For on this airless, waterless hadean world, the day was only five hours long.[1]

Nightfall brought the rise of the moon, an awesome globe so close as to appear to touch the earth's surface as it loomed over the horizon, brightening the austere landscape with its huge glowing face. Each time as it ascended rapidly, its pull played in tidal oscillations on the viscous molten lava pouring onto the earth's surface from the many eruptions. The moon revolved just beyond Roche's limit of 2.86 radii (11,000 miles) and escaped the destruction into a ring system like the outer ring circling Saturn at 2.3 times the planet's radius. In quick succession the months passed, as the moon spun around the earth in 6.5 hours in an orbit approximately 46^0 to the ecliptic.

As bleak as the rocky exterior may have appeared, within its creation the inner earth contained the essence of a new existence. The planet was still essentially an unsorted conglomerate accreted at a temperature low enough to have retained the volatile constituents within its rocky structure, but also trapped in its interior were the radioactive isotopes of the elements, potassium, uranium and thorium. As time passed, the heat generated from the radioactive disintegration of ^{40}K, ^{235}U, ^{238}U and ^{232}Th, unable to escape, was absorbed by the rocks and their temperatures began to rise. After millions of years the accumulating heat drove the temperatures above the melting point of the silicates. As the rocks melted, they expanded, and being less dense, migrated upward while the denser material moved downward. A differentiation of the interior of the earth based on density, begun during the accretion stage, now accelerated by a new dynamic mechanism.

Volatile components held in chemical bonds were liberated by the heat and created immense pressures beneath the weak rocky surface. After a while, no longer able to detain the cauldron within, the crust opened in fissures and the volatiles and molten material spewed out in volcanic eruptions, fumaroles and hot springs. Oxygen, hydrogen, nitrogen and carbon, long frozen in the non-volatile combinations with the metals as oxides, hydrates, nitrides and carbides were freed from the non-gaseous elements and blown and sweated to the surface where they began forming a new atmosphere. Any free oxygen quickly reacted with the reduced gases to form water; and the gaseous envelope that began to form over the globe consisted of hydrogen, nitrogen, water vapor, carbon monoxide, carbon dioxide and the acids of sulfur and chlorine. Phosphorus, bound in rock as the mineral apatite, was freed by the intense heat and belched to the surface with volcanic ash to react quickly with water.

Beneath the hot surface, the cauldron began churning in great convection currents, moving the heat and lighter substances outward and the dense iron-nickel melt toward the center of the earth. The radioactive elements, bound selectively in the crystal lattice of minerals of less density, were carried toward the surface. There was no distinct crust at this time but only the outer surface of the yet unsorted conglomerate. The inner core, heated from the radioactive decay from above and the intense pressure of gravity, began to grow from the inward migration of the molten iron.

The surface was not stabilized as it is today by being lighter material and continued to subside to displace magma that flowed to the top and poured out in great floods of lava. The molten rock that reached the surface, solidified, and took on the fine-grained texture of basalt, a volcanic rock coal black to dark gray in color, with the principal minerals being the ferromagnesium silicate pyroxene and calcium-bearing plagioclase.

The earth was an aggregation of rocky materials in which most of the rock-forming minerals were silicates of iron, aluminum, magnesium, calcium, sodium and potassium. The oxides of iron were present, as was apatite, the calcium phosphate mineral. Only four elements, — iron, oxygen, silicon and magnesium — comprised 93 percent of the total weight. Most of the iron migrated toward the center of the earth to build the core; whereas, silicates became the principal minerals of the outer layers.

Igneous rocks, those crystallized from the silicate melt called magma, are the closest approximation to the primordial earth material. Rocks may be a single mineral like quartz (SiO_2), but generally they are a combination of minerals, the composition and physical properties characterizing the rocks. When magma solidifies at or near the surface, it gives principally basalt; but when it cools far beneath the surface, the slow growth of constituent minerals creates plutonic rocks, of which granite is a common type. Granite is one of the lightest rocks, having

PRINCIPAL MINERALS IN THE EARTH'S CRUST

Mineral	Percent weight
SiO_2	60.18
Al_2O_3	15.61
CaO	5.17
Na_2O	3.91
FeO	3.88
MgO	3.56
K_2O	3.19
Fe_2O_3	3.14
TiO_2	1.06
P_2O_5	0.30

F.W. Clarke and H.S. Washington, U.S. Geol. Survey, Profes. Paper 127 (1974)

66 percent or more silica; basalt has less than 50 percent; and andesitic rocks make up the intermediate range.

For hundreds of millions of years the earth was a hot, inhospitable place as volcanism poured out noxious fumes and vapors at an enormous rate. There were no oceans, a scant atmosphere, and a surface, barren, pitted and scarred by fissures and fiery eruptions from within. The earth would have seemed to have little destiny. But vast amounts of water bound in the rocks as hydrates were being liberated into the atmosphere and remained there as the surface was hot. After a very long time, with the air saturated and the surface of the earth cooling, a new phenomenon took place.

It rained.

It rained, and it evaporated, and it rained some more. It poured down on the bare rocky surface and ate the rock and collected in great flat basins. It was not the sweet rain of the earth's spring; it was the bitter corrosive acid rain from the bowels of the earth heavy-laden with H_2S, CO_2 and HCl. The principal volatiles from the volcanoes were water, carbon dioxide and hydrogen chloride in a ratio of 20:3:1; the rain was approximately 1 molar hydrochloric acid.

But as the rains were acid, bringing with them the chloride, bromide, sulfide and carbon dioxide, the rocks were basic with sodium, potassium and calcium. The acid rain dissolved the rock until it was neutralized,

VOLATILE MATERIALS NOW ON OR NEAR THE EARTH'S SURFACE UNACCOUNTED FOR BY ROCK WEATHERING

Volatile	**Wt. (10^{20} grams)**
Water	16,600
C as CO_2	910
Sulfur	22
Nitrogen	42
Chlorine	300
Hydrogen	10
B, Br, Ar, F etc.	4

Modified from W.W. Rubey, Bull. Geol. Soc. Am **62** 1111-1147 (1951)

and the salts formed broad flat salt plains where the water evaporated.

As the volcanoes continued to spew out the outgassing of the earth's interior, they were restoring the atmosphere and creating oceans. It was a reducing atmosphere devoid of oxygen and the oceans were merely shallow catchbasins for gathering the rains. It was yet to be nearly 2 billion years before oxygen was to be in the atmosphere in significant quantities; and the oceans came into being only by growing throughout the ages from the water expelled from the earth's rocky interior.

Two billion years in the future the oceans would achieve their modern characteristics as we know them. But the oceans of Hadean Earth were solutions resulting from an acid leach of basaltic rock. The atmosphere was void of oxygen so that anaerobic deposition environments with CO_2 pressures of about $10^{-2.5}$ atmospheres, or 10 times today's level, were prevalent. Under these conditions, the pH* of early ocean water was lower that today's, the calcium concentration was higher, and the ocean was probably saturated with respect to amorphous silica. In addition to the other ions from the basaltic rocks, reduced iron and sulfur would have been in their proportions found in the rocks. Only when the pH approached neutrality would aluminum ions begin to

*pH: a logarithmic scale of hydrogen ion concentration. Neutral solutions have pH 7; 0-7 is acidic, 7-14 is basic.

precipitate as the hydroxides and combine with silica to form cation-deficient alumino-silicates. As long as the HCl was in exess of CO_2, the oceans would have had a high content of calcium chloride and the carbonate would not have been precipitated as it was at later times.

As the atmosphere was being restored, important changes began to take place. In the upper level, radiation from the sun dissociated water molecules to hydrogen and oxygen; the hydrogen escaped to outer space and the oxygen reacted quickly with the reduced atmospheric gases reverting back to water. The photodissociation continued to consume some of the atmospheric water, but being the principal volatile brought to the surface by volcanic activity, it accumulated much faster than it was consumed. As carbon dioxide poured into the atmosphere from the volcanoes, the amount built up was restricted by absorption of the carbon dioxide into the oceans. In this way the level of atmospheric carbon dioxide was kept at a relatively low level.

It has generally been believed the earth heated to a hot stage at this time forcing out the water and the outer volatiles into a dense atmosphere only to condense out at a later time after the earth cooled sufficiently. William Rubey,[3] who studied the matter, has found convincing evidence this could never have happened. Instead, it appears that at no time in the earth's history was there ever more than a fraction of the excess volatiles of the earth's interior in the atmosphere.

The amount of carbon dioxide buried as carbonates and organic carbon in sedimentary rocks is 600 times greater than all in the atmosphere, hydrosphere and biosphere. If even as much as 1 percent of the carbon dioxide now locked in these rocks had been in the atmosphere the oceans of today's volume would have gone from their pH of 8.2 down to 5.9.

The equilibrium of atmospheric carbon dioxide and that absorbed by the oceans proved to have a profound significance. Carbon dioxide in the atmosphere creates what is called the "greenhouse effect." Like the glass of a greenhouse, it is transparent to visible light, but absorbs the heat-generating infrared rays. When sunlight is absorbed by the surface of the earth, the warmed solid substances re-emit much of the energy as invisible infrared radiation. If the level of carbon dioxide in the earth's atmosphere is too high, this energy would be reabsorbed by the air

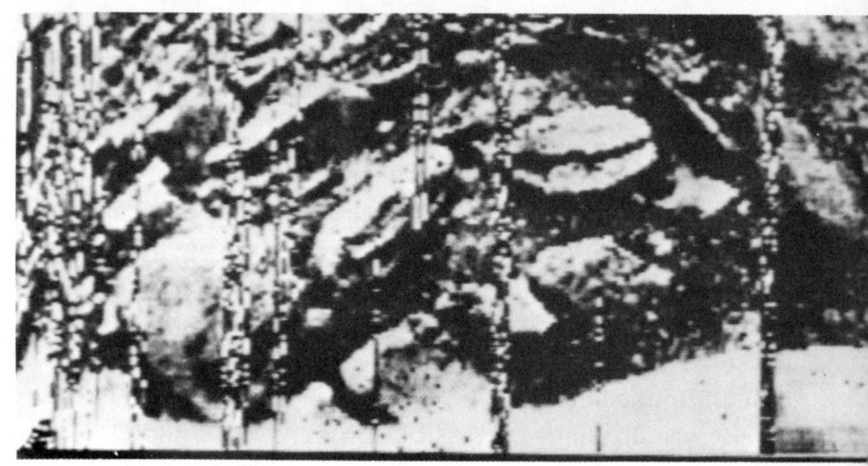

instead of being radiated into space, and the earth would heat up. By maintaining the atmospheric carbon dioxide at a low level (about 0.024 percent today), the oceans have controlled the greenhouse effect of the earth.

While the earth was going through her formative years, so too was her sister planet, Venus. Of all the other members of the family of planets, none resembles the earth in size and mass more than does Venus. Both sister planets lost their initial atmospheres, but soon replaced them by the outgassing of the volatiles from the interior. But, whereas the earth became hospitable, Venus turned mysterious, always shrouding her face behind a thick veil of clouds. Only recently has the story of Venus' past been learned.

On December 14, 1962, the U.S. spacecraft Mariner II approached within 22,000 miles of Venus and radioed scientific data the 36 million miles back to earth of its findings. The peak behind the veil was disappointing to all who envisioned Venus to be a planet with lush rain forests. The surface of Venus was dry and far too hot for the existence of life.

The U.S.S.R.'s Venera 4 probed the atmosphere and landed on the surface of Venus in October, 1967, its instruments radioing back measurements of atmospheric temperatures, pressures and

Panorama of the Venus surface taken in the place of Venera-9 landing. The light spot at the bottom is a part of the landing capsule. The vertical stripes in the picture meant the transmission of technical data. (Tass Wirephoto release)

composition. This was followed by the Soviet Venera 9 and Venera 10 touching down on the surface on the far light side of the cloud-shrouded planet on October 22 and 25, 1975. The spacecrafts sent back measurements that revealed the atmosphere on the surface to be 472° C (882 °F) and the pressure 90 times the atmospheric pressures on the earth. From these data, those of Venera 4, and the U.S. Mariner probes, the composition of the Venusian atmosphere was found to be 90 to 95 percent carbon dioxide, 0.4 percent water, no more than 7 percent nitrogen, and less than 1.6 percent water and oxygen. Venus is a very hot and dry planet with a surface temperature higher than the melting point of lead. Our sister planet failed to create the conditions conducive to life.

What went wrong? How could two planets so similar be destined for roles so different in our solar system? The answer apparently lies in the fact that the earth is 92 million miles from the sun; whereas, Venus is 67.2 million miles. On earth the water condensed into oceans, and the carbon dioxide, as it was continually poured into the atmosphere, was absorbed and precipitated out as carbonates. But Venus was closer to the sun. The ultraviolet light, much more intense than on earth, dissociated the water too efficiently. The water formed by the volcanoes never appreciably exceeded the rate of dissociation so that the oceans did not form as they did on earth. Without the oceans, the carbon dioxide was never absorbed out of the atmosphere. As the carbon dioxide in the atmosphere built up, the temperature rose. Within a short time, Venus was trapped in a runaway greenhouse effect. The hotter the atmosphere became, the less the chance for the water to condense out. After a while, Venus became hotter than the boiling point of water and passed the point of no return. She became a hot, waterless world, devoid of life. If the earth had been a scant 5.5 million miles closer to the sun, she too would have gone the way of Venus.

Michael Hart[4], an expert in planetary atmospheres at the Goddard Space Flight Center at Greenbelt, Maryland, traced the evolution of the earth's atmosphere from its beginning 4.6 billion years ago. Data on the composition of gases, the quantity absorbed by the oceans, chemical reactions between atmospheric gases and numerous other processes were programmed and the conditions throughout geologic time were calculated. Hart discovered the zone for life in which the earth travels as it revolves around the sun lies within a narrow margin. If the earth had been 6 percent closer to the sun, the atmosphere would have become the dense CO_2 clouds like Venus; if the earth had been 1 percent farther, the oceans would have frozen solid 2 billion years ago.

The latter result came unexpectedly. Nevertheless, it is consistent with the findings of Hayes, Imbrie and Shackleton[5] that Ice Ages occur when the earth is farthest from the sun during the summer. The earth's distance from the sun varies between 92 and 93 million miles, or about 1 percent. An additional 1 percent to the distance as calculated by Hart could conceivably have caused drastic circumstances.

As the earth was developing an atmosphere and the rains were shaping the surface and collecting in juvenile oceans, the earth's interior was undergoing an evolution. Seismic studies show the earth today to be composed of three well-defined concentric spheres: the crust, the mantle and the core. The core, or innermost zone, has a diameter of about 6,946 km (4,316 mi), or just over half the earth's 12,810 km (7,942 mi) diameter. It consists of a solid inner portion about 1,600 miles in diameter within a fluid shell. The inner core is believed to have a density of about 10 to 12 times that of water and is iron-nickel in the vicinity of 4,000°C (7,200°F), but solidified by the extreme pressure.

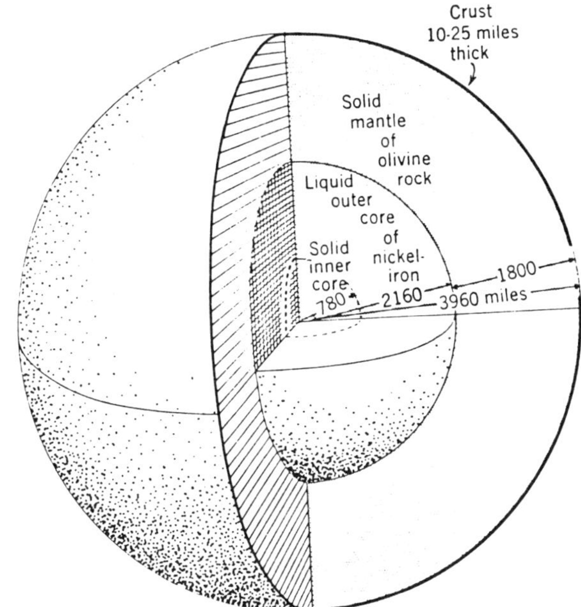

Principal zones of the earth's interior. (From A.N. Strahler, **Physical Geography,** *4th ed., John Wiley & Sons, New York, 1975)*

In contrast, the mantle, which represents the largest volume, is rocky rather than metallic, and extends from the rim of the core to the base of the crust. Seismic data show emphatically the earth is essentially solid to the depth of 2,900 km (1,790 mi). The continental crust of the outer shell is 30 to 40 km (average of 20 mi) in thickness; the oceanic 6 to 9 miles. Whereas the crust has a density of 2.75 times that of water, the mantle progresses inwardly from a density of 3.3 to one of 5.5. There is then a discontinuity across to the core where the density runs from 9.5 for the outer rim to 12.3 at the center.

The mantle is rigid enough for the passage of seismic waves, although it may also possess qualities of plasticity due to the enormous pressures on it. A project of geophysicists has been to search for mixtures of materials that have the same densities and exhibit the same properties under high pressure observed by the inner earth. Alfred Ringwood[6–8] and his colleagues at the Australian National University at Canberra found in their studies with high pressure that olivine crystals collapsed under increasing pressure to make denser crystals. Olivine, a mineral composed of iron, magnesium, silicon and oxygen, by far the most abundant elements on earth, is also a principal component of meteorites. When the mineral was subjected to conditions simulating depths up to 600 km (370 mi), olivine transformed under the pressure into a more compact crystal structure. Furthermore, upon release of the pressure, olivine relaxed and returned to the less dense configuration. From these studies, it appears olivine exhibits the same behavior observed for the earth's inner layers, and this mineral is most likely the principal component in the earth's composition.

But on Hadean Earth, there were no continents and the crust was the outer surface of the mantle. The radioactive elements were not yet concentrated in the crust or upper mantle as they are today, but were still distributed throughout the undifferentiated mantle. Nonetheless, the accumulating heat from the nucleoclides over hundreds of millions of years was differentiating the earth into concentric layers. And as the radioactive elements migrated toward the outer crust, they brought with them their heat-producing capacity nearer to the surface. The magma would have concentrated in a transitional layer below the surface as it is today between the crust and the upper mantle.

Toward the end of Hadean times the buildup of radiogenic heat, the partial melting of the mantle and the upward convection of heat in the magma must have reached climactic proportions and the original crust underwent modification in areas around the globe. The intrusion of igneous rocks and the extrusion of lavas deformed the surface and accelerated erosion, and the earliest sedimentary rocks were formed.

It was probably too early yet for the formation of true crystal rocks; the sea-floor spreading process did not occur during this time. There was still not the irreversible differentiation of the initially homogeneous mantle. But the passing of the Hadean time was marked by the release of the heat buildup by great floods of lava spewing out from the volcanoes onto the earth's surface and beneath the waters of the growing oceans.

It was the end of the first long age of the earth's history. It had seen the birth of the earth's atmosphere and the oceans — it had lasted 800 million years.

Far into the future an incredibly long 3.8 billion years, the rocks crystallized from the magma in that primordial scene were to play a significant role in science. In 1966, Vic McGregor, a young geologist from New Zealand working with the Geological Survey of Greenland, began mapping in detail the mountain area around a fjord named Amerlik on the western coast near Godthaab, the capital. It was not an easy task. The great assortment of rocks and their complex arrangements made interpreting the geologic history difficult, but after several years McGregor began to piece together a distinctive sequence of events that had occurred down through the ages. The rocks recognized to be the oldest from that region were the Amitsôq gneisses, igneous rocks that had undergone metamorphosis and deformation by mighty forces acting on the earth's crust. By McGregor's interpretation, there should be rocks that were formed even earlier than the Amitsôq gneisses.

Stephen Moorbath of Oxford joined McGregor in the summer of 1971 and the two geologists began to collect rock samples to be sent back to England for age measurements by radioactive isotopes. At Isua, a mountainous area 100 kilometers northeast of Godthaab at the very edge of the great inland ice sheet, a mining company was exploring a large iron ore deposit. The ore was a part of a great arc of highly metamorphosed volcanic and sedimentary rock 12 to 25 kilometers in diameter and 3,000 meters thick. When McGregor and Moorbath reached the site, they saw the arc of rock was supracrustal, that is, laid down on a surface, and flanked by granite gneisses with edges of contact sheared and deformed. Samples were collected and sent back to Oxford for rubidium-strontium and uranium-lead measurements to determine the ages. When the results were finally received, McGregor and Moorbath learned that in that bleak Arctic upland near the great ice sheet where the rock is totally exposed, they had been walking on a section of what may have been the original continental crust of the earth. The age of the rocks was found to be 3.76 ± 0.10 billion years.[9] They were the oldest rocks on earth.

References

1. B.G. Marsden and A.G.W. Cameron, **The Earth-Moon System**, Plenum Press, New York, 1966, p. 73.
2. George Howard Darwin, **The Tides**, W.H. Freeman and Company, San Francisco and London, 1962.
3. William W. Rubey, Geologic history of seawater, *Bull. Geol. Soc. Am.* **62**, 1111-1147 (1951).
4. Michael H. Hart, Earth was born under critical conditions: just missed a lethal sheet of ice cover, *Astronomy News* **15**, No. 7, 2 (1977).
5. J.D. Hays, John Imbrie and N.J. Shackleton, Variation in the earth's orbit: pacemaker of the Ice Ages, *Science* **194**, 1121-1131 (1976).
6. S.P. Clark and A.E. Ringwood, Density distribution and constitution of the mantle, *Rev. Geophys.* **2**, 35-88 (1964).
7. D.E. Green and A.E. Ringwood, The genesis of basaltic magma, *Contr. Miner. Petrol.* **15**, 103-190 (1967).
8. A.E. Ringwood and D.E. Green, An experimental investigation of the gabbro-eclogite transformation, *Tectonophysics* **3**, 383-427 (1966).
9. S. Moorbath, R.K. O'Nions and R.J. Pankhurst, Early Archean age for the Isua Iron Formation, West Greenland, *Nature* **245**, 138-139 (1973).

6
The Archean

Formed by the accretion of the unmelted mass of dust, aggregates and stones, the earth in the beginning would have looked much like the dry barren face of the moon. But throughout the Hadean Era the internal heat distilled to the surface the volatile materials bound to the rocks and a primitive atmosphere and hydrosphere were born. By the time of the Isua Iron Formation 3.76 billion years ago, there was enough water on the surface for rain, erosion and sediments. Following the Hadean, the earth entered the Archean Era.

The development of a hydrosphere and erosion by rain brought the earth's surface into the rock cycle. Whereas igneous rocks are primary, sedimentary rocks are secondary. Minerals weathered from igneous rocks and laid down in sediments undergo lithification to give rise to sandstone or shale, depending on the nature of the deposit; or chemicals leached from rocks and carried to oceans, lakes and groundwater can precipitate as minerals to form limestone ($CaCO_3$) and dolomite

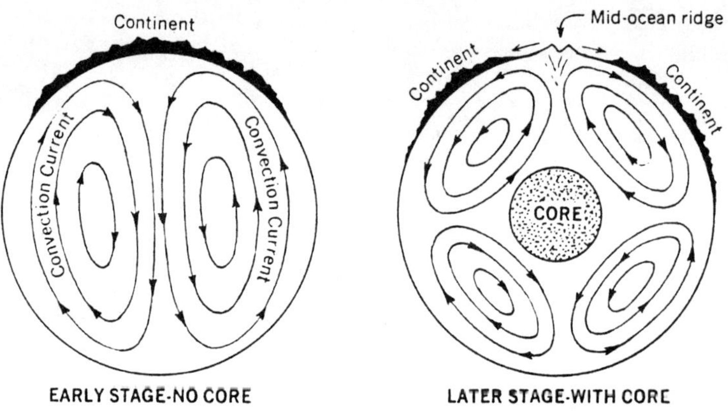

Formation of the earth's core. The system of flow allowed the lighter material to accumulate on the surface to form a primordial continent, and heavy material to sink, forming the core. The growing volume of the core broke the circulation pattern into separate cells whose flow tore the continent apart and formed a midocean ridge along the line of rupture.

($CaMg(CO_3)_2$). The sediments are commonly deposited in great troughs in the earth's crust where they eventually may become the loci of subsequent mountain building. When they are at great depths and are subjected to enormous pressures and high temperatures, the rocks are altered and metamorphosed, new crystals develop, and preexisting crystals enlarge or are rearranged into orderly patterns. By this means, limestone becomes marble, and shale, slate.

Within the earth, the unsorted conglomerates continued to differentiate by density. The core of iron-nickel melt was growing. And in the mantle, the deep plastic region below the surface was churning slowly in vast convection cells, rising in some regions, cooling and sinking in others. The earth was becoming a gigantic heat machine.

These convection cells, before the core had grown to any great size, would have passed through the whole earth. But as the core became larger, they fragmented into smaller cells that circulated only within the mantle. With differentiation of the mantle throughout the earth's history and concentration of the radioactive elements toward the surface, the generation of heat and the convection cells shifted outward. Today the cells appear to be confined to the upper 700 kilometers (444 miles) of the mantle;[1] but during the Archean Era they presumably passed much deeper, driven by the radiogenic heat and conduction from the core, churning in great loops at a rate of a few centimeters per year.

The early Archean would have been a consolidation interval following the great eruptions that ushered out the Hadean. Over the hundreds of millions of years erosion wore down the old volcanic mountains and deposited thick layers of sediments on their margins. While the surface was being weathered, within the earth's interior the heat of radioactive decay continued to accumulate on a worldwide scale for the next episode.

Then around 3 billion years ago, when shallow primitive oceans skimmed the earth's surface, the earth underwent another series of crustal formation. The cauldron no longer contained, the crust split into huge rifts and the molten magma upwelled out onto the surface. The pressure from this outflow of magma caused the adjoining sections of crust to decouple from the upper mantle and slide over the layer of molten rock at the interface. The movement wasn't much — only a centimeter or so a year — but over the millions of years it was enough to force the surface of the earth to lose this increase in its crust in some manner elsewhere. In order to relieve the pressure the crust split at other places and the section under pressure began to slide over the neighboring section, driving down the edge of cleavage into the mantle beneath it.

As the subducted surface slid deeper into the mantle, it melted at the subterranean temperatures — the lighter silica-rich rock moving upward while the ferromagnesium rocks sank. Where one edge of the surface slid beneath the other, a deep trench resulted; and parallel to the trench the subducted crustal material extruded as magma onto the surface, creating an arc of volcanic islands. These island arcs must have appeared in a number of locations on the face of the earth.

The magma that erupted along rifts in the earth's crust, pouring

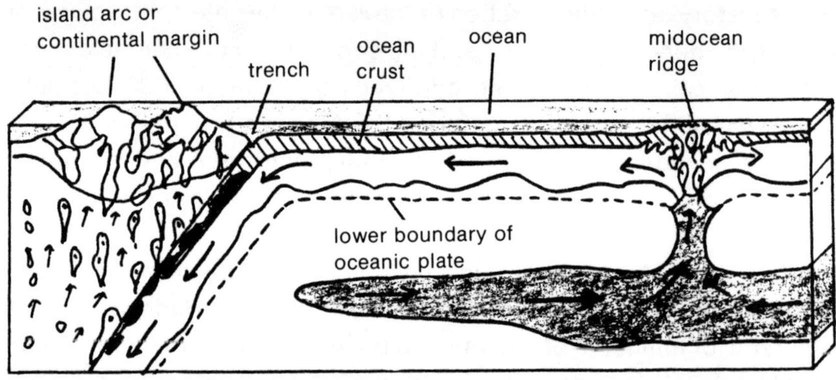

Subduction of a tectonic plate. Spreading of the ocean floor forces the opposing edge of the oceanic plate to drive under an adjoining section. As the edge descends, it is melted and undergoes fractionation of the lighter and heavier constituents.

out vast quantities of lava became the basement rocks of the continental shields. These foundation rocks, although 3 billion years old and folded and metamorphosed, can be seen as long successions of pillow lava as much as several kilometers thick, formed by the rapid chilling of being erupted under water. There is evidence these belts, known as greenstone belts because of their greenish tinge from chlorite, hornblende and epidote, may have been crustal regions that have subsided 10 to 15 kilometers (6 to 9 miles) as volcanic rocks and sediments accumulated layer after layer over a long period.

The rocks in greenstone belts have no exact equivalent among contemporary active volcanic regions, although they show some resemblances to present volcanic island arcs, such as the Kuriles north of Japan and southwestern Aleutian islands. The rocks around greenstone belts are often predominantly granite, and many Archean provinces consist of strongly folded, steeply dipping volcanic successions compressed between granitic bodies. During the Archean the distribution of land and water are not well known, but the sediments and volcanic rocks were accumulating under water.

The island arcs were probably then as they appear to be today — a significant evolutionary intermediate between oceanic and continental crusts. Oceanic crust is basaltic and represents the surface of the mantle; whereas continental crust, thicker and of lower density, is principally granite. Island arcs are of crustal material thicker than oceanic crust but not as thick as continental, and composed of rocks common to both.

The earth's crust was undergoing a fractionation where, on each eruption, lighter rock was being accumulated on the outer surface. These volcanic rocks of the greenstone belts characteristically occur in sequences that begin with minerals high in iron and magnesium and pass with time to the granitic-type rock rich in potassium and sodium. Such sequences may be repeated several times within a single greenstone belt.

For hundreds of millions of years widespread volcanic eruptions poured floods of lava out in succession. The rains that cut at the surface and washed down the intrusions of basalt left predominantly primitive volcanic sediments. The earth's crust was not yet differentiated into granitic rock making it light enough for a stable platform, and as lava and sediments layered atop it, it yielded.

Toward the end of the Archean another stage of crustal development occurred. As oceanic crusts slid beneath the overriding plates, the molten rock from the subducted crusts rose by its buoyancy and moved into emplacements on the inland margins of the island arcs. Confined by the pressure of the solid crust to thousands of feet below the surface these magma bodies, called batholiths, cooled very slowly. As they gradually cooled in place, minerals with the highest melting points, which generally are the minerals with the highest densities, crystallized first. Olivine, the mineral containing iron and magnesium, and the calcium-bearing plagioclase crystallized and sank in the melt, taking with them most of the iron, magnesium and calcium. Next came pyrozene, hornblende, biotite and others following in a discontinuous sequence of crystallization of the various minerals resulting in a crude fractionation of the components of the molten rock in an order worked out years ago by the petrologist, N.L. Bowen.[2] Only when all the metal ions that can form silicate minerals were used up did the remaining silicate melt crystallize out as quartz, or silicon dioxide. Gold, silver, copper, lead, zinc and tin, which do not fit readily in the structures of common rock minerals, concentrated in the residual melt fraction of the magma where they eventually flowed into cracks and solidified as veins or remained in place to become pockets of ore.

This stage of mountain building, or orogeny as it is called by geologists, went on over hundreds of millions of years. Some times the magma extruded onto the crust, pouring out thick series of volcanic rock. More often, it remained intruded until the final stage of orogeny. Then, at a time when the confining pressure over the intrusive body weakened, its buoyancy drove it upward like a cork through the crust in the last spectacular step of mountain building.

In this way the continents have grown step by step from their nucleus of granite by addition to their margins the lighter material fractionated from the mantle. The entire procedure of mountain building apparently has occurred in six or seven episodes throughout the earth's history, each episode taking approximately 800 million years.

The thrust of the mountains on the margins of the greenstone belts severely metamorphosed and deformed the rocks. The continual subsidence of the belts created the flat low-lying terrain known as the continental shields. These are the cratons, or nuclei, from which the continents grew by subsequent mountain building episodes. The Canadian Shield, the largest of these features, lies like a gigantic saucer with its center holding the Hudson Bay. The mountains are gone now, long worn down to their root stocks, but the area remains a vast hoard of mineral deposits.

The greenstone belts, dating from 3.4 to 2.5 billion years ago, are the oldest belts of metamorphosed and deformed rocks. From about 2.7 billion years onward, individual sedimentary basins formed from the erosion of the ancient mountains. The Witwatersrand Basin of southern Africa is one of the oldest of these basins. It was the wash of the greenstone belt and granitic rocks that carried the gold down to be concentrated in the conglomerates of the basin to supply half of the world's production today.

The cratons upon which the continents were growing may have been 5 to 10 percent of the present continental area 3.8 billion years

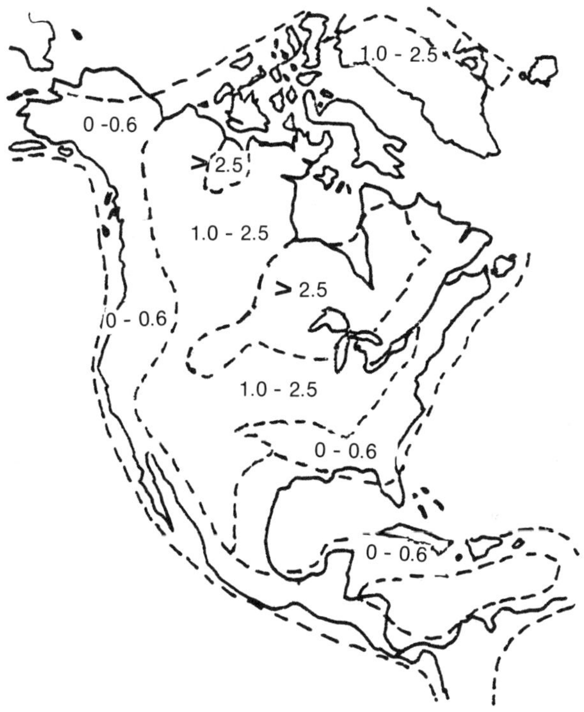

The growth of North America. The numbers indicate the ages of rocks of the continental platform in billions of years.

ago, but between 2.9 and 2.6 billion years ago they grew in area until they were 50 to 60 percent of the present area. The earth's crust was becoming stable enough by 2.7 billion years ago to allow sediments to accumulate in large basins without being altered by subsequent stresses.

During the Archean the atmosphere was still without oxygen, but contained nitrogen, and the carbon dioxide content was probably 4 to 10 times today's value — and it was a scorcher. According to geologists L. Paul Knauth and Samuel Epstein[3] in studies at the California Institute of Technology by isotopic analysis of 66 samples of chert from central and western United States, 3 billion years ago the average temperature may have been as high as 70°C (160°F). The findings are based on measurements of the relative abundances of isotopes of oxygen and hydrogen in water of hydration of chert from different past geologic ages. The data indicate climatic temperatures have been generally declining from that time with some fluctuations.

The Archean Era lasted until 2.5 billion years ago. When it ended the crust was stable enough to hold heavy platforms of sediment and sufficiently rigid to withstand intrusions of magma. From then on the geologic column is characteristically cratonal sediments deposited on submerged continental margins.

The Archean was followed by the Proterozoic — an Era that extended for nearly 2 billion years through the remainder of the Precambrian. It came to an end 570 million years ago with the beginning of the Cambrian Period — and fossils.

References

1. D.P. McKenzie and Frank Richner, Convection currents in the earth's mantle, *Sci. Amer.* **235**, 72-89 (1976).
2. Robert J. Foster, **Physical Geology**, Charles E. Merrill Publ. Co., Columbus, Ohio, 1971, p. 57-62.
3. L. Paul Knauth and Samuel Epstein, Hydrogen and oxygen isotope ratios in modular and bedded cherts, *Geochim Cosmochim. Acta* **40**, 1095-1108 (1976).

7
Life on the Cellular Level

The fossil record beginning abruptly at the base of the Cambrian created a biological problem. It looked as though life had suddenly appeared on earth with no ancestry. But, as is so often the case with seemingly insurmountable obstacles, the answer was extremely simple. Life exists on two dimensions. There are those multicellular plants and animals large enough to be visible, and beyond the range of our visual detection exists the microscopic realm of the microbe which we are tied to by an invisible evolutionary thread.

The discovery of the cellular level of life paralleled the development of the microscope. It was a Dutchman by the name of Anton van Leeuwenhoek with no formal scientific schooling, but with an absorbing hobby of grinding lenses and using them to study minute things, who brought to light a whole new world hitherto neither seen nor suspected. The microscope had been invented in 1590 by two Dutch brothers, Francis and Zachary Janssen, when they placed a lens at each end of a tube and obtained a magnification of ten times. It was a crude device, but an advancement over the magnifying glass. Leeuwenhoek, on the other hand, made high quality lenses of a very short focal point with a magnification 50 to 275 times and a resolving power far exceeding the early compound microscope. He ground lenses of many sizes — some no larger than the head of a pin — and mounted them between two thin brass plates. And as Leeuwenhoek peered through his lenses at samples of rainwater, pond water, and scrapings from his own teeth, he saw a strange tiny universe teeming with life.

He saw for the first time in history the "very little animalcules," as he called them in 1677, describing bacteria and protozoa. Leeuwenhoek was a man of insatiable curiosity and powers of careful observation. He discovered a new world and he investigated everything in it he could find, correcting many misconceptions. In long rambling letters to the Royal Society of London he explained that weevils in grainaries were not bred from wheat, but were grubs from tiny eggs; that fleas bred in the regular manner of winged insects and did not sprout from sand or dust; that shellfish were spawn and not generated out of sand; and that embryos of fresh-water mussels were sometimes eaten by his little animalcules. He studied the circulation of the blood in the capillaries of the tail of an eel, the web foot of a frog and an ear of a rabbit, and in his letters he illustrated the red corpuscles of various animals. In 1677 he described for the first time the spermatozoa from insects, dogs and man. For fifty years he revealed to the world the fascinating universe he had discovered on the other side of his lenses.

Leeuwenhoek's discoveries led to the recognition that there is a level of life smaller than that visible to the eye. The world was awakened by the appearance of a missing dimension between life as was known and its creation, and in the wake of Leeuwenhoek's discoveries the existence of a smaller and simpler life form reactivated interest in Aristotle's concept that higher organisms had evolved from lower forms of life.

While Leeuwenhoek studied his tiny universe, Robert Hooke in 1665, using a crude microscope with lenses of fused glass, observed the honeycomb appearance of thin slices of cork and called the structure cells. For a hundred and fifty years this was believed to be the basic structure of plants. It was the German botanist, Hugo Mohl, who realized it was not the cell wall seen by Hooke that was the basis of life, but the translucent, semi-fluid substance inside, and he named it protoplasm. Nevertheless, the name cell became recognized as the fundamental unit of living systems.

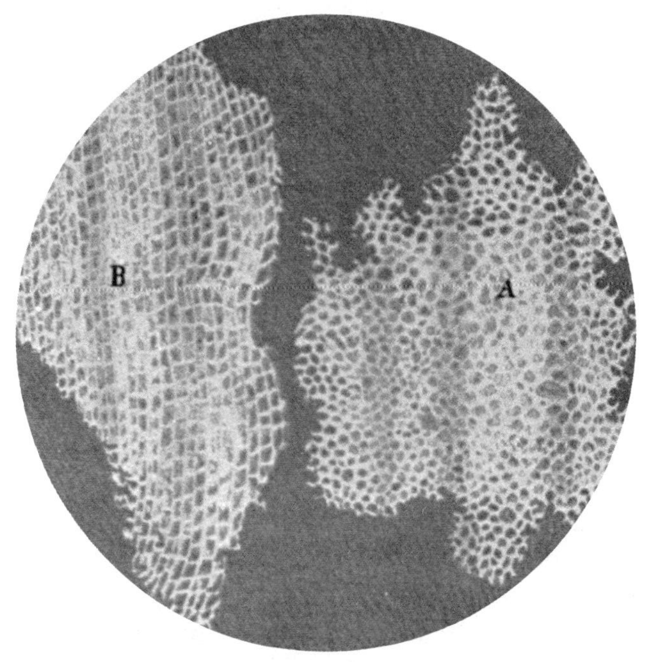

Drawings of a piece of cork from Hooke's book **Micrographia.** *A is a cross section; B is a longitudinal section.*

Animal cells, lacking the cell wall of plant cells, are smaller, and except for a few like eggs, spermatozoa and blood corpuscles, were more difficult to see with the early microscopes. Then in 1827, Lister invented the achromatic microscope, later improved upon by Amici, which corrected the chromatic aberration that plagued microscopists and permitted a more detailed study of cells. Four years later, Robert Brown detected a dark object in the protoplasm of plant cells and discovered the nucleus. It was Matthias Schleiden, however, who recognized the importance of the cell nucleus and associated it with cell division, thus showing that cells came from pre-existing cells.

A year later, following a dinner conversation with Schleiden, the German anatomist, Theodor Schwann, sensed that the animal cells he was studying behaved like Schleiden's plant cells. The general impression had always been that the organism was the fundamental unit of life. Then suddenly, in one of the most sweeping generalizations in the history of science, Schwann saw there was a great common denominator for all living things — plants and animals were constructed from the same basic cellular unit. In 1839, Schwann published his thoughts in a paper entitled *On the Correspondence in the Structure and Growth of Plants and Animals,* and the cellular theory of life was established.

The cell is the smallest autonomous biological system — the basis of life — and all living things consist of either a single cell or they are multicellular. The cell is, in effect, a biochemical machine capable of self-replication. Given a source of energy and the essential raw materials, it can construct its own components and reproduce its entire composition. Considering the fact the number of individual constituents can run into tens of thousands packed into a sphere so small it needs a magnification of several hundred times to be visible, it is a remarkable package.

When viewed through a conventional light microscope, all cells appear to be capsules of transparent and largely homogeneous material. The only structures discernible are chromogenic particles such as chloroplasts of the plant cells which contain chlorophyll, or pigmented substances in animal cells. In order to study cells, the microscopist used various chemical stains to selectively color or darken internal features of the cell. For over a century this was the principal means of studying cells.

When the biologists of the 19th century began viewing the microscopic world, they found it was populated with such a variety of unicellular organisms that it strained their classification method. There were protozoa, unicellular animals with relatively large and complex cells; there were bacteria, smaller and simpler; and there were the algae and fungi. It was an odd assortment of creatures on a level where the distinction between animal and vegetable became blurred. But of all the unicellular organisms, only the bacteria and the blue-green algae lacked a distinct nucleus and were grouped together in a class to become known as the procaryotes; the cells of all the other plants and animals had membrane-bound nuclei and were called eucaryotic cells.

The light microscope went through several modifications and innovations over the century to improve the instrument's capability. There were developed the phase-contrast, the inference, the polarizing, the ultraviolet and the dark-field microscopes; but detailed descriptions of cellular structure always remained agonizingly beyond the observable. Resolution, dependent on the wavelength of light, was limited to about 0.24 micron* (2,400 Angstroms). Since procaryotes range from 0.3 to 2 micra in diameter, and eucaryotic cells with their more complex composition about 10 times larger, the resolution was able to show the cell, but was not fine enough for structural detail.

Then in 1924, de Broglie hypothesized that electrons should travel in characteristic waves like light with the wavelength being inversely proportional to the root of the voltage. Theoretically, electron beams could have wavelengths much shorter than light, and a microscope using electrons instead of light would have a much greater resolving power — a 100 kv electron beam would improve the resolution over a light microscope by approximately 140,000 times. Based on this principle, the first electron microscope was built in Germany in 1932 using magnetic lenses, and the Siemens-Halske Company produced a prototype of a commercial model in 1938.

The electron microscope revolutionized the knowledge of the way cells are organized. It showed the difference between the two kinds of cells was more than the presence or absence of a nucleus — it was

---

1 micron = 0.001 millimeter (0.0004 inch)

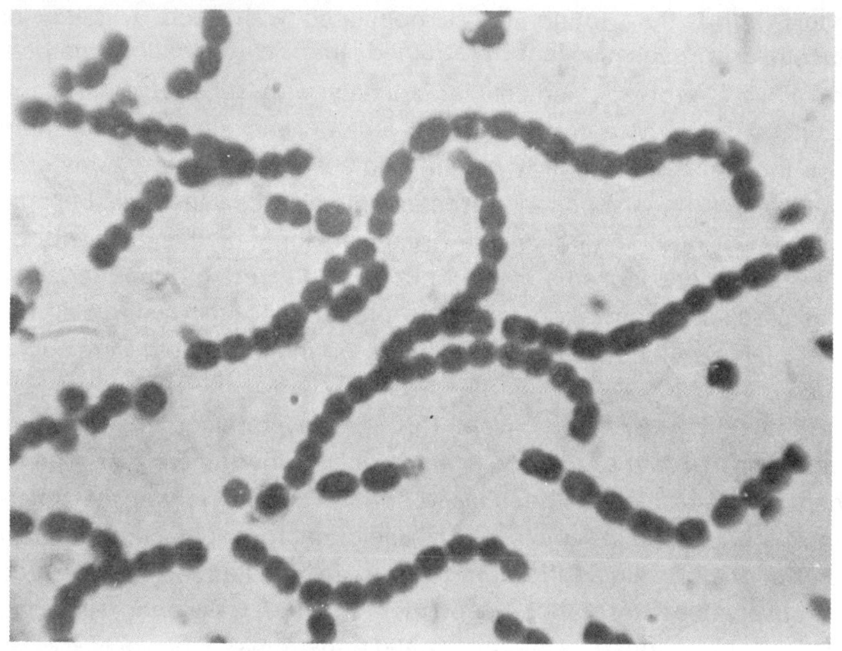

*Blue-green algae (**Nostoc**) as seen through a microscope. Magnification is 1,000 X. (Carolina Biological Supply Co.)*

an extreme difference in subcellular architecture. After the complexity of the structure and chemistry of eucaryotic cells became known, it was recognized the gulf between procaryotic and eucaryotic cells is so great that the development of the latter had to have been one of the major steps in evolution.

Both kinds of cells are bound by membranes of similar profiles, resolvable at high magnification as triple-layered structures about 80 Å (Angstroms)* thick. In the procaryotic cells there are no membrane-bound units; the nuclear material and cytoplasm appear uniform and not separated. The principal structural units are subcellular particles about 100 Å in diameter known as ribosomes which are the site of protein synthesis.

The eucaryotic cell, on the other hand, when observed under the

---

*100 Å = 0.01 micron = 0.00001 millimeter.

electron microscope is no longer a homogeneous cytoplasm, but a labyrinth of sections separated by membranes. This system of membranes is called endoplasmic reticulum, and all the membranes result from convolutions of the cellular membrane and are continuous with one another. The nucleus of the cell is surrounded by a membrane and contains nucleic acids and proteins. In other regions of the cell there are discrete organized structures called organelles which play specific roles in the cellular functions: ribosomes, as in the procaryotic cells, for the synthesis of proteins; mitochondria, the powerhouses of the cell, as highly organized double-walled sacs where pyruvic acid is oxidized to CO_2 and water giving energy which is used by the rest of the cell; Golgi bodies; lysosomes and others.

It is the nucleus of the cell that is the storage site for the blueprint to the entire organism. In eucaryotes it is a distinct organelle, whereas with procaryotes it lacks a nuclear membrane. The hereditary information for the cell is stored in the chemical structure of a long linear polymer called deoxyribonucleic acid (DNA).

The DNA is the informational molecule for a living system. It is its coded structure that determines the amino acid sequence of proteins. But proteins make the organism; they are the workhorses that make it all possible. Almost all fundamental operations of a cell are performed by proteins. They are responsible for structure, for the transport of material, the regulation of processes, and above all, they are the enzymes that catalyze all biochemical reactions. All cells, procaryotic or eucaryotic, have to synthesize proteins, and this task is carried out in small subcellular particles called ribosomes.

Ribosomes are about 25 millimicra in diameter with a total molecular weight of 4,000,000 for higher organisms; about 2,700,000 for bacteria. Each ribosome is composed of two subunits, one approximately twice the size of the other. The smaller subunit has one large molecule of ribonucleic acid (RNA); the larger has two RNA's of unequal size. Additionally, there are about 20 different proteins in the smaller unit; 40 in the larger. As far as can be determined, the proteins are present as only one molecule each.

The functional arrangement of the constituents of the ribosomes is highly specific. This constancy of organization is manifested by the fact that at least some ribosomes have been crystallized. The ribosomes of avian embryos, for instance, can be induced to crystallize merely by cooling the cells.[2]

Unlike ribosomes, the mitochondria are common only to the eucaryotes. These are sausage-shaped particles 0.5 to 1.0 micron wide and 5 to 10 micra long. They are surrounded by an outside

Cross section of the major part of a mammalian cell viewed through the electron microscope showing the nucleus, nuclear membrane and nucleous area. In the cytoplasm one can see vesicles and mitochondria. The bar represents 1,000 nm; magnification is 7,500 X. (Courtesy of Dennis O'Callaghan, University of Mississippi Medical Center. Photograph by Nan Mansfield)

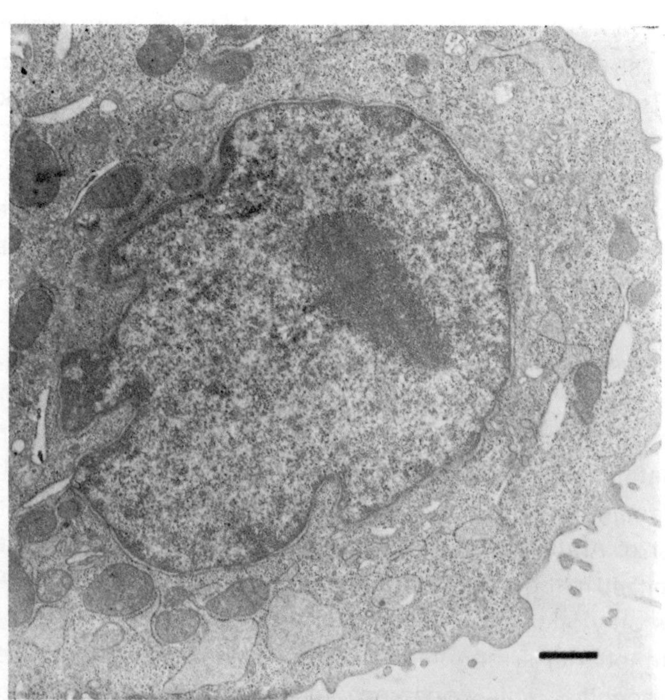

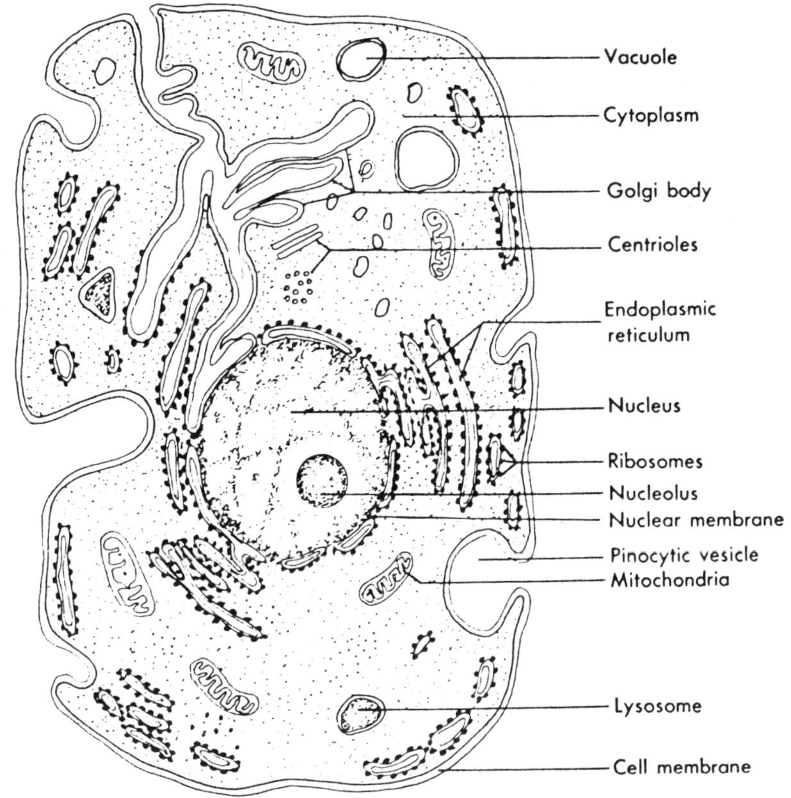

Diagram of a eucaryotic cell

membrane (thylakoid) and are partitioned into a series of chambers by inner membranes called christae. Plant cells tend to have fewer mitochondria than animal cells; the number range from one for the unicellular alga, *Microsterias,* to 500,000 for the giant amoeba, *Chaos chaos.*

When seen in a living cell, mitochondria appear to be in constant motion. They are the respiratory centers for the cell. It is in the mitochondria where carbohydrates, fats, and to a lesser extent, proteins are metabolized to supply energy for the cell. In a series of chemical reactions catalyzed by enzymes, compounds of higher chemical energy are converted to compounds of a lower chemical level, and the energy difference is used to synthesize the high energy-molecule, adenosine triphosphate (ATP). It is this energy-rich chemical that the mitochondria distribute around to the various sites of synthesis to activate compounds for conversion to other chemical structures.

In green plants the organelle that serves to trap sunlight is a structurally complex particle called the chloroplast. The number of chloroplasts for plant cells varies. In some algae, such as the filamentous *Spirogyria*, there is only a single chloroplast to each cell; whereas, a cell in the spongy part of a grass leaf may have 30 or 40 chloroplasts.

There are other organelles in eucaryotic cells that have evolved as forms of life became more advanced. The Golgi apparatus, for instance, is a system of membranes used in the packaging of proteins secreted, such as digestive enzymes. These proteins are accumulated in the Golgi apparatus, carbohydrate is added, and a large number of molecules are wrapped in a membrane. The package is then passed to the edge of the cell where it releases its contents to the outside.

Lysosomes are membranous sacs which contain enzymes capable of digesting proteins, DNA, RNA and carbohydrates. One function of the lysosomes is to digest pieces of food taken into the cell. The lysosome has also one final function. When the cell dies, the lysosome sac bursts and the released enzymes digest the cellular biopolymers back to their monomeric units, thus obliterating the chemical organization that made the cell a biological entity, and returning the building blocks to be used again.

All cells are encased in a membrane structure with unique properties for the containment of cellular components and as a semipermeable barrier to the outside environment. One of the universal features of cellular membranes is their protein-lipid nature; and of the lipids, phospholipids have characteristics that make them particularly suitable for the membrane.

When eucaryotes evolved, they retained the architecture of the cellular membrane and extended it greatly. When viewed by an electron microscope, the interior of a eucaryotic cell is seen as a maze of

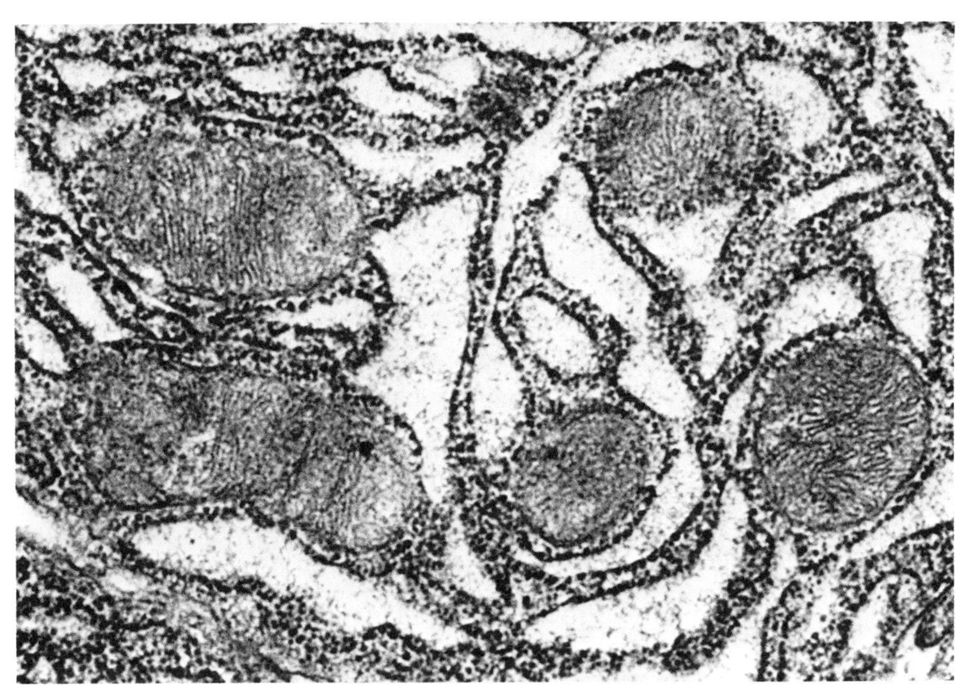

Mitochondria in close association with the endoplasmic reticulum. The labyrinth of inner membranes is clearly visible in the individual mitochondria. Magnification is 46,400 X. (Courtesy of K. Naserian, USDA Laboratory)

sections housing the cytoplasm and the subcellular particles. Invaginations of the membrane intrude deep into the cell and the elaborate cytoplasmic membrane system meanders through the cell as a continuation of the cell membrane. This involved system of membrane, the endoplasmic reticulum, serves more than to increase the surface area, and is now recognized as an important part of the cell for the manufacture of cellular products; within the structure are enzymes which control reactions in strategic parts of the cell. The endoplasmic reticulum is a major adaptive modification of the eucaryotic cells not found in the procaryotes. Its channeling through the interior of the cell apparently permits some direct transport of various molecules and ions from one part of the cell to another, and even out of the cell.

The cell is the basic structural unit of life, but there are three major types of living organisms: the procaryotes, the eucaryotes and the multicellular plants and animals. Since evolution has a tendency to move from the simple to the more complex, it is reasonable to believe life began with a primitive type of procaryotic cell. But there is no transition between procaryotic cells and the eucaryotes. One is a simple capsule of cytoplasmic reactions and the other is an assembly of complex subcellular units all working in a concerted operation. This single step is viewed as a biological leap equal to or greater than the crossover from single-celled microscopic eucaryotic organisms to the *Metazoa,* or multicellular animals, and man.

References

1. J. Cairns, from Braum: **Bacterial Genetics**, 2nd ed., W.B. Saunders Co., Philadelphia, 1965.
2. B. Byers, Structure and formation of ribosome crystal in hyperthermic chick embryo cells, *J. Mol. Biol.* **26**, 155-167 (1967).

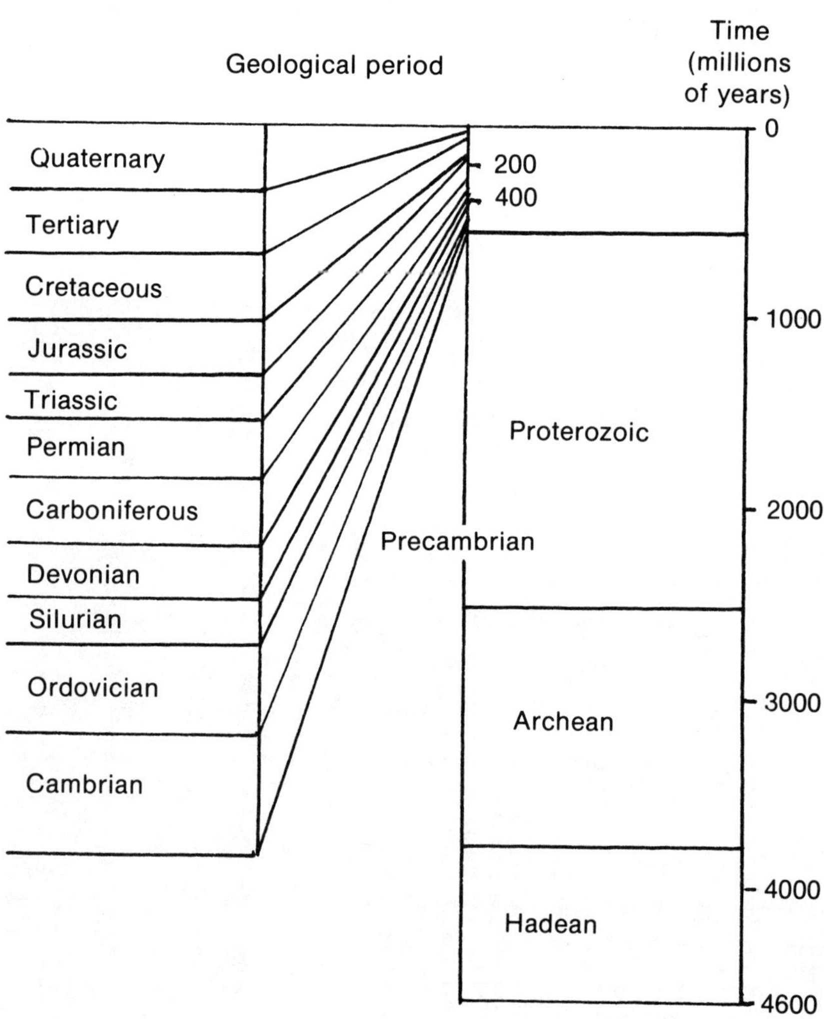
Geological period
Time (millions of years)
Quaternary
Tertiary
Cretaceous
Jurassic
Triassic
Permian
Carboniferous
Devonian
Silurian
Ordovician
Cambrian
Precambrian
Proterozoic
Archean
Hadean
0
200
400
1000
2000
3000
4000
4600

8 *Life in the Precambrian*

The enormous thicknesses of Cambrian strata attest to the millions upon millions of years that life existed only on the level of sponges, jellyfish and the trilobites. In the Ingo Mountains of California the strata containing trilobites and archaeocyathids, an extinct type of calcareous sponge, extend for 14,000 feet, or nearly 3 miles. Yet, this is not down to the point when life first appeared. There is tangible evidence that living organisms existed on earth for a very long time before the Cambrian Period.

The Ediacara fossils and others found below the Cambrian strata that began 570 million years ago have caused a restriction in the definition of Cambrian rocks to those strata that contain fossils recognized to be characteristically Cambrian. As more geological surveys were conducted, it became apparent the Cambrian fossils emerged from a trail that led back deep into the Precambrian. In Morocco it was found that 3,000 feet of archaeocyathid-bearing strata conformably underlie the lowest Cambrian, and in turn rest upon 10,000-foot-thick limestone containing the ancient remains of "water-biscuits," the calcareous masses of fossiliferous mats and tufts with concentric laminations that grew in shallow water.

These cabbage-shaped or branched laminated structures called stromatolites are the most widespread and abundant fossils of the Precambrian. They are generally composed of limestone or dolomite, but in some cases they are siliceous. Stromatolites were probably formed in an intertidal environment in the Precambrian in the same manner they are still being formed today — by blue-green algae. Many of these hemispheroidal fossils are as small as buttons, but others can be thousands of feet in area. The giant stromatolite domes in the Belt Series near Helena, Montana, are up to 15 feet thick and extend for thousands of feet.[1]

The stromatolites were formed in greatest abundance during the Middle and Late Precambrian, but their occurrence extends back into the Archean where they have been found in the African Pongola Formation dated at around 3 billion years. Like most fossil stromatolites, those of the Pongola show no cellular detail. Nevertheless, they resemble structures of the type being formed today in the Bahamas and at Shark Bay, Western Austrailia,[2] and well-preserved stromatolites of various ages have yielded microscopic cellular detail. No inorganic processes are known which form such structures.

Stromatolites are not only evidence that the blue-gree algae must have an extremely old ancestry. An additional testimony is the oxygen. The earth's atmosphere containing 21 percent free oxygen is an oddity in a universe that is 87 percent hydrogen. The oxygen-liberating photosynthesis has created an oxidizing atmosphere that has elevated all life to a thermodynamically unstable situation.

Recent stromatolites at Shark Bay, Australia. (Reproduced with permission of the Palaeontological Association from M.R. Walter, **Special Papers in Palaeontology 11**, *1972.*

Oxidation of organic compounds is a spontaneous reaction, which means that without a continual input of energy, all biological matter would ultimately revert back to the oxidized state of carbon dioxide and water. This unstable condition is maintained by the absorption of energy from sunlight for the reduction of carbon dioxide and the liberation of oxygen — 90 percent being generated by the planktonic algae of the oceans. It has been estimated that if photosynthesis were to cease today, all the oxygen in the atmosphere would disappear within 2,000 years through absorption by rocks unsaturated with respect to oxygen.[3]

Despite the earth losing its protoplanetary atmospheric hydrogen, the atmosphere formed by outgassing was also reduced and devoid of free oxygen. For photosynthetic organisms to oxidize the constituents of the atmosphere and the hydrosphere before the buildup of free atmospheric oxygen was possible must have taken an extremely long time. But there is geological evidence that free oxygen began to accumulate in the atmosphere as long ago as 2 billion years. Between 2.3 and 2.0 billion years ago there was the last apparent occurence of abundant and easily oxidized detrital pyrite and uranite.[4] These minerals which were eroded from rocks and transported considerable distance before being laid down in sediments would have been oxidized if the atmosphere at the time had contained significant levels of oxygen. The fact that they do not occur in later sediments as detrital deposits in abundance suggests that atmospheric oxygen was beginning to build up at this time.

And between 2.2 and 1.9 billion years ago, virtually the last and volumetrically the greatest phase of the deposition of banded iron formation took place.[5] The reducing conditions of the Archean and Early Proterzoic favored the formation of minerals containing ferrous iron from the alteration of basaltic rocks. The characteristic minerals that occur in the iron formations are siderite (iron carbonate), greenalite (iron silicate) and pyrite (iron sulfide) in association with chert, originally an amorphous silica. But much if not most of iron ore formation was biogenic. Ferrous salts are relatively soluble, whereas oxidized iron is not. The liberation of oxygen by photosynthetic organisms oxidized the ferrous iron creating deposits of precipitated iron. These became banded iron formations, unique rocks consisting of alternating layers of iron-rich and iron-poor silica representing rhythmically banded precipitated sediment.

It is uncertain whether the cherty iron zones of the 3.76 billion-year-old Isua Iron Formation of West Greenland[6] or the 3.4 billion-year-old Onverwacht Group of Africa resulted from biological activity. The last major episode of banded iron formation was 1.8 to 2.0 billion years ago. Thereafter, with much or most of the iron oxidized, the oxygen was added to the atmosphere. Younger iron generally consists of red beds, individual grains coated with ferric oxide.

The paleochemistry of oxygen can thus be traced back to the Precambrian red beds and limestones. But additionally, there are Precambrian "coals" containing beds of almost pure carbon found in Michigan and Finland. It is difficult to explain these except that they apparently were formed by well-organized photosynthetic life. As impressive as some of the evidence is of early life forms, it is circumstantial in that these are products of Precambrian life — not fossils of the actual organisms.

Then in the early 1950's, Stanley Tyler of the Department of Geology, University of Wisconsin, was prospecting for iron along the Michigan shores of Lake Superior when he came upon ancient coal deposits. The coal contained what he thought to be microscopic plants. Tyler showed the coal to William Shrock, the chairman of the geology department at the Massachusetts Institute of Technology. Shrock thought the plants looked like the fungus that grows on a jar of jelly that has been left open too long and suggested to Tyler that he show them to Harvard botanist, Elso Barghoorn.

The result of this consultation was that Tyler and Barghoorn teamed up and made a field trip to the site for a closer study. A search for whatever had wrinkled the seam of coal led the two to the Canadian side where they found black shales and chert known as the Gunflint Formation, a layer of Precambrian rock on the northern shores of Lake Superior near Schreiber, Ontario, just east of Thunder Bay. The Gunflint chert is overlain by shale and is generally regarded as Middle Hurian of the Canadian Shield.

Samples of the chert were collected and cut with a diamond saw into slices so thin that light could pass through them. When Barghoorn viewed the thin sections through a microscope, he saw microscopic plants — fossils of minute organisms too small to be seen by an unaided eye that had lived during the Precambrian.

Tyler and Barghoorn cut more than 800 thin sections of the flintlike black chert for study. Hydrofluoric acid was used to dissolve the silica of the bedded chert to free fragments of the primitive plants, and the organic residue showed spores and filaments. Five morphologically distinct forms of biota were recognized: two were algal, two fungal, and one appeared to be calcareous flagellate. These small primitive plants seemed to be representative of blue-green algae and simple forms of fungi. The Gunflint Formation has been dated at 1.9 to 2.0 billion years old, making these fossils at that time the oldest structurally preserved organisms.[7]

In a subsequent paper in 1965, Barghoorn and Tyler[8] reported finding an array of microscopic fossils in other samples of the Gunflint Formation. In this paper they show 12 assemblages of unicellular spheroidal and filamentous microfossils. From their morphology the spheroids appeared to be related to the coccoid blue-green algae, and the filamentous fossils to the modern iron bacteria, *Sphaerotilus* and *Siderococcus.* These were all excellent specimens preserved by permineralization of the cellular structure in a siliceous matrix. Here, entombed in 2 billion-year-old chert were the remains of the microorganisms that precipitated the ironstone formations and generated the free oxygen that made future life possible.

Soon thereafter, J. William Schopf,[9] a former graduate student with Barghoorn and presently at the University of California, Los Angeles, found varied assemblages of excellently well-preserved spheroidal and filamentous plant microfossils in the Bitter Spring Formation of Northern Territory, Australia. These fossils of microbiota occurred in carbonaceous cherts of the Late Precambrian strata in the Ross River area of Central Australia and were thought to be approximately 1 billion years in age. The fossils resulted from algae that apparently grew as laminar sheets or mats in a marine environment forming widespread algal stromatolites. Of 19 species that Schopf found, 14 were of modern algal families. The filamentous and coccoid

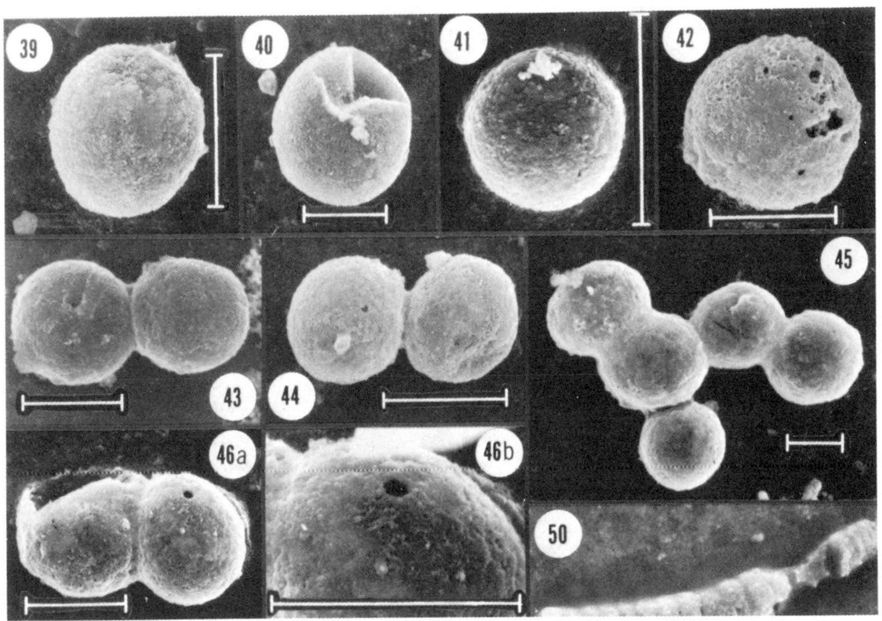

Scanning electron micrographs showing well preserved microfossils from the Late Precambrian (ca. 850 million year-old) Bitter Springs Formation of central Australia. (Courtesy of J.W. Schopf. Proc. XXIV Internat. Geol. Cong., Sect. 1, Montreal, 1972, pp. 68-77)

blue-green algae were predominant and must have been highly diversified at this time 1 billion years ago.

Apparently the blue-green algae were flourishing as early as 2 billion years ago and may well have been responsible for the Bulawayan stromatolites of Rhodesia which formed 2.6 billion years ago, and the the Pongola stromatolites at 3 billion years. Nevertheless, these primitive plants would have had to have predecessors that existed even earlier — microorganisms that were more ancient than the oldest blue-green algae. A goal of paleobiology became a search to push back the fossil record as close as possible to the moment when life began on earth.

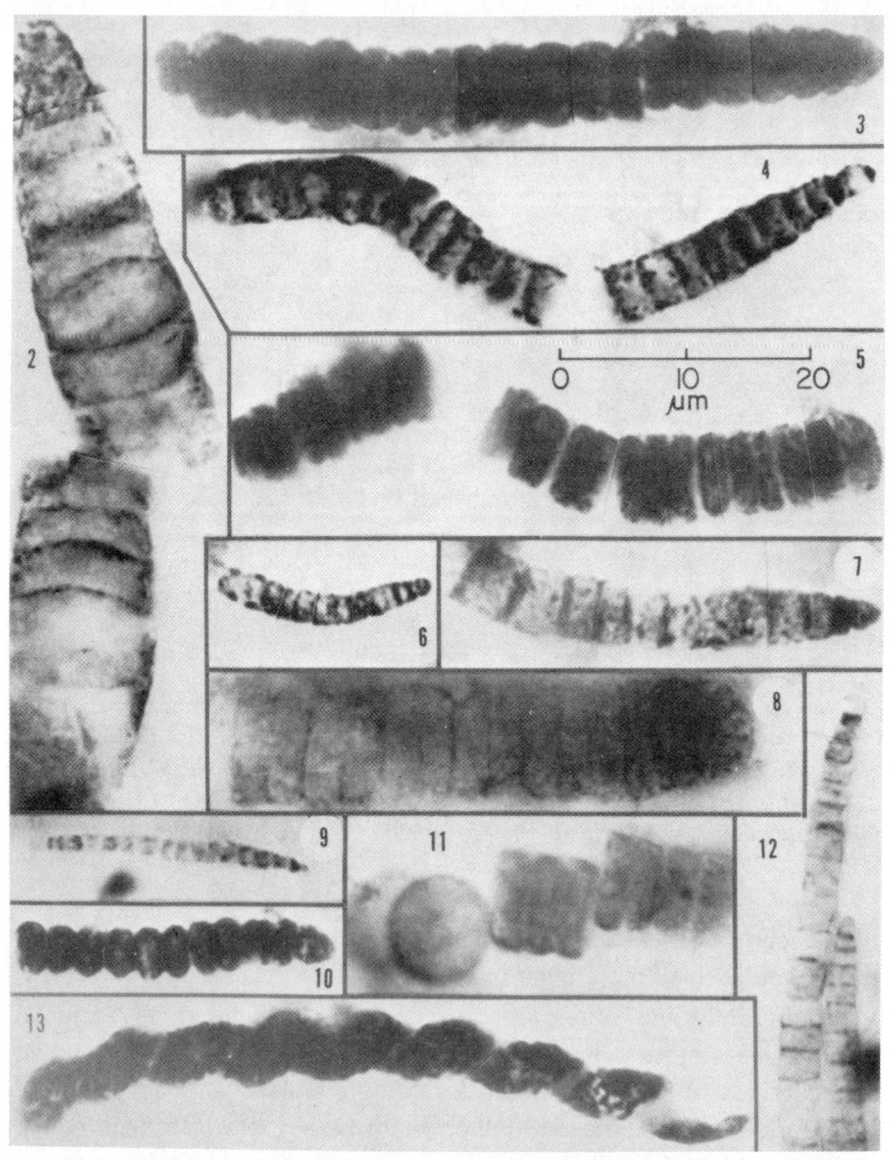
3
4
5
0
10
20
μm
6
7
8
9
11
12
10
13
2

Optical photomicrographs showing cellularly preserved, filamentous, blue-green algae from the Late Precambrian Bitter Springs Formation of central Australia, about 850 million years in age. Similar types of blue-green algae dominated the earth's biota beginning at least as early as 2,300 million years ago and extending to near the close of the Precambrian about 600 million years ago. (Courtesy of J.W. Schopf. Proc. XXIV Internat. Geol. Cong., Sect. 1, Montreal, 1972, pp. 68-77).

In 1965, Barghoorn was collecting cherts from several localities in the Barberton Mountain Land of the area of eastern Transvaal in South Africa near the Swaziland border where the waters of the Umbilizi River flow through rolling hills on their way to Mozambique and the Indian Ocean. The Barberton Mountain Land is a few hundred square miles of hills formed of Archean greenstone belts whose ages date back as far as 3.4 billion years. The Swaziland Series of the formation consists of the Fig Tree Group underlain by the Onverwacht Series. Carbon is widespread in the formation, and in some places shales that were converted to graphitic schists by metamorphism are found. Some black cherts contain as much as 0.20 percent organic matter.

Barghoorn and Schopf examined rocks of the Fig Tree Group by light microscope. The rock matrix contained many laminations of dark-colored, nearly opaque particles of organic substances. The laminations being aligned parallel to strata of chert suggested deposition in an aqueous environment. Nothing resembling fossils of microorganisms could be seen by the microscope. But then Schopf polished the surface of the rock sections and viewed them through an electron microscope. Under the greater magnification it was possible to see what had not been seen before. There were rod-like structures 0.5 to 0.7 millimicron long and 0.2 millimicron in diameter. They resembled rod-shaped bacteria! Later, spheroidal microfossils 17 to 20 millimcra in diameter resembling modern blue-green algae of the coccoid group were also found. In all, 28 well-defined specimens were detected in the fossils of the microbiota. These were fossils of what appeared to be bacteria that had been living on earth 3.0 to 3.3 billion years ago.[10]

About the same time, Hans Pflug[11] of the Justus Leibig University of Giessen, West Germany, was examining cherts and shales of the Fig Tree sediments for structured organic remains. In samples collected in the vicinity of the Sheba Gold Mine near Barberton he found assemblages of remains of organisms. Chemical and optical studies of the organic material showed these structures to have cell walls. Pflug suggested a similarity to ocalean blue-green algae. The radiometric dating placed the age of 3.2 billion years.

These microfossils from the Fig Tree Group have to be regarded almost certainly of biological origin and are probably remnants of single-celled alga-like microorganisms. The organic composition, the constant morphology, the limited size range and the similar appearance to the excellently preserved microfossils of the Gunflint cherts and the blue-green algae of the Bitter Spring Formation are strong indications of a unicellular non-colonial alga-like form of life on earth over 3 billion years ago.

Approximately 35,000 feet below the Fig Tree Group lie the Onverwacht Series, covering 400 square miles of the southern part of the Mountain Land and 50,000 feet thick. In 1968, A.E.J. Engel and others[12] reported finding cup-shaped and spherical microstructures in this group of Archean rocks. The size of 590 structures range from 6 to 193 millimicra with no dominant size. This variance of 30-fold appeared, however, to be too much of a spread to be characteristic of organized biological systems.

Following this report, Jim Brooks and Marjorie Muir[13] investigated specimens of the Onverwacht strata by first treating slices of uncrushed rock with 20 percent hydroflouric acid to digest the inorganic matrix. They recovered a concentrated dark residue of organic material representing 0.2 to 0.48 percent by weight of the samples. When viewed with an electron microscope the organic material was seen to be fossil remains of what appeared to be cell walls of microorganisms. There are basically two types: spheroids 7 to 10 millimicra in diameter; and filamentous forms, 15 to 20 millimicra in size. These fossils of microorganisms showed morphological similarities with those of the overlying and younger Fig Tree Group.

Chemical extraction and analysis of the organic matter from the

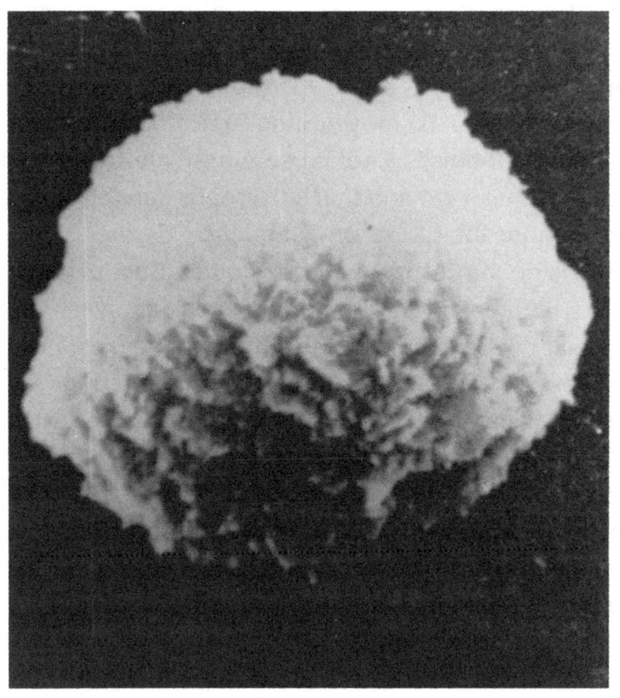

Microfossil from the Onverwacht Formation. (Reproduced with permission, J. Brooks and G. Shaw, **Origin and Development of Living Systems,** *Academic Press, 1973)*

Fig Tree Group have shown 0.003 to 0.015 parts per million of aliphatic hydrocarbons (C_{15}-C_{25}) and larger amounts of pristane.[14] The Onverwacht chert had free aliphatic hydrocarbons, fatty acids, *n*-paraffins C_{12}-C_{24}, pristane and phytane.[15] Pristane and phytane, being isoprenoid hydrocarbons, are indicative of biogenic origin. But Nagy,[16] examining the porosity and permeability of the Onverwacht chert, showed that the hydrocarbons could have percolated into the rocks from above.

Nevertheless, most of the organic material in the rocks is kerogen, an intractable and insoluble residue that would have been formed in place.

The kerogen was analyzed in a different manner by Dorothy Oehler[17] while working on her thesis with Schopf at UCLA. Photosynthetic organisms show a preference for $^{12}CO_2$ over $^{13}CO_2$ when they absorb carbon dioxide. By measuring the $^{13}C/^{12}C$ ratio in kerogen it is possible to establish whether or not it came form photosynthesis. Oehler's results[18] suggest that it did and that autotrophs capable of fixing CO_2 had been on earth more than 3 billion years ago.

Using the carbon isotope method, Schopf and his students[19] applied it to study the oldest stromatolites then known — those of the Bulawayan Formation. They confirmed that these structures were created by photosynthetic organisms and Schopf suggested their age of 2.6 billion years might be minimal for the time of origin of blue-green algae or photosynthetic bacteria as filamentous, integrated biological communities. The blue-green algae, or at least the photobacterial primitive ancestors of the algae, may go back as far as the earliest known fossils of living organisms on earth — those of the Onverwacht Series 3.4 billion years old.

These microfossils from the Archean and Proterozoic resembling bacteria and blue-green algae have been found in Ontario, eastern California, southern Africa, central and southern Australia and the U.S.S.R.[20] But there is a degree of uncertainty about organized structures over around 2 billion years old. Organic material will commonly aggregate into spheroids, so this alone is not sufficient in extablishing biogenic origin. Of the more than 20 papers describing fossil-like microstructures in excess of 3 billion years, many are probably not fossils of organisms.[21] Nevertheless, stromatolites of probable algal origin were flourishing as much as 3.0 to 3.1 billion years ago, and the algae responsible for them could be related to forms seen in the Fig Tree and Onverwacht sedimentary rocks.

These possible microorganisms of the Archean are assumed to have been procaryotes, the most primitive form of a living cell. At some time in the Precambrian Era the eucaryotic cells that gave rise to all higher forms of life had to have appeared. If Preston Cloud, a geologist at the University of California, Santa Barbara, is correct, eucaryotes emerged between around 2.0 and 1.3 billion years ago.

In 1966, Cloud and his coworkers collected samples from black chert found 18.5 meters below the upper contact of the Beck Spring Dolomite in eastern California. When thin sections were studied, they revealed preserved unicells and spiny sporelike bodies. These fossils were a line of microscopic spherical and filamentous shapes not unlike older fossilized microorganisms — except for two important differences: they were much larger than older forms; and some of the filamentous forms were branched.[22] Recent analysis of microfossils for size and distribution show that eucaryotes are generally about ten times larger than the procaryotes.[23]

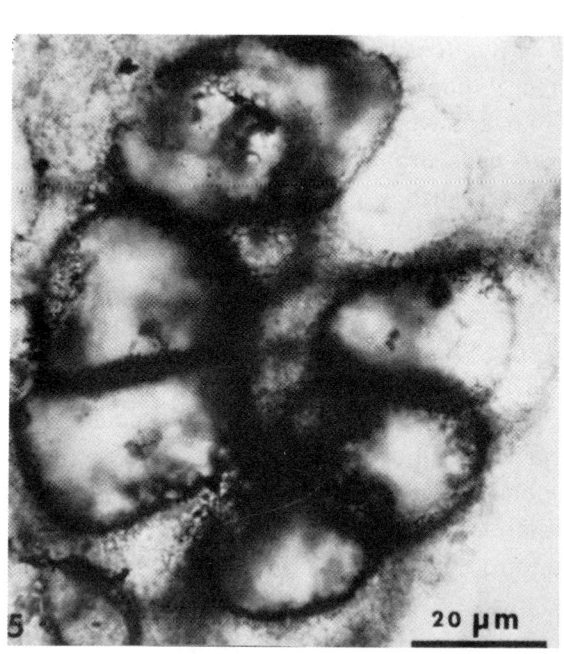

Photomicrographs of Beck Spring Dolomite microfossils showing what appear to be eucaryotic cells. (Courtesy of Gerald R. Licari, East Los Angeles College)

Fossiliferous outcrops occur 2,900 meters below the lowest metazoan trace fossils and are younger than 1.7 billion years. These have been correlated to another group dated at 1.2 to 1.4 billion years of age. The most numerous fossils from the various localities are filamentous blue-green algae placed in the new genus, *Beckspringia.*[24] By studying the microflora in formations of determined radiogenic ages, Licari and Cloud have attempted to bracket the origin of eucaryotes between about 1.3 and 1.6 billion years ago.[25]

A dispute exists as to when the eucaryotes first appeared. Helen Tappan[26] of the University of California, Los Angeles, believes they existed at the time of the Gunflint Formation 2 billion years ago. Knoll and Bargoorn,[27] on the other hand, deny the existence of fossilized cell organelles and the appearance of eucaryotic cells before the *Metazoa.* If Preston Cloud, Gerald Licari and the others are correct about the Beck Spring Dolomite fossils, however, these fossils will then mark the appearance of the greatest biological breakthrough in the history of life on earth — the eucaryotic cell.

The fossil record of the transitional period from the unicellular microorganisms 1 billion years ago to the Ediacara fauna 680 million years ago when the metazoae, or multicellular animals, were emerging with cells organized in layers of tissue is still sketchy. Nonetheless, a recent discovery has helped to bridge the gap. Bonnie Bloeser and Schopf at UCLA, Robert Horodyski of Tulane University and William Breed of the Museum of Northern Arizona[28] have reported finding microfossils in Precambrian rocks in the Grand Canyon in Arizona belonging to a distinctive group of one-celled planktonic organisms called chitinozoans and having an age of 750±100 million years. The chitinozoans are thought to be unicellular heterotrophs, which mean they, like all animals, cannot produce their own food, but depending upon the photosynthesis of plants for food. The chitinozoans are heterotrophs that exist between the multicellular animals and the autotrophic algae.

References

1. Adolph Knopf, The boulder batholiths of Montana, *Amer. J. Sci.* **255**, 81-103 (1957).
2. M.R. Walter, **Stromatolites and Biostratigraphy of the Australian Precambrian and Cambrian**, The Palaeontological Association, London, 1972.
3. Preston Cloud and Aharon Gibor, The oxygen cycle, *Sci. Amer.* **223**, 110-123 (1970).
4. P. Cloud, Evolution of ecosystems, *Amer. Scientist* **62**, 54-66 (1974).
5. S.S. Gildrich, Ages of Precambrian banded Iron-Formation, *Econ. Geol.* **68**, 1126-1134 (1973).
6. S. Moorbath, R.K. O'Nions and R.J. Pankhurst, Early Archean age for the Isua Iron Formation, West Greenland, *Nature* **245**, 138-139 (1973).
7. S.A. Tyler and E.S. Barghoorn, Occurrences of structurally preserved plants in Pre-Cambrian rocks of the Canadian Shield, *Science* **119**, 606-608 (1954).
8. E.S. Barghoorn and S.A. Tyler, Microorganisms from the Gunflint chert, *Science* **147**, 563-577 (1965).
9. J.W. Schopf, Microflora of the Bitter Spring Formation, Late Pre-Cambrian, Central Australia,*J. Palentol.* **42**, 650-688 (1968).
10. E.S. Barghoorn and J.W. Schopf, Alga-like fossils from the Early Precambrian of South Africa, *Science* **156**, 508-512 (1967).
11. Hans D. Pflüg, Structured organic remains from the Fig Tree Series (Precambrian of the Barberton Mountain Land, South Africa), *Rev. Palaebot. Palynol.* **5**, 5-29 (1967).
12 A. Engel, B. Nagy, L.A. Nagy, E.G. Engel, G.O.W. Kremp and C.M. Drew, Algal-like forms in Onverwacht Series, South Africa: oldest recognized life-like forms on earth, *Science* **161**, 1005-1008 (1968).
13. J. Brooks and M.D. Muir, Chemistry and Morphology of the micro-organisms in the Early Precambrian rocks of the Onverwacht Group, I.U.P.A.C. International Symposium on Chemistry in Evolution and Systematics, held at Strasbourg, France, July 3-8, 1972.
14. J. Oró and D.W. Noones, Aliphatic hydrocarbons in Precambrian rocks, *Nature* **213**, 1082-1083 (1967).
15. J. Han and M. Calvin, Occurrence of fatty acids and aliphatic hydrocarbons in a 3.4 billion-year-old sediment, *Nature* **224**, 576-577 (1969).
16. B. Nagy, Porosity and permeability of the Early Precambrian Onverwacht chert: origin of the hydrocarbon content, *Geochim. Cosmochim. Acta* **34**, 525-527 (1970).
17. D.Z. Oehler, **Carbon Isotopic and Electron Microscope Studies of Organic Remains in Precambrian Rocks**, Ph.D. thesis, Univ. Calif. Los Angeles, 1973.
18. D.Z. Oehler, J.W. Schopf and K.A. Kvenholden, Carbon isotopic studies of organic matter in Precambrian rocks, *Science* **175**, 1246-1248 (1972).
19. J.W. Schopf, Biogenicity and significance of the oldest known stromatolites, *J. Palentol.* **45**, 477-485 (1971).
20. A.S. Lopuchin, Structures of biogenic origin from Early Precambrian rocks óf Euro-Asia, *Origins of Life* **6**, 45-57 (1975).

21. J. William Schopf, Are the oldest "fossils," fossils? *Origins of Life* **7**, 19-36 (1976).
22. P.E. Cloud, G.R. Licari, L.A. Wright and B.W. Trowel, Proterozoic eucaryotes from eastern California, *Proc. Nat. Acad. Sci.* **62**, 623-630 (1969).
23. J. William Schopf and Dorothy Z. Oehler, How old are the eucaryotes? *Science* **193**, 47-49 (1976).
24. Gerald R. Licari, Biogeology of the late pre-Phanerozoic Beck Spring Dolomite of eastern California, *J. Paleontol.* **52**, 767-792 (1978).
25. G.R. Licari and P. Cloud, Prokaryotic algae associated with Australian Proterozoic stromatolites, *Proc. Nat. Acad. Sci.* **62**, 56-62 (1972).
26. H. Tappan, Possible eucaryotic algae (Baugiophycidae) among early Proterozoic microfossils, *Geol. Soc. Am. Bull.* **87**, 633-639 (1976).
27. A.H. Knoll and E.S. Barghoorn, Precambrian eukaryotic organisms: a reassessment of the evidence, *Science* **190**, 52-54 (1975).
28. B. Bloessner, J.W. Schopf, R.J. Horodyski and W.J. Breed, Chitinozoans from the Late Precambrian Chuar Group of the Grand Canyon, *Science* **195**, 676-679 (1977).

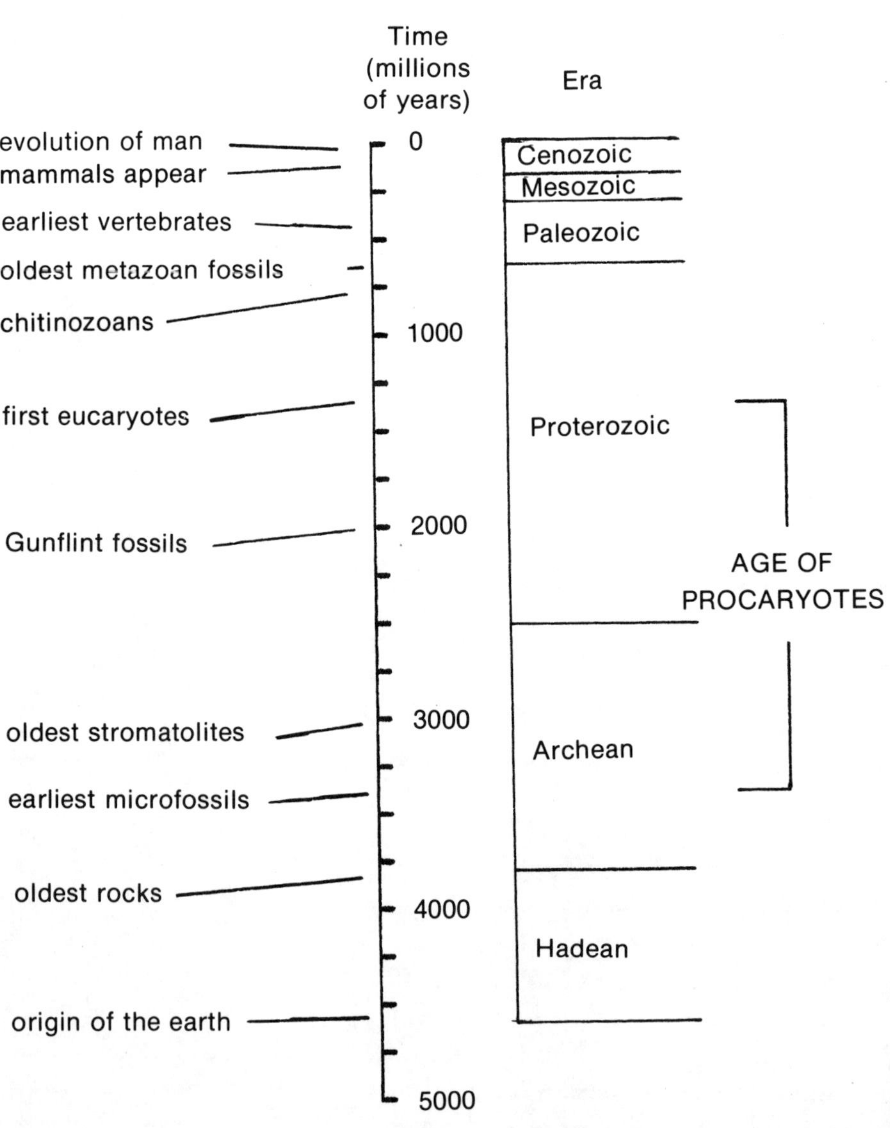
Time
(millions
of years)
Era
evolution of man
mammals appear
earliest vertebrates
oldest metazoan fossils
chitinozoans
first eucaryotes
Gunflint fossils
oldest stromatolites
earliest microfossils
oldest rocks
origin of the earth
0
1000
2000
3000
4000
5000
Cenozoic
Mesozoic
Paleozoic
Proterozoic
Archean
Hadean
AGE OF
PROCARYOTES

9
The Age of the Procaryotes

The earth had traveled around the sun over one billion times before even the simplest form of living thing appeared that has left any trace of its existence. It was a world much different from today. The barren rocky surface that thrust above the primordial ocean was the dark gray and black face of volcanoes; the atmosphere had no oxygen and consisted of nitrogen, some hydrogen, carbon monoxide and carbon dioxide at less than 1 percent but still as much as ten times the present; and the oceans were shallow basins of hot wash of the basaltic surface.

The sediments were the detritus from the erosion of predominantly basaltic rocks of volcanic origin being deposited in an anaerobic marine environment. The reducing conditions of the atmosphere and the oceans resulted in an appreciable amount of ferrous and sulfide ions in the seawater. The oceans were not to begin taking on modern characteristics until the recycling of sediments predominated over the erosion of basaltic rocks and the atmosphere contained free oxygen. This time was still far in the future.

It was a strange setting — quite alien to what we normally associate as conducive to life. But there it happened. Sometime before 3.4 billion years ago an aggregation of relatively small and simple organic compounds assembled in a lipid envelope, and between them, began to mediate elementary reactions. Those cells that were able to assimulate available substances and condense them into polynucleotides and polypeptides, replicated and took on the nature of primitive bacteria. Metabolism developed from reactions the cells were able to use to degrade materials for their chemical energy and reactive products. In order to accomplish this, chemical energy had to be held in a carrier and transferred to other molecules to be converted to activated derivatives. Pyrophosphates, and particularly ATP, were adopted early and possibly initially. Once activated derivatives were formed, they were energetically favored to follow spontaneous degradation — reactions that proceed on their own, but often slowly, unless promoted by a catalyst.

This level of development probably soon gave rise to another organism that was able to draw from the inexhaustible supply of CO_2 for its carbon. In order to do so it needed a source of energy and hydrogen. Both were in plentiful supply. All that was needed was a chemical procedure which could be used to extract and harness them. The earth's surface was bathed in boundless radiation from the sun each day, and the visible light was absorbed by colored substances and converted to heat. If, instead of being squandered as thermal energy, the light energy were trapped and held in a chemical structure long enough to be used to generate ATP and reduce CO , the organism would have a supply of energy even when no food substances existed.

It apparently was at this stage that the first ferredoxin appeared. Formed from a complex of polypeptide and the abundant iron sulfide, this biochemical became incorporated into the biochemical system early and has remained as a universal constituent of living cells ever since. As a component of the photosynthesis apparatus, ferredoxin was able to accept the energy of light absorbed by pigments and retain it as an electron energy level until it could be used to reduce CO_2.

The earliest photosynthetic organism would then have required a pigment, ferredoxin and a source of hydrogen. A donor of hydrogen for the beginning organism would have been substances which required the least amount of energy to extract the hydrogen and were still readily available. This supply appears to have been accessible organic matter.

Presumably, the earliest organisms were heterotrophs that thrived by metabolizing a reservoir of organic matter, but developed a rudimentary form of photosynthesis when the food supply neared exhaustion. There survives today a pigmented bacterium called *Athiorhodacea* that seems to be of this early stage of life. The *Athiorhodacea* is able to grow anaerobically as a heterotroph in solutions containing butyric acid and other organic nutrients and use the chemical energy it derives from them; but this organism is also able to absorb light and carry out the photocatalytic transfer of hydrogen and reduce CO_2. Its source of hydrogen in this case is the nonutilizable organic matter.

But when the organic matter was no longer available or in short supply, another source of hydrogen was needed. Photosynthetic bacteria evolved that were capable of using H_2S as their hydrogen donor. This type of anaerobe is still today as the purple sulfur bacteria *(Thiorhodaceae)* and the green sulfur bacteria *(Chlorobacteriaceae)*, found in shallow lagoons and sea inlets that are rich in H_2S. In each of these types of photosynthesis, oxygen is not a by-product.

These bacterial forms of photosynthetic life may have been the dominant organisms on earth for several hundred million years; the fixation of CO_2 was certainly being carried out for a considerably long time before organisms evolved to the point of being capable of an oxygen-liberating photosynthesis. Eventually, however, because of the failing supply of the other hydrogen donors, or perhaps because of its sheer abundance, an organism became biochemically sophisticated enough to extract hydrogen from the most plentiful supply on earth — water. It requires 10 times as much light energy to remove hydrogen from water than from H_2S, but the supply was inexhaustible. The organism that developed the photocatalysis of water became the blue-green algae and began the 3-billion-year history of oxygen production.

It has not been established exactly at what time the blue-green algae emerged on the scene. The carbon isotope studies of Oehler[1] indicate that the fixation of CO_2 was coterminous with the oldest microfossils at 3.4 billion years ago. This process could have taken millions of years to develop and would still have coincided with the earliest fossils. Nevertheless, the Bulawayan stromatolites of Rhodesia apparently are the result of blue-green algae activity. Since they are dated at 2.6 billion years, an interval of 800 million years, or longer than it has taken man to evolve from a single-cell protozoan, passed from the first appearance of life to when the blue-green algae were growing in abundance in the tepid waters of the Archean seas.

The blue-green algae (*Cyanophyla*) are certainly among the most ancient forms of life to appear on earth — and one of the most successful. These simple microscopic organisms thrive even today and occur in greatest abundance in small freshwater bodies — ponds, ditches and shallow lakes — during and immediately after periods of high air temperature. To some extent they are found everywhere from the polar regions, throughout the temperate zones to the warm waters of the tropics. And, except for some bacteria, they grow where no other organisms can — in the 80°C (176°F) waters of hot springs of New Zealand and Yellowstone.[2]

The bacteria and blue-green algae belong to a particular division of life called the Monera; all other living things are either eucaryotic unicellular microorganisms or eucaryotic multicellular forms of life. Unlike the traditional two-kingdom system of plants and animals, evolutionary relations are better represented by a five-kingdom classification. Members of the Monera are the procaryotes, distinguished by the simplicity of their cellular structure; whereas, all other forms of life are either singular or multiple eucaryotic cells in which the nucleus, the mitochondria, and other subcellular components are sheathed in a membrane. In the procaryotes, there is no separate membrane-bound constituents except for the cell itself.

The cells of blue-green algae are encased in an outer mucilaginous sheath, a middle pectin layer, and an inner wall of cellulose. In contrast to the cell walls of the other algae, those of the blue-green algae contain amino acids, as do bacterial walls. The blue-green algae developed early as a sturdy but efficient packet of photosynthesis. By extracting CO_2 and using water as the hydrogen donor, they convert it to cyanophycean starch. These algae were and still remain the simplest food-producing plants.

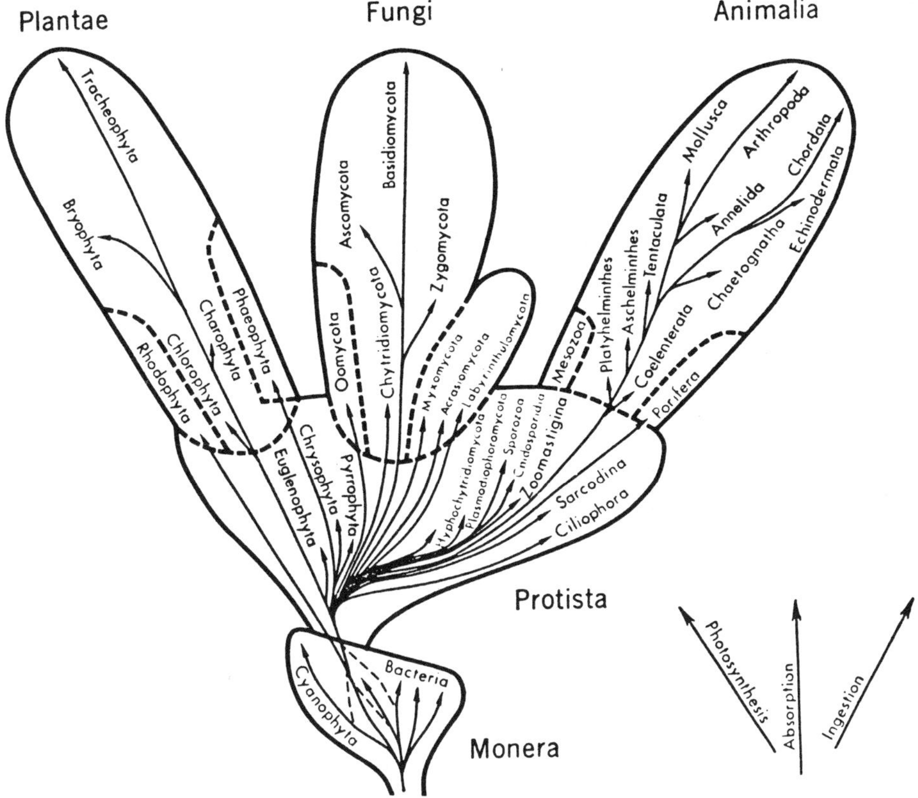

The five kingdoms are based on three levels of development: the procaryotic (Monera); eucaryotic unicellular (Protista); and eucaryotic multicellular. Each level diverges in relation to modes of nutrition. Monera have photosynthetic and absorptive; the two higher levels are divided into photosynthetic, absorptive and ingestive. (R.H. Whittaker, Science **163**, *150-160, 1969)*

The Archean ended 2.5 billion years ago with the climactic uplifting of mountains. With the Canadian Shield, this became the Kenoran province that added to the margins of the growing continent, extending from the Slave providence in the northwest to Labrador eastward across Greenland to terminate in the continental shelves of the Atlantic between

Greenland and Scotland. Comparable developments occurred in western Australia, southern India and in central and southern Africa. The sedimentary basins that were forming were of cratonal origin, in contrast to the volcanic sediments of earlier times.

When life began on earth it was in an anoxygenic environment. The atmosphere contained a small amount of hydrogen, and the rocks and most minerals in solution in the oceans were in their reduced and

*Blue-green algae (**Gloeocapsa**) magnified 40,500 times in the electron microscope. This is a longitudinal section of a cell dividing. The light central area contains the DNA; the concentric striated lines are the lamellar where photosynthesis occurs. (Courtesy of H. Stuart Pankratz, Michigan State University)*

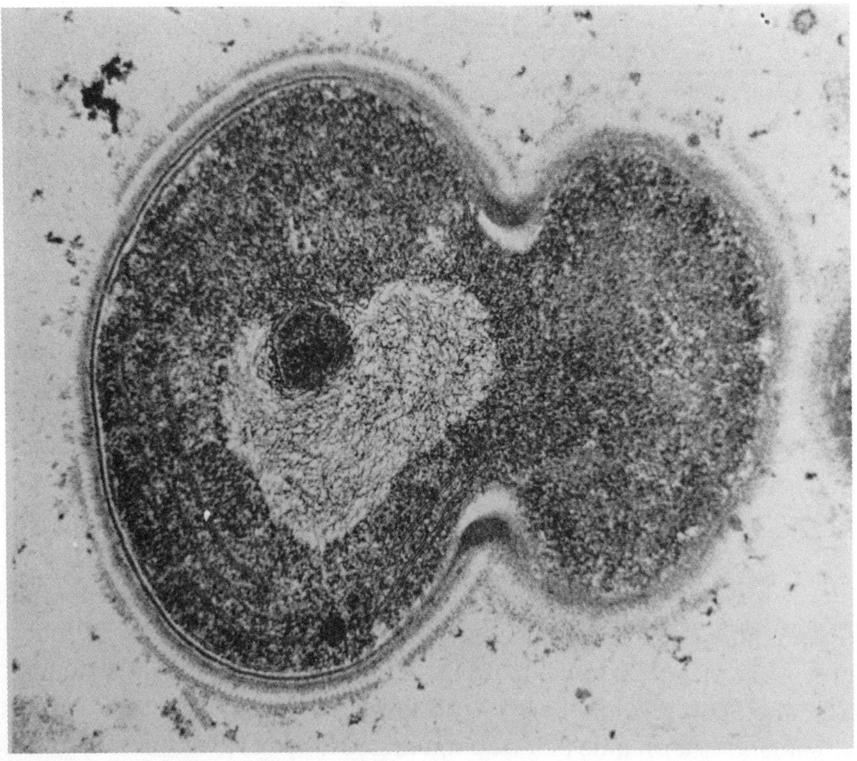

lowest valence state. This is particularly notable for iron and sulfur. Ferrous salts are relatively soluble, but oxidized iron is not. As a result, the concentration of dissolved iron in seawater today is extremely low (less than 10^{-7} M), but this was not the case during the Archean. Sulfur, which is easily oxidized, exists principally as the sulfate ion in the present oceans. But in early times, it was as the sulfide from dissolved H_2S of volcanic origin.

The primitive life that evolved under these circumstances were the anaerobic microorganisms. They metabolized their carbohydrates by fermentative degradation, extracting the energy stored in the chemical bonds when CO_2 was reduced by photosynthesis to sugars in the manner of yeast today. It was a perfectly adequate biochemical system for a simple form of life under the environmental circumstances.

But the liberation of oxygen by the blue-green algae in their photocatalysis of water introduced a perilous form of pollution to all life. Free oxygen is an extremely reactive agent that readily oxidizes reduced substances, mineral or biological. To prevent being destroyed by their own waste, the blue-green algae had to have the oxygen neutralized or removed from their immediate environment as it was generated. In the Archean oceans the most available and reactive chemical species for this role was the ferrous iron; and as the ferrous salts reacted with oxygen, the insoluble ferrous oxide precipitated. In time the evolution of oxygen was to change the character of the oceans. The blue-green algae were widespread and flourishing by the end of the Archean; after another 500 million years they were generating so much oxygen they were depleting the oceans of ferrous iron. Vast deposits of this precipitated iron banded with chert from precipitated silica became the iron ore of North America around the Great Lakes and in Labrador, in the Hemesley region of western Australia, and in Mauritania of northwest Africa.

The climatic temperature was slowly declining from the 70°C (160°F) of the Middle Archean 3 billion years ago. Between 2.2 and 2.0 billion years ago the earth entered one of its cooling cycles and the first known Ice Age occurred. From that time on this was to be a recurring episode in the earth's history.

The last great deposition of banded iron formation was 2.0 to 1.8 billion years ago; thereafter, with much or most of the iron oxidized, the oxygen was leaked to the atmosphere. Some ironstone deposits from this time contain öolites and other structures indicative of shallow water deposition, marking some of the oldest shorelines in the earth's past. The remains of these can be seen today in Labrador and in Karelia, near the border of Finland and the U.S.S.R.

By this time the kinds of microscopic life-forms had become much more diverse. This is the time of the Gunflint Iron Formation which left the multitude of bacterial and alga-like microfossils. Nevertheless, all life was on the microbial level and confined to the oceans; the land surfaces stood sterile and barren of even the most primitive form of vegetation.

Life in the oceans, however, was teeming. The efficient biological system of the blue-green algae for drawing on the unlimited reservoirs of CO_2, water and sunlight to construct their organic components allowed them to expand in an ocean-wide ecological niche. By the Middle Proterozoic, they were so much the dominant life form the time could be called the "Cyanophycean Period." And although the blue-green algae are themselves microscopic, they were leaving in shallow waters monumental evidence of their presence.

Living at a time when there was no oxygen in the atmosphere, the early biological systems were without the benefit of the ozone layer to screen out the deadly ultraviolet rays. Any organism under these circumstances survived only in sheltered niches or at depths that afforded protection from the lethal radiation. For this reason, blue-green algae evolved from predecessors most suitably adapted for weak illumination. Eventually these phytoplankton evolved thick individual gelatinous sheaths, either colored or colorless, as protection against light too intense. Many lived in colonies or shapeless masses or layers of mucus, developed as the result of dissolving and coalescing the individual sheaths. Being phototactic, they moved through any covering sediment that shut out the light completely, and as they did so their mucus cemented the particles in place. Many had sticky mucus sheaths that formed loose networks of filaments which sediment fell into, creating columnar shapes. So despite being of perishable cellular matter, blue-green algae left enduring monuments of their past existence in the widespread Precambrian stromatolites.

Around 1.5 billion years ago, the oldest deposits of calcium sulfate were being formed. Although sulfate ions may have existed in solution for some time before this date, this nevertheless indicated that there was sufficient free oxygen at this time to oxidize the sulfur acids in the oceans. With the passing of nearly three-quarters of geologic time, the oceans must have been at this time much like they are today in size, and they were taking on modern characteristics.

Having developed and evolved in an oxygen-free environment, all the microbiota that populated the oceans were anaerobic organisms; that is to say, they did not use oxidative respiration. They neither needed nor desired oxygen. To them oxygen was a deadly poison. But with the last of the ferrous iron laid down in banded iron formations, from about 1.8 billion years onward free oxygen had been going into the atmosphere from the photosynthesis reaction of the blue-green algae. It was taking over a billion years for the oxygen from photosynthesis to oxidize all the substances of the earth's atmosphere and hydrosphere, but the pace went on unabated. Eventually, this changing of the earth's environment from reducing to oxidizing conditions constituted an encroaching peril to the occupants who had been the undisputed masters of the earth for nearly 2 billion years.

Many that lived to meet the threat developed oxygen-mediating enzymes, peroxidase and catalase, to protect their biochemical constitutents from destruction by oxygen. Some presumably survived by retreating to oxygen-deficient niches and exist today as the anaerobic bacteria. But the age of the procaryotes was coming to an end. Their dominance was foredoomed by the ever-increasing oxygenation of the air and water.

It was Louis Pasteur who discovered that obligate anaerobes cannot tolerate oxygen concentrations above 1 percent of the present atmospheric level. Following the oxidation of the salts and minerals of the oceans and the reduced gases of the atmosphere, the concentration of free oxygen in the air began moving toward the Pasteur point. The level of oxygen may have reached a critical level for the anaerobes by 1.4 billion years ago when the changing environment brought the emergence of the eucaryotes.

References

1. D.Z. Oehler, J.W. Schopf and K.A. Kvenvolden, Carbon isotopic studies of organic matter in Precambrian rocks, Science **175,** 1246-1248 (1972).
2. Josephine E. Tilden, *The Algae and Their Life Relations,* The University of Minnesota Press, Minneapolis, Minn., 1935.

Cambrian sea life. (Courtesy, Field Museum of Natural History, Chicago)

10

The Advance of the Eucaryotes

Only the most primitive type of cell could have lived at the high temperatures of Archean times on earth. But by 1.3 billion years ago, climatic temperatures had declined from around 70° C (160° F) to 52° C (126° F) --- a temperature just below the spontaneous denaturation temperature of complex proteins. The eucaryotic cell developed when the overall temperature had dropped to a level compatible with its complex molecular and cellular structure. It was also better equipped to cope with the presence of free oxygen than the anaerobic organisms. But the procaryotes had had their age. They had been the only form of life on earth for 2 billion years.

From their emergence between 1.4 and 1.2 billion years ago onward, the eucaryotes began their advance in efficiency of their revolutionary new cellular organization. But as long as the atmospheric oxygen remained less than 1 percent of today's level, only the fermentative metabolism of carbohydrates was possible and they remained on the microscopic level of yeast.

After 500 million years the earth's environment had undergone an appreciable transition and the eucaryotes were reflecting the change as their complex cellular structure continued to evolve into more efficient organisms. By 750 million years ago they reached the level of complexity of chitinozoans.

The climate was cooling and the oceans were much like they are today. The only forms of life were still confined to the seas; and the continents, now approximately 30 percent of the earth's surface, stood broad and barren, with rivers and lakes --- but neither plants nor animals. The day had extended to 20 hours with 442 days in the year;[2] and the moon was no longer the awesome sphere dominating the night sky, for it had been receding from the earth throughout the ages, until toward the close of the Precambrian, it appeared only about twice its present size.

It was around this time that some eucaryotic cells began to forsake their solitary ways and began to share a colony as a loosely associated collection of individuals. In a comparatively short time the colony took on a character of its own as the individual cells became more dependent upon being a part of it. The cells interacted with each other by excreting chemicals and ions which affected the biochemical synthesis governing reproduction and products in each other. In this way cells within the colony became specialized and different from each other in the group. The colonies most successful with this group living for the gathering of nutrients and protection against predation evolved and passed on a genetic propensity for differentiation necessary for colonial organization.

The scenario is not purely conjectural. There are found today living systems in this intermediate stage of organization in which cells become colonies, united and specialized, but not to the extent to be classified as multicellular organisms. Among the green algae there is a one-cellular form which has a chloroplast, an eyespot and two flagella or thread-like projections used for locomotion and movement of water currents. Within this family are the *Pandorina,* some of whom form colonies of four to thirty-two cells. These colonies are not merely aggregates because the cells swim by coordinated movement of their flagella. The *Gonium* is another member of this group that forms colonies.

But the most evolved colony formation is by the *Volvox*. This genus of pale green flagellates forms a colony of 500 to 50,000 cells arranged in a hollow sphere about one-fiftieth of an inch in diameter. Whereas cells of the *Pandorina* and *Gonium* look alike, the cells of the *Volvox* in the colony became specialized; the cells at the front of the ball have larger eyespots, and only some of the cells reproduce themselves. Thin strands of protoplasm connect the cells one to another in the colony. The colony is reproduced when cells in the back begin to divide, producing a new small ball of cells that is released to the inside of the parent colony. When the old colony dies, the young colonies inside are released to disperse and repeat the cycle.[3]

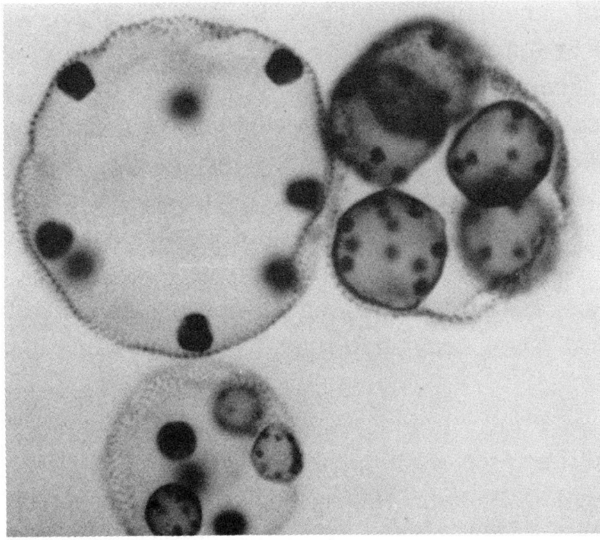

Volvox*, a green alga that forms colonies. (Carolina Biological Supply Company)*

From colony formation the eucaryotes were crossing the threshold to becoming metazoae, or multicellular animals. As with most stages of evolutionary development, there are living species who have resisted change and have survived in the ecological niche that was prevalent at the time that level of development was widespread. The sponges are animals that lie at the border-line between the unicellular and multicellular development.

The surface of a sponge is formed by the ectosome, a layer or layers of cells perforated by minute pores. The body is crossed by numerous canals which run into and from flagellated chambers like little thimbles lined with cells bearing a funnel-shaped collar. The sponge takes in food and oxygen by drawing water through the pores and canals to the flagellated chambers with the collared cells and out again through vents, the waste products from digestion and respiration being discharged by the exhalant current.

On the East Coast from Nova Scotia to South Carolina there is a small sponge found growing commonly on oysters called *Microciona prolifera.* It begins life as a thin incrustation, but as it ages, it sends up vertical finger-like lobes with rather large openings at the ends as vents. These projections increase in number as the sponge gets older to form a bush-like structure with interwoven branches. Some specimens grow as tall as eight inches. The color of *M. prolifera* varies seasonally, but in the summer and autumn, it is tomato red.

In 1907, H. V. Wilson,[4] a biologist with the University of North Carolina at Chapel Hill, spent his summer in the U.S. Bureau of Fisheries laboratory at Beaufort Harbor doing research on his special interest, the degeneration and regeneration of tissue. Being aware of the regenerative powers of *M. prolifera,* Wilson decided to attempt an experiment with the little red sponge.

He took the sponge and cut it into small pieces with scissors and strained the tissue through fine bolting cloth. As he held the pieces of sponge in the cloth like a bag, he immersed it in a saucer of filtered seawater and squeezed it with forceps. Red clouds of cells passed out through the cloth into the water and quickly settled to the bottom of the saucer like a fine sediment. After the sponge was disintegrated and the constituent cells strained into the saucer of water, Wilson carefully studied the behavior of the sediment.

As he watched, the cells immediately began to fuse with each other until, after a short time, they had conglomerated into many little balls. Following this, protusions of protoplasm or pseudopodia reached out from the balls over the surface of the saucer. When they made contact with other groups of cells, the conglomerates came together to make one. Eventually, all the balls of cells fused into a single incrustation. Differentiation of the cells began, and as the days went by, flagellated chambers appeared in great number connected by canals formed in the structure. Short vent tubes began to grow vertically from the incrustation, and after six or seven days, the little red sponge had regenerated itself!

Sponges are at the lowest level of development of multicellular animals, but the experiment was remarkable in showing that metazoae result from individual living cells which have come together in coordination in a specific way to create a higher order of life. Moreover, it supported the thesis that the single cell is the primary unit of developmental function.

Wilson tried next specimens of the coelenterates, that phylum best known by the jellyfish and which is at a transitional stage to all higher animal phyla. The structure of coelenterates, being composed of two layers of tissue, the ectoderm and the endoderm, are more evolved than the sponges. Nevertheless, when polyps of hydroids were cut into fragments and squeezed through fine cloth, these dissociated cells also selectively reaggregated themselves to reform the animal.

Little became of Wilson's fascinating experiment for the next thirty years. Then in 1939, Johannes Holtfreter,[5] a biologist at the Kaiser-Wilhelm Institute in Berlin, dissociated the cells of a frog embryo in a solution free of calcium and magnesium ions. When the suspension of cells was allowed to stand undisturbed, the cells first started to sort themselves out and eventually reformed the original embryo. The experiment was performed with avian embryos in 1952 by Moscona,[6] followed by other researchers working successfully with embryonic tissue from mammals. For reasons that are explained later, the experiment works only for the early stages of the embryo.

The human body as well as all other metazoae develops from one cell, a cell that divides repeatedly, first forming tissues by making layers of a definite pattern, these tissues then growing into organs. In this way the embryo reenacts the evolutionary stages of development that took place hundreds of millions of years ago. In the end the fully structured animal with its own individual qualities is built of trillions of cells working together as a unit. It has been estimated the number of cells in the human adult is of the order of 100 trillion, and all of these are ultimately derived from the single fertilized ovum. It seems like a very large number, but only 45 generations of cell division would be sufficient to attain it.

Multicellular organization meant a large increase in the number of genes to express the function of not only the single cell but of the whole organism. The functions of the higher animal result from differentiation of cells; that is, cells specializing to generate various tissues, organs, bone and hair. Because of the manner in which metazoae evolved from organized amassing of progeny of a single cell, every cell in the body has the full complement of genes and chromosomes for the complete animal. They differ in that all the genes are not expressed. Only those genes that are for producing proteins relative to the specific cell's function are used; all the other genetic material in the particular cell is shut off from transcription by basic proteins called histones that combine with the gene and prevent it from being copied. In this way eucaryotic cells were able to achieve and coordinate various functions from basically the same cell and were able to advance from the unicellular stage to the higher forms of life.

About a hundred million years was needed to advance from the tissue level of development of coelenterates to animals with organs; but when the breakthrough was made, the effect was explosive. The new type of organization of tissue for interacting with the environment was so superior to the relatively passive predecessors that this type of animal life quickly became worldwide and dominant. These animals, the arthropods, mollusks and others grew exoskeletons of chitin-like material or mineralized shells to protect their fragile organs and tissue; but they remained in their sheltering ocean depths, and the land was still barren.

While the eucaryotes were advancing, one of the great mountain systems in the earth's history --- the Appalachian-Caledonian --- began to be thrust up. Between 1,100 and 750 million years ago, long periods of sedimentation had laid down platforms on the margins of North America and Europe. But the ancient ocean that separated the two land masses shrank as powerful forces within the earth brought the continents toward each other. When eventually they collided, the sedimentary platforms caught in the collision buckled and folded, pushing up towering peaks. From the heat and pressure, limestone was metamorphosed to marble, shales to slate and schist, sandstones were transformed to quartzite, and intrusions of magma formed bodies of granite. Whereas the mountains of five or six episodes more ancient that the Appalachian-Caledonian have long been obliterated by erosion, the Appalachian range in eastern North America and the Caledonia mountains of Scotland, worn and sculptured by the ceaseless action of water, stand today among the oldest mountains on earth.

The late Precambrian, which began as warm and moist, ended cold and dry as glaciation extended over eastern Canada, and the earth experienced another Ice Age. With the start of the Cambrian, the climate grew mild. The climatic temperature was around 34°C (111°F), and atmospheric oxygen was now probably several percent above the Pasteur point. Trilobites, looking like a type of horseshoe crab, inarticulate brachiopods, primitive mollusks, the echinodermates, ancestors of the starfish, annelids (segmented worms) and the arthropods, primitive centipedes with their segmented bodies, crawled along the sea bottoms.

The Cambrian, lasting from 570 to 500 million years ago, was followed by the Ordovician with a major expansion of the invertebrates into new species, genera and families. It was an age of marine animals with mineralized skeletons and shells: corals, starfish, brittle stars and crinoids colonized the shallow sea floor. The cephalopods, some straight, some curved and some coiled shells, appeared, and among them was the nautilus, much like today, a formidable predator cruising in the ocean depths.

By the Ordovician Period, 500 million years ago, with shallow seas covering large areas of the world, primitive plants began to adapt themselves to life on the fringes of the land. It was a new condition where they had to develop structural support against gravity and a vascular system to carry fluids upward to their exposed parts. Then around 450 million years ago there appeared in fresh water in what is now Colorado an animal that was probably a jawless fish. The fossils are so rare and fragmentary that the form of the animal is unknown. They are found in the Harding sandstone as dissociated and broken plates of bony structure, but they indicate the presence of the missing phylum --- the chordate with vertebra, and our ancestor.

Since most fossil records are of marine origin, the account of freshwater and terrestrial development is more difficult to assemble. But colonization of the continents apparently occurred during the Silurian (420-395 m.y.) and Devonian Periods (395-345 m.y.). Presumably it began with the primitive plants, followed by the arachnids: scorpions and millipedes. North America was low and flat during this time except for mountains and volcanoes in eastern United States and Canada; Europe was mountainous with arid basins. It was around 370 million years ago that an amphibian ancestor of all terrestrial vertebrates, including man, pulled himself out of his freshwater habitat onto a riverbank and found himself in Greenland. Or at least his earliest fossil remains were found there 370 million years later.

Colonization of the land areas by plants led to the Carboniferous Age from 350 to 270 million years ago. Large trees, some 100 feet tall, stood in swampy forests throughout many continents. There were the relatives of the horsetails, the club mosses and tree ferns of today, as were primitive gymnosperms of conifers. Insects were diverse and included a giant dragonfly with wings 28 inches long, a five-foot millipede and enormous cockroaches and scorpions. Trilobites were nearing the end of their long history, and among the vertebrates were large sharks. Amphibians, descendants of the air-breathing vertebrates of the Devonian, were present; and the synapsids, the earliest known reptiles.

During the Permian Period that followed, 280 to 225 million years ago, the synapsids were primarily predacious and they became predominant. A subclass of the *Synapsidia* were the therapsids, small, unimpressive relation, but active carnivores. During the Triassic Period (220-180 million years ago) these small creatures developed special secreting glands to nourish their young with milk and became the first mammals.

The continents, like huge rafts of granite slowly skimming on the earth's mantle, had become fused into a supercontinent called Pangaea within the preceding hundred or more million years. But during the Triassic the parts that were eastern North America and New Zealand were experiencing an outbreak of volcanic eruptions. Africa and South

Carboniferous forest. (Courtesy, Field Museum of Natural History, Chicago)

America as a unit swung away from North American dividing Pangaea into Laurasia of the north and Gondwanaland to the south. India and Antarctica split from Africa.

As the Triassic entered the Jurassic Period, the great trees of the coal swamps had already yielded to ginkgos, conifers and cycads. Dinosaurs filled nearly every niche of terrestrial life, many attaining gigantic sizes. And a rift formed between North America and Europe. It was a small narrow body of water much like the Red Sea or the Gulf of California, but it was the beginning of the Atlantic Ocean. Mountains from Alaska to Mexico arose, and there were eruptions in the northwest.

The Cretaceous Period saw the appearance of flowering plants. Propagating by airborne seeds had an explosive effect resulting in their being spread rapidly throughout the world. Bees followed in their wake. The mammals, living in the shadow of the dinosaurs for 150 million years, were on the sidelines as the giants lumbered into extinction.

With the decline of the dinosaurs 70 million years ago, the mammals rose to become the dominant form of animal. The concentrated energy in the seeds of flowering plants made possible the rapid metabolism for flight, and birds evolved. In western United States, the Laramide orogeny, one of a succession of mountain-building events from the late Devonian was climaxing by plutonism that consolidated the marginal belt of the continental crust.

Sixty-five million years ago there were small forest-living creatures with the build and gait of squirrels. They were not yet specialized in tree climbing, but these were the earliest primates, a separate order of *Mammalia.* During the Oligocene, 40 to 25 million years ago, the Alps and the Himalayas were thrust up. Saber-tooth cats evolved to prey upon the grazing mammals.

The Miocene, 25 to 10 million years ago, saw the uplift of the Sierras and the Rockies. Except for rodents, all but two of the three recognized mammal families already existed. The fauna included deer, hyenas, the earliest giraffes and the bovines. A huge bear-dog, Amphicyon, was conspicuous, and mastodonts spread into North America grasslands to join the evolving horses and camels as grazing became dominant over browsing life.

When the Pliocene began 10 million years ago, a chill was on the tropics and grasslands were widespread. The mammals reached the peak of their size and abundance. It was about the middle of the Pliocene 4 or 5 million years ago, a scavenger on the plains of eastern Africa appeared, competing with the hyenas for what food he could snatch from kills by the predators much stronger than he.

He was an errant primate that remained on the ground while the others developed a way of life in the trees. He lacked the teeth or the speed of a carnivore, but his cunning and group actions gave him an advantage that allowed him to survive.

Eventually he began to shape stones as weapons and tools. His teeth show he evolved on a diet of roots, fruit, nuts and other eatables he could gather. And his bad digestion — he couldn't eat green fruit and some raw foods like the baboon — led him to use fire to predigest foods he couldn't eat raw in order to expand his available food supply.

This of course was man. He evolved as a separate species sometime around 4 and 5 million years ago. Life had existed for 3.4 billion years; for 2.7 billion years, or 80 percent of the time, it remained at the level of one-celled organisms. Only within the last 2 percent of the time life has existed on earth did mammals appear. And since the first appearance of life in the Fig Tree and Onverwacht Series in South Africa, 99.9 percent of life's existence passed, and only in the last 0.1 percent of the time span, did man finally evolve.

Why did it take so long?

Presumably the eucaryotes evolved from the procaryotes, but there remains a large biological gap between the bacteria and blue-green algae and the complex eucaryotic cell. Instead of a transitional evolution, there is a quantum jump. What happened over 1 billion years ago when the temperature was becoming cooler, the oceans became oxidized, and free oxygen began to build up in the atmosphere that could have created a cellular life-form so advanced over the primitive procaryotes? Why was becoming multicellular so explosive an innovation? And why was life confined for nearly 90 percent of its existence to the sea to venture out on the land only a few hundred million years ago.

The answers to these mysteries have systematically fallen into place within the last decade. It has already been pointed out that the high climatic temperatures of early earth excluded the development of any but the simple and hardy procaryotic cells. Although the temperature fluctuations that permitted an Ice Age during the early Proterozoic and the areas of probable lower temperatures like the polar regions would dismiss this as a sole reason. Apparently eucaryotes appeared when they did and without transition for another reason.

The answer seems to lie with the mitochondria and chloroplasts, those principal subcellular particles of the eucaryotic cells. Blue-green algae do not have chloroplasts, but they themselves are about the same size as chloroplasts. Actually, when the sizes of mitochondria and chloroplasts are compared to procaryotes, they are approximately the same. Furthermore, ribosomes and the other subcellular particles of eucaryotes are synthesized by the nucleus, except for the mitochondria and chloroplasts — they reproduce themselves by division. As long ago as 1890, Richard Altmann,[7] a professor of anatomy at Leipzig, proposed a theory that these two particles were comparable to bacteria and were actually symbionts. That is to say, their relationship with the eucaryotic cell was one of symbiosis where they and the cell join together to function for mutual benefit. The concept was received with much criticism at the time and was eventually forgotten.

Then in 1962, Ris and Plaut[8] reported finding DNA in chloroplasts; and two years later, DNA was discovered in the mitochondria in both plants and animals.[9-12] Not only was there DNA present, the DNA of the chloroplasts was in a closed circle like the looped chromosome of bacteria. This was all suggestive that these subcellular particles had self-replicating properties as well as protein synthesis capabilities. Upon further examination, it was seen the blue-green algae, the mitochondria and the chloroplasts all have similar lamellar structures independent of the internal membrane of the cell, all have DNA, enzymes, carotenoids, cytochromes and other constituents in common for their activities; they all divide, can mutate and evolve. The answer to the mystery began to reveal itself.

It now appears what happened a billion or so years ago is that at some time a large single-celled ancestor of green plants ingested, but did not digest, a blue-green algal-like cell. In so doing, it acquired a photosynthetic symbiont which became a permanent tenant as the chloroplast. Instead of the organism having to seek out its food now, the live-in chloroplast was able to supply it directly. In return the smaller chloroplast had santuary from predators and a hostile environment. It was a relationship too good not to become permanent.

Like the chloroplasts, the mitochondria too were presumably free-living microorganisms at one time. But being anaerobes, life was becoming precarious as the level of oxygen continued to mount — survival was only for those who could evolve enzymes to counteract the oxygen or find an escape from it. There is good reason to believe the mitochondria solved their crisis by either being ingested by some pre-eucaryotic cell, or deliberately taking refuge within the cell to avoid being oxidized.[13,14]

The accumulation of free oxygen from photosynthesis must have taken a very long time. The concentration of free oxygen may have been low until late in the Precambrian. Minimal concentrations of oxygen that would support the physiological processes of complex metazoa-like annelids and arthropods probably existed for a sufficient period prior to the Ediacara times to allow for the evolution of these animals.[15] But at this time one of the great developmental leaps on earth was taking place. The explanation was suggested by the Canadian biologist, J.R. Nursall,[16] in 1959, and was later expanded upon by L.W. Berkner and L.C. Marshall.[17]

The Pasteur point, or when atmospheric oxygen is at 1 percent of the present level, is lethal to anaerobes, but it is also the concentration at which oxidative metabolism can take place for aerobic organisms. Microorganisms such as yeast which break down glucose by fermentation derive 47 kilocalories of energy per mole of sugar. This energy comes from the chemical energy in converting glucose to pyruvic acid. But the amount of energy actually stored in glucose by photosynthesis in the reduction of CO_2 and the concomitant release of oxygen is 686 kilocalories per mole.

$$6\,CO_2 + 6\,H_2O \longrightarrow C_6H_{12}O_6 + 6\,O_2$$

The revolutionary achievement of the multicellular animals 600 million years ago was to evolve a metabolic pathway whereby they could metabolize glucose by oxidizing it with oxygen back completely to the CO_2. In so doing, they realized an effective boost of energy 18 times greater than by fermentation by deriving 36 ATP molecules from glucose by oxidative phosphorylation, compared to only 2 from the fermentative breakdown of glucose to pyruvic acid. It was this tremendous increase of energy that fueled the development of the higher animals.

But even as the atmosphere built up a surplus of oxygen, plants and animals remained in the sea for several hundred million years. It is now believed the reason for this long delay was for the oxygen level to reach an atmospheric concentration 10 percent of the present level, for only at this level is it sufficient to build the ozone shield.[17]

Ultraviolet light has a profound effect on living matter. It destroys bacteria and other microorganisms rapidly, and it is the cause of sunburn. Today, practically all the ultraviolet radiation is screened out by the layer of ozone in the upper reaches of the atmosphere. This ozone layer is generated by the action of shortwave ultraviolet light from the sun on oxygen in the atmosphere. At the pressure of one atmosphere the amount of ozone in this protective shield would be a layer of pure gas only 3 millimeters thick, or one-eighth of an inch. It of course is diluted with other air gases and is at an altitude of 10 to 40 miles so that the ozone-containing layer is actually several miles. Nevertheless, if the amount of ozone in the atmosphere were reduced to one-third, our skins would be destroyed on exposure to the sun in a matter of minutes. And on the other hand, if the amount were doubled, the human race would probably die out for lack of an essential vitamin while being smothered by an accumulating mass of bacteria.[18]

It appears the reason plants and animals were confined to the sea until around 500 million years ago was because the oxygen level had not yet reached the point sufficient to produce the ozone barrier as protection against the lethal ultraviolet radiation that streamed down on the earth's surface. During most of the Precambrian the ultraviolet rays penetrated seawater to a depth of 10 meters. But as the ozone layer began to build, it screened out most of the radiation so that its penetration was only a few centimeters by the Late Precambrian and Early Cambrian. Within a few hundred million years more the radiation was reduced to the level where plants and animals could leave the protective seas and live permanently on the surface of the continents.

References

1. L. Paul Knauth and Samuel Eptein, Hydrogen and oxygen isotope ratios in nodular and bedded cherts, *Geochim. Cosmochim. Acta* **40**, 1095-1108 (1976).
2. B.G. Marsden and A.G.W. Cameron, **The Earth-Moon System**, Plenum Press, New York, 1966, p. 73.
3. Dorothy Hinslow Patent, **Microscopic Animals and Plants**, Holiday House, New York, 1974, p. 61.
4. H.V. Wilson, On some phenomena of coalescence and regenerative sponges, *J. Exptl. Zool.* **5**, 245-258 (1907).
5. J. Holtfreter, Gewebeaffinität ein Mittel der embryonalen Formbildung, *Arch. exptl. Zellforsch. Gewebezücht* **23**, 169-209 (1939).
6. A. Moscona and H. Moscona, The dissociation and aggregation of cells from organ rudiments of the early chick embryo, *J. Anat.* **86**, 287-301 (1952).
7. R. Altmann, Die Elementarorganismen und ihre Beziehungen zu dem Zellen, Veit und Comp, Leipzig, 1890.
8. H. Ris and W. Plaut, Ultrastructure of DNA-containing areas in the chloroplast of Chlamydomonas, *J. Cell Biol.* **13**, 383-391 (1962).
9. P.R. Bell and K. Mühlethaler, Evidence for the presence of deoxy-ribonucleic acid in the organelles of the egg cells of **Pteridium aquilium**, *J. Mol. Biol.* **8**, 853-862 (1964).
10. D.J.L. Luck and E. Rich, DNA in mitochondria of **Neurospora crassa**, *Proc. Nat. Acad. Sci.* **52**, 931-938 (1964).
11. M.M. Nass, S. Nass and B.A. Afzelius, The general occurrence of mitochondria DNA, *Exp. Cell Res.* **37**, 516-539 (1965).
12. F.L. Schuster, A deoxyribose nucleic acid component in mitochondria of **Didymium nigripes** a slime mold, *Exp. Cell Res.* **39**, 329-345 (1965).
13. J.E. Wallis, **Symbionticism and the Origin of Species**, William and Wilkins, Baltimore, Md., 1927.
14. L. Margulis, **Origin or Eukaryotic Cells**, Yale University Press, New Haven, Conn., 1970.
15. R.A. Raff and E.C. Raff, Respiratory mechanisms and the metazoan fossil record, *Nature* **228**, 1003-1005 (1970).
16. J.R. Nursall, Oxygen as a prerequisite to the origin of the metazoa, *Nature* **183**, 1170-1172 (1959).

17. L.W. Berkner and L.C. Marshall, The history of oxygenic concentration in the earth's atmosphere, *Discussions Faraday Soc.* **37**, 122-141 (1964);------, History of major atmospheric components, *Proc. Nat. Acad. Sci.* **53**, 1215-1226 (1965).
18. Brian O'Brian, Stratosphere exploration, in **The Origin of the Solar System**, T. Page and L.W. Page, eds., The Macmillan Co., New York, 1966, pp. 141-142.

11

The Architecture of Biochemical Compounds

We find ourselves atop an evolutionary column so high the entire existence of man as a species is compressed into the top 0.1 percent of the time span of life on earth. But what are we and how did we come into being? These are questions that have been central in every culture of every age. The replies have been as varied as the societies, each reflecting the cultural experiences and impressions of the physical world. The answer given by science lies in understanding the chemical nature of living things before attempting to derive how it originated.

The physical character of biological systems is so complex and different from terrestrial material that contemplating a chemical origin of life a few centuries ago was inconceivable. Then a revolution in thought began to take root. A hundred and fifty years ago a few men of science began a series of discoveries that eventually led to revealing the very chemical basis of all life.

In the past it was natural to think of living things as separate and different from the elements of the earth, sky and water. The animate and the inanimate appeared worlds apart. A lizard and a rock had nothing in common. The lizard was alive with the spark of life. Even if the lizard were killed, the loss of life brought a dramatic change, and the body of the lizard underwent decomposition unlike the rocks.

By the 18th century, scientists had established several basic principles of chemistry and physics which were valid for inorganic substances, but the complexity and less predictable nature of biological systems seemed to exclude them from these physical tenets. This impression was given formal recognition in 1707 when the German physician, Georg Ernst Stahl, enunciated the principle that life was governed by special non-physical laws. This was the theory of Vitalism which held that all living things contained a vital force, an inseparable non-physical component that directed and made possible the functioning of all life processes.

Since living things were of a different nature than the rocks and minerals of the earth, their chemical constitution was different. From early times, man realized that substances used for food, and consequently, things from plants and animals, fell into distinct categories. There was the white chalky starch that was extracted from wheat, potatoes and rice used to stiffen the collars of burghers. There were oils from plants and animals that were used for food and burning in lamps. Being insoluble in water and greasy to the touch, fats and oils were lumped together as lipids. And there was a third group found in foods but different from the other two. This was comprised of the albuminous substances in solution in the whites of eggs, milk and blood. Members of this catagory were particularly unstable and coagulated when heated.

The early chemists were aware that substances from living things were clearly different from the mineral world. Unlike most inorganic compounds, products of organisms were unstable to heat, usually changing irreversibly; and most could be burned. Elemental analysis showed starch to be composed of carbon, hydrogen and oxygen; lipids were mostly carbon and hydrogen with a small amount of oxygen; and albuminous substances contained carbon, hydrogen, oxygen, nitrogen, and sometimes sulfur and phosphorus. With so much carbon and hydrogen, it became apparent why these substances burned. Except for limestone, carbon is not a common element among minerals — with living systems, it was always present.

By the early part of the 19th century some of the fundamental principles and methods of chemistry were already known. Gravimetric analysis had been introduced by Friedrich Hoffmann and the inorganic aspects of analysis were developed even before 1800. But it was the work of Jöns Jacob Berzelius in Sweden in the early 1800's from which much of modern chemistry grew. He developed improved analytical methods, and using oxygen as sixteen times the weight of hydrogen, composed a generally accurate table of atomic weights for the known elements. By determining the weight percentage of each element in a compound by analysis, it was then possible to use atomic weights to learn the molecular formula. With this procedure Berzelius established the exact elementary composition and formula of some 2,000 compounds. He also gave the world many chemical words, including polymer for a large molecule formed by the linking together of small subunits, and catalyst, a substance that promotes a chemical reaction without itself being consumed.

In Berzelius' time, a few pure biological compounds were already commonly known. Several crystalline sugars had been isolated from a number of sources and urea was known as crystals found when urine evaporated to dryness. The purified compounds derived from living organisms seemed to have many common properties which they did not share with inorganic chemicals. It was inconceivable that the two types of chemistry could be related. Berzelius coined the word organic and divided chemistry into organic and inorganic, organic chemistry being the domain of compounds from living systems, distinct and separate from inorganic chemistry.

The chemical distinction was defined. The Vitalists were satisfied. No matter how life originated, it remained a philosophical question because its worldly substance could not have come from the soil or minerals. If there were to be a scientific explanation of life's origin, its primary issue was the same problem then as it was a hundred years later: How could organic substances come from the inorganic materials of the earth?

Berzelius' distinction between organic and inorganic chemistry stood only twenty-one years. One of his own students, the German chemist Friedrich Wöhler brought down the barrier abruptly. It was a simple experiment — but indisputable. By heating the inorganic salt, ammonium cyanate, Wöhler produced urea, the common substance excreted in mammalian urine. It was a hard blow to the Vitalists. They recovered somewhat to redefine their position, but Wöhler's experiment was only the beginning in the breakdown of the division between the chemistry of the animate and the inanimate.

Eleven years later in 1839, Schwann swept all living things into a common mold by recognizing the cell as the basic unit of life. And for the remainder of the century while biologists studied the composition and function of cells, chemists unveiled, step by step, the architecture of organic compounds.

In 1812, Kirchhoff had astonished everyone by boiling ordinary starch with a little acid and obtaining grape sugar, a compound whose taste and properties were quite different. He had hydrolyzed the starch, that is, ruptured the covalent bonds with the addition of water, by a kind of digestion catalyzed by the acid. Seven years later the French chemist Braconnet boiled several plant materials, including sawdust, and generated the simple sugar, glucose. It was subsequently learned that a substance named cellulose, a principal constituent of plants, was the source of Braconnet's glucose.

Gay-Lussac investigated starch, cellulose and the various sugars and discovered each analyzed one carbon atom for each oxygen and two hydrogens. There appeared to be a water molecule for each carbon giving the formula CH_2O for the members of this group. This prompted him to name them carbohydrates, or hydrated carbon.

The sugars were the simplest molecular structures obtainable by hydrolysis. When the molecular weight of glucose was measured, it was found to be 180, or six times the molecular weight of CH_2O. The molecular formula, therefore, must be its multiple by six, or $C_6H_{12}O_6$. Other simple sugars gave the same formula. Since starch and cellulose were considerably larger, a size immeasurable by techniques of that time, they were apparently formed by the linking of the simple sugars.

A Dutch agricultural chemist, Gerardus Mulder, studied the

albuminous substances found in foodstuffs, and in 1838 upon a suggestion by Berzelius, applied the term protein for the group. Biologists quickly realized that protoplasm, the viscous solution found in all cells and regarded as the basis of life, was composed mostly of proteins. Unlike the carbohydrates, hydrolysis of proteins gave a mixture of smaller nitrogen-containing compounds which were difficult to separate. The first of this series to be isolated was found as a white crystalline chemical in 1820 and was called glycine. These are the alpha (α) amino acids, distinguished by having a carboxylic acid and amino group joined to the same carbon atom, and named in 1848 by Berzelius. It would be over a century before all of the twenty-two common amino acids of proteins would be isolated and identified.

General formula for α - amino acids

$$\begin{array}{c} \quad\quad COO^{-} \\ \quad\quad | \\ H_3N^{+}\!-\!C\!-\!H \\ \quad\quad | \\ \quad\quad R\ \text{group} \end{array}$$

By 1827 William Prout was already suggesting that the organic matter of living systems was made up of essentially three classes of substances: the carbohydrates, lipids and proteins. As chemists continued to investigate them, they learned a feature of starch, cellulose and proteins was that they were extremely large molecules. This distinguished them from inorganic compounds which rarely exceeded a molecular weight of a few hundred. The size of these organic polymers was beyond the range of the methods to measure available to the chemist of the mid-19th century, but the scientists had discovered an important fact. Life was constructed of giant molecules.

Berzelius, who had set chemistry on its course, died in 1848. That same year a young French chemist with the name of Louis Pasteur presented to the Paris Academy of Sciences a paper telling of a remarkable discovery he had made — certain chemical compounds existed as "right-handed" and "left-handed" components, each being mirror images of the other. Tartaric acid, discovered in particular industrial processes, had been found to have the same composition as the native acid from grape fermentation, but markedly different properties. One of these properties was that natural tartaric acid viewed through a polaroscope gave a rotation to a beam of polarized light; the synthetic acid failed to do this. Pasteur studied the crystals of the synthetic tartaric acid under a microscope and discovered two crystalline forms, mirror images of the other. By painstakingly separating the crystals with forceps, he discovered the two forms had opposite effects on polarized light. He established that this was due to molecular asymmetry and further showed that this isomerism — having the same molecular formula but different physical and chemical properties — occured in other organic compounds, but that only one form occurred in natural products. In chemical syntheses both forms were produced in equal proportions so that the substance exhibited no rotation of polarized light. Since only one isomeric form was found in nature, Pasteur deduced that organisms were selective toward isomers, a fact that prepared him for another great discovery.

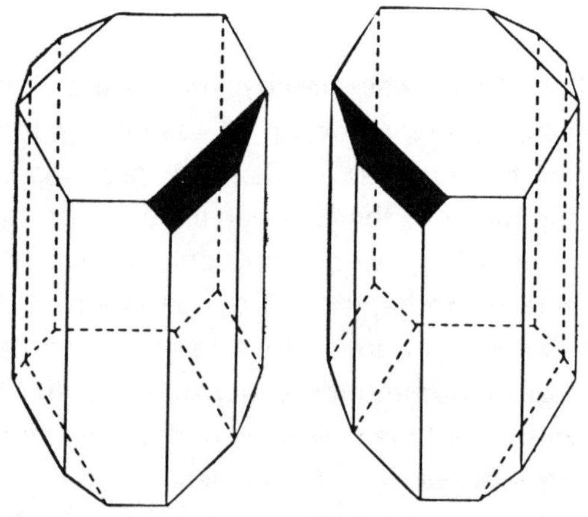

Drawings of crystals of tartaric acid showing the mirror images of the two asymmetrical isomers.

Until Pasteur's time, yeast was not regarded as a microorganism but merely an organic catalyst in the levening of bread and the fermentation of fruit juices. When asked by the wine industry to investigate the problem of their product going bad, Pasteur studied fermentation and correctly guessed that the conversion of sugar to alcohol was the result of the biological activity of a living organism, the yeast. He further concluded that it was a specific microorganism that was responsible for the fermentation of juices, the souring of milk and the putrifaction of meat. Through his monumental achievements in microbiology, Pasteur brought to light a better understanding of life at the microscopic level. By a simple experiment, he proved that each microbe was derived from a pre-existing microbe, thus giving even microorganisms an ancestry and dismissing the principle of spontaneous generation. Pasteur was instrumental in revealing to the world that life on the cellular level had prodigious powers of synthesis, but he could not go so far as to accept a chemical basis of life and continued to back the cause of the Vitalists.

The chemistry of organic compounds entered its second period in 1858 with the birth of the structural theory. By this time it was becoming increasingly more difficult to reconcile so many molecular formulas for the growing number of organic compounds. For compounds with different properties to have the same formula, they must differ in some distinguishing manner. The man to discover the distinction and to launch organic chemistry into an era of building molecular structures was one, who probably by no mere coincidence, had the intentions of becoming an architect. But August Kekule', while a student at the University of Giessen, came under the influence of Justus von Liebig and switched to chemistry. Kekule' studied the problem confronting chemists on the formulae, and in 1858, showed carbon to be tetravalent, and thus each carbon formed four chemical bonds with its neighboring atoms. But most importantly, he recognized that carbon was able to link, not just with other elements but also with other carbon atoms, resulting in long chains called the aliphatic series.

This hypothesis opened the door for structural organic chemistry. As an example, the formula of the common fatty acid, oleic acid, with the molecular formula, $C_{18}H_{34}O_2$, became

```
  H H H H H H H H H   H H H H H H H   O
  | | | | | | | | |   | | | | | | |  //
H-C-C-C-C-C-C-C-C-C=C-C-C-C-C-C-C-C-C
  | | | | | | | |   | | | | | | | |  \
  H H H H H H H H   H H H H H H H H   OH
```

or as more routinely written,

$$CH_3-(CH_2)_7-CH=CH-(CH_2)_7-COOH$$

Not only did carbon have four valence bonds, but the single bonds could be doubled or tripled, giving multiple bonds with their particular chemical properties.

This solved the problem of many compounds, but there still remained a group of non-aliphatic chemicals, including benzene, C_6H_6, whose properties and composition did not fit the new theory. These compounds had too few hydrogens for the tetravalent carbons to form open-chain structures. Kekule' struggled with the problem for years. Then one night in 1865, after an evening of heavy drinking, he dozed off on a horse tram and dreamed of the benzene molecule as a snake biting its own tail while in a whirling motion. From that drunken stupor the concept of the six-carbon benzene ring was born, and all the data of the aromatic series of organic compounds fell into place. This doctrine of linking together carbons in alternating single and double bonds to form compounds was dubbed "Kekule's sausages" by his contempories. Organic compounds are still distinguished as "open chain" and "ring" derivations, attesting to the importance of Kekule's hypothesis.

C_6H_6

Molecular

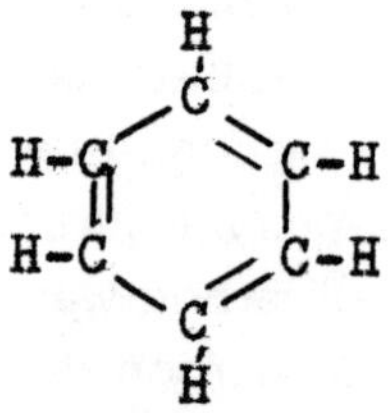

H
C
H-C C-H
H-C C-H
C
H

Structural

Conventional Shorthand

Benzene Formulae

A new dimension was added in 1874 when Van't Hoff and Le Bel proposed that the four valence bonds of carbon are directed toward the four corners of a tetrahedron with carbon at the center. The architecture of organic compounds became three-dimensional. Although the representation of carbon bonds as a flat picture directed at right angles has been retained out of convenience, it was realized that bonds oriented toward the corners of a tetrahedron gave a spatial expansion to organic substances.

In 1875, Emil Fischer, who had been one of Kekule's students, discovered that phenylhydrazine formed easily identifiable derivatives with simple sugars. Using this technique, he was able to isolate and identify the various closely related sugars from natural sources. He showed that sugars were carbon atoms linked together with each bearing a hydroxyl group except the terminal aldehyde. The sugars with the same molecular formula that had different properties differed structurally by the orientation of their respective hydroxyls. The five-carbon pentoses and six-carbon hexoses cyclized by interaction of the aldehyde with the terminal hydroxyl to form a ring structure. Fischer succeeded in

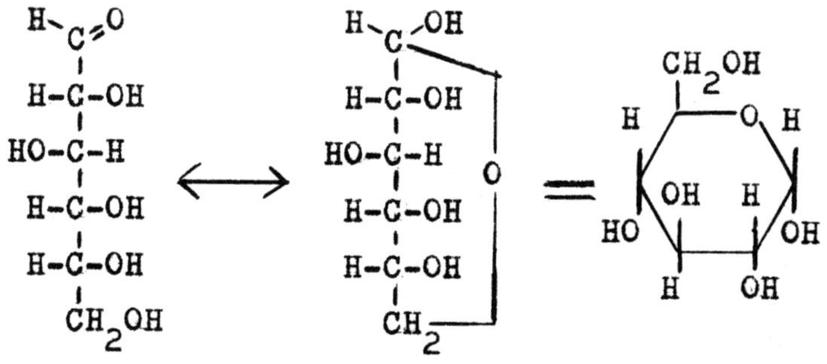

Structural formulae of D-glucose, $C_6H_{12}O_6$

elucidating the three-dimensional structure of these sugars and confirmed their structure formulae by synthesis, generally the final confirmation of the correctness of a formula.

Since starch was glucose linked together in a polymer, its structure was then recognized to be

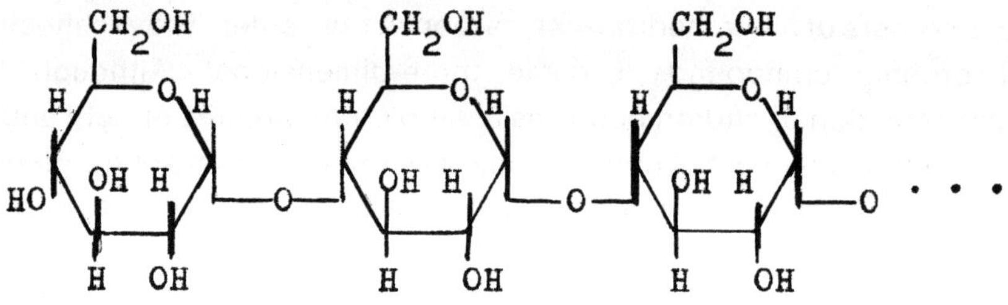

There were two basic types of starch molecule, the linear polymer and the branched. When the molecular weights were eventually determined, the linear polymer was found to vary in size from 100 to 1,000 glucose units.

The architecture of substances isolated from plants and animals was the largest and most complex of chemicals ever encountered. The powers of chemical synthesis exercised by biological systems were certainly impressive, even intimidating to the chemist. Organisms produced natural products of immense size and extreme complexity like chlorophyll, $C_{55}H_{72}M_{9}N_{4}O_{5}$, and hemoglobin, $(C_{738}H_{1166}FeN_{202}S_{2})_{4}$, with incredible ease and at 37°C or less. To synthesize even simple compounds in the laboratory, the chemist had to use elevated temperatures and highly active reactants, and generally obtained only a low yield of the desired product. With the biological systems, how was it possible?

The controversy raged for over fifty years during the last half of the 19th century between the Vitalists championed by Pasteur and the Mechanists by Liebig. The Vitalists maintained biological reactions were possible only because of the living organism; the Mechanists believed biological processes to be reactions of chemicals, very complicated, but nevertheless, chemical compounds.

Back in the 1830's men had studied the digestive process and discovered hydrochloric acid in the extracts from the stomach. Since acid hydrolysis of carbohydrates and proteins was known, it seemed apparent this was the process of digestion. Then in 1835, Schwann isolated from gastric juices an organic powder which was not an acid, but very actively broke down meat. He gave it the name pepsin from the Greek word for digestion. Other organic catalysts were found. In 1833,

Payen and Persoz isolated diastase from malt which hydrolyzed starch to sugar, Liebig and Wöhler in 1837, reported emulsin from bitter almonds, and later, Dubrunfaut extracted an organic catalyst from yeast which degraded sucrose to the simple sugars, glucose and fructose, and called it invertase. Since each of the organic catalysts effected a hydrolysis, they were regarded by the Vitalists as agents of digestion, a process that can proceed outside the body. But to transform one organic compound into another the way yeast changes sugar to alcohol in fermentation, they argued, required the living organism.

In 1897, Eduard Büchner, a German chemist, attempted to analyze this process of alcoholic fermentation. He ground the yeast cells with sand until they were all fragmented, then removed the sand and the cellular debris by filtering. When Büchner added sugar to the filtrate — now free of any yeast cells — rapid fermentation began at once. Fermentation did not need the cell! The biological reaction was being carried out, not by the living organism, but by some substance extracted from the cell. Büchner recognized that fermentation was not a physiological process but a chemical reaction catalyzed by an enzyme, and he called the enzyme, zymase. Why did Büchner's experiment work where others failed? The answer lies in the fact that enzymes are frail structures. Always before, the method used to kill yeast cells also destroyed the fragile configuration of the enzymes molecules, thus rendering them inactive.

Büchner's discovery established that the biological processes carried out by organisms were really chemical reactions catalyzed by organic components called enzymes that could be investigated separately outside the cell. It was quickly realized that pepsin, emulsin, diastase and invertase were also biocatalysts which belong to the enzyme class. Little else, however, was known of enzymes concerning their chemical make-up or mode of action except that they were very large and unstable.

This encountering of molecular sizes too large to measure had always been an unsettling obstacle to the study of biological material. With no definite estimate of molecular size, the image of starches, proteins and enzymes remained vague and mystical.

Advances in measuring large molecular weights were begun in 1877 when the German botanist Wilhelm Pfeffer attempted to use a principle discovered seventeen years earlier by Thomas Graham of Scotland. Graham had learned that a thin parchment between a salt solution of protein and pure water allowed the salt to pass through its pores but not the protein, the latter being too large. Actually, small ions of salt and molecules of water pass freely until they equilibrate with an equal number of each on both sides. But if one side contained a substance like protein which was too large to pass through the semipermeable membrane, when it equilibrated to the same number of water molecules on each side, the volume of the protein solution increases because initially, a unit volume of protein solution had less water than a unit of water. This increase of volume was called osmotic pressure. What Pfeffer realized was that osmotic pressure depended on the number of protein molecules, and since the number in a weighed sample depended on the molecular size, osmotic pressure related to molecular weight. It was the Dutch physical chemist van't Hoff who refined the procedure. The difficulty was to chart a reliable correlation between osmotic pressure one read in the experiment and some known molecular weights. After the calibration of the method was accurately established, one was able to measure the osmotic pressure of a weighed sample of protein and compute its molecular weight.

The molecular weights of proteins were found to be huge. Egg albumin was 34,000, hemoglobin, 67,000, few proteins were less than 10,000 and many were larger than 100,000, the upper range to the method of measurement. This meant that egg albumin was a biopolymer of about 300 amino acids, and hemoglobin, over twice that number. When osmotic pressure was superseded by the ultracentrifuge in the 20th century as the means of determining molecular weights, the size of proteins larger than 100,000 came within the scope of measurement. But the possibility of ever knowing the order of sequence of all the amino acids and shape of such giant structures appeared remote.

Enzymes were the tantalizing mystery of life. Neither their chemical nature nor mode of action was known. Since enzymes were such powerful catalysts, only minute amounts were needed to promote the specific chemical conversions; consequently, it was easier to measure the result of their activity than to detect the enzyme itself. Some enzymes, such as carbonic anhydrase which dehydrates carbonic acid, can transform over a million molecules a minute for each molecule of enzyme. Analysis of an enzyme concentration required a measureable quantity of purified sample, a level of preparation that was difficult to achieve with the laboratory methods at the turn of the century. One thing that was known was that enzymes were notoriously unstable and lost their activities quickly if warmed to 56° C, only nineteen degrees above body temperature. It was an intriguing feature and one reminiscent of proteins. Because of this, many biochemists began to believe enzymes were really proteins with catalytic properties.

The controversy stormed on for and against this concept a couple of decades, neither side being able to gather adequate data to settle the dispute. Then in 1920, Richard Willstätter, a renown German chemist and Nobel Prize winner, studied the problem. He purified an enzyme solution with extreme care until he was satisfied no other substance remained. The resulting clear solution still retained enzymatic activity, despite the fact that no protein could be detected. Confident of his results, Willstätter announced to the scientific world he was convinced enzymes were not proteins. He was in error. Willstätter failed to realize that enzymes could exhibit their activity at concentration levels far below the amounts needed to detect proteins by the methods at that time.

Then in 1926, an incredibly simple experiment was carried out by a biochemistry professor at Cornell University which changed several ingrained impressions. James B. Sumner had been working for nine years to isolate the enzyme, urease, from jack beans. The crux of the problem was to find a means of selectively precipitating the urease from crude extract to isolate a purified product. One day, following a suggestion by his former professor at Harvard, Sumner used acetone to extract his jack-bean meal. After allowing the solution to filter overnight, he examined a drop of the filtrate under a microscope. There were tiny octahedral crystals. He had never seen these before. Collecting the crystals by centrifugation, he dissolved them and tested the solution. They showed intense urease activity. Subsequent work revealed the crystals to be a protein with a molecular weight of 483,000.

Not only had Sumner shown an enzyme was a protein, he had actually crystallized it. The substances that promote the fundamental processes of life were compounds that crystallized in the manner of common chemicals.[1-2]

References

1. J.B. Sumner, Isolation and crystallization of the enzyme urease, *J. Biol. Chem.* **69**, 435-440 (1926).
2. ————, Recrystallization of urease, *J. Biol. Chem.* **70**, 97-98 (1926).

12
The Molecular Basis of Life

The astonishing feature of living things is that they can reproduce facsimiles of themselves generation after generation. The conclusion is inescapable. Organisms must possess within their makeup some means of retaining and passing on a store of information that is the inheritance from the preceding generations. This information contains the instructions for synthesizing the organism and all its components.

Since prehistoric times man has realized that heredity was an influence in the physical characteristics of plants and animal, but the mechanism remained obscure and mystifying. Not until the middle of the last century was a systematic study of inheritance carried out. In 1856, an Augustinian monk named Gregor Mendel, growing varieties of the common pea in the cloister gardens in Brünn (Brno), Moravia, Czechoslovakia, began experiments in cross breeding them and observing the transmission of various traits to the 1st, 2nd, 3rd ... generations. As early as 1866, Mendel published statistical rules regarding inheritance in the Proceedings of the Naturforschender Verein in Brünn. The paper received little attention at the time and was forgotten ony to be rediscovered in 1900 when three European botanists, Carl Erich Correns (Berlin), Erich Tschermak von Seysenegge (Vienna) and Hugo de Vries (Leiden) simultaneously and independently reported results similar to Mendel's, only to find the experimental data and theory had been published 34 years previously.

The great controversies over evolution raged throughout the latter half of the 19th century and into the 20th. In order to explain Darwin's theory, biologists formulated the concept that biological characteristics are inherited through physical factors that are passed on through successive generations. The English biologist, William Bateson, gave this branch of biology the name genetics (from genesis) in 1906, and in a peculiar retrogressive derivation, the inheritance factors became known as genes. But what is the actual chemical nature of the gene?

The genetic substance was isolated from the nuclei of cells nearly 70 years before its true biological significance was realized. In 1868, Friedrich Miescher, a young medically trained Swiss chemist from Basel near the borders of France and Germany set out for Tübingen. At twenty-four he had just completed his doctoral examination and was going to work for Hoppe-Seyler, the great German physiological chemist. It was autumn before Miescher began his postdoctoral research, but by February of 1869 he wrote to his former professor in Switzerland of isolating a new substance from cell nuclei.

Little was known of the nucleus of the cell at this time and the function of cellular material was almost completely obscure. Miescher had initially planned on carrying out his investigation on lymph cells, but the limited availability compelled him to use pus cells he extracted from surgical bandages. Contaminated with grease and carbolic acid, the cells were first washed with sodium sulfate solution, filtered and treated with alkali. Miescher then shook the cell fragments vigorously for a long time in a mixture of ether and extremely dilute hydrochloric acid. The fats, decomposition products and detritus either dissolved in the ether or went to the interface of the immiscible liquids; the slightly denser nuclei slowly settled to the bottom of the water layer as a fine whitish sediment.

Miescher's substance from the nuclei of pus, which he called nuclein, contained a substantial percentage of phosphorus. Until this time, lecithin was the only phosphorus-containing natural product known. The nuclein was a complex of protein and nucleic acid; but subsequent purification procedures were to enable the nucleic acid to be separated as a mass of long fibrous, thread-like material that is collected from the precipitated matter by entwining it on the end of a glass rod. Apparently Miescher, without knowing the structural nature of his nuclein, realized it had some connection with the genetic function. It was not until 1944 that an experiment by Avery[1] verified that the young Swiss had isolated the substance that is the chemical basis for the hereditary features of all living things — the nucleic acid.

Miescher's preparation of nuclein came ten years after Darwin published **On the Origin of Species.** By about 1880 the mitotic process was established and biologists, working with the light microscope, discovered that all cells contain nuclear material of a definite number of rodlike units they called chromosomes. Chromosomes are the carriers of the specific hereditary factors (genes) and elegant microscopic studies revealed their mode of replication in cellular reproduction. When isolated and analyzed, chromosomes were found to contain protein and nucleic acid in nearly equal proportions.

Nucleic acid is the phosphorus-containing polymeric substance found in Miescher's nuclein he had isolated from pus cells in 1868. The German chemist, Albricht Kossel, working at Heidelberg with nucleic acid from the thymus gland of calves, discovered it contained nitrogenous bases called purines and pyrimidines, and he isolated and identified two different derivatives of each base. Being a polymer with only four kinds of subunits, nucleic acid, like starch, seemed to be a long monotonous chain molecule.

For the first few decades of this century, while biologists expanded genetics by clarifying the mathematical relation of biological inheritance, biochemists achieved considerable success in showing the role of enzymes in controlling the life proceses. Neither had any clear concept of the chemical nature of a gene or how enzymes were made. Then in the 1930's, the American geneticists George Beadle and Edward Tatum,[2] working with *Neuospora crassa,* the common red bread mold, linked Darwinism to chemistry by showing that enzymes control structure and genes control enzymes. They recognized that genes somehow code for enzymes, and they postulated that for each enzyme there is a specific gene.

It was an impressive feat that cells reproduced proteins containing hundreds of amino acids repeatedly in the exact sequence. For protein to be synthesized time and again in identical composition, it was reasoned, the amino acids must be polymerized in their precise order on some type of template. Such templates would contain in their composition the information of heredity.

Because of the immense amount of information an organism would need in its heredity material, biologists generally accepted that any substance to be the genetic factor would have a large number of subunits to act as letters in the informational code. Since proteins contain over twenty kinds of amino acids, these macromolecules appeared ideally suitable for the role; and throughout the 1930's, most biologists and biochemists believed the protein found in chromosomes was the genetic material and regarded the nucleic acid to be of little significance.

During that same decade in 1935, Wendell Stanley[3] at the Rockefeller Institute of New York did an astonishing thing. He crystallized a virus. Viruses are biological entities that occupy a zone between living cells and inanimate chemicals. They consist of protein and nucleic acid without the cellular machinery for reproduction or metabolism. Lacking the means of regeneration, viruses are perpetuated by inserting their genetic factor into cells and the machinery of the infected cell is taken over to produce copies of the virus. For a virus to be crystallized like so much salt impressed upon scientists that genes may eventually be isolated and studied as chemical compounds. The basis of life moved one step closer to being purely a matter of chemistry.

Then in 1944, Erwin Schrödinger,[4] the renoun Austrian-born physicist living in Dublin as an émigré from Nazi Germany, published a small book, **What is Life?** In it he stressed upon his fellow physicists that biology was on the threshold of the crucial question of the basis of life and they must not be discouraged by the difficulty of interpreting life by

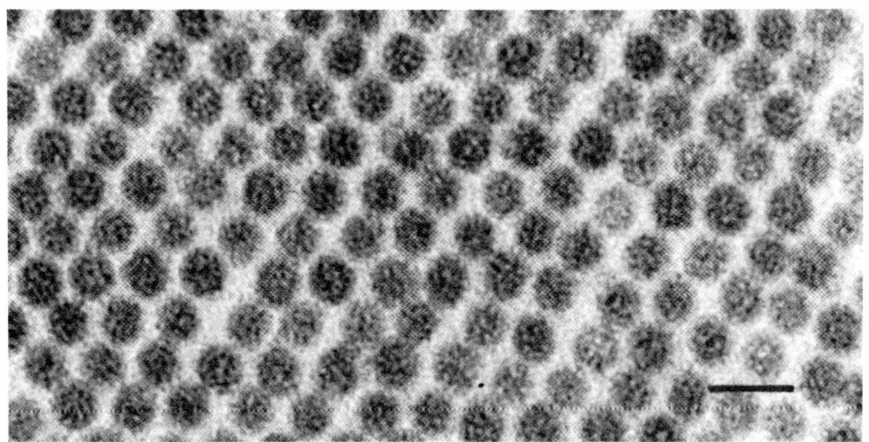

Electron photomicrograph of human wart virus. The virus is an icosahedral shell containing DNA. This particular virus has no envelope. The bar represents 100 nm; magnification is 120,000 X (Courtesy of Dennis O'Callaghan, photograph by Nan Mansfield, University of Mississippi Medical Center)

the ordinary laws of physics. He emphasized that they should consider finding how biology can be explained on the molcular level.

The key to the puzzle lay in viruses that infect bacteria and are called bacteriophages. In 1952, Alfred Hershey and Martha Chase, using radioactive phosphorus and sulfur as labels to follow the respective biochemicals, demonstrated that the DNA of a bacteriophage entered the bacterium and it alone was responsible for the reproduction of new viruses. This compelling evidence that the chemical form of genes was the nucleic acid astounded biologists who regarded protein to be the material of inheritance and marked the beginning of molecular biology.

When Kossel analyzed nucleic acid in the last century, he found two purines he called adenine and guanine, and two pyrimidines, cytosine and thymine. Later research with plant nucleic acid led to the discovery of a third type of pyrimidine called uracil.

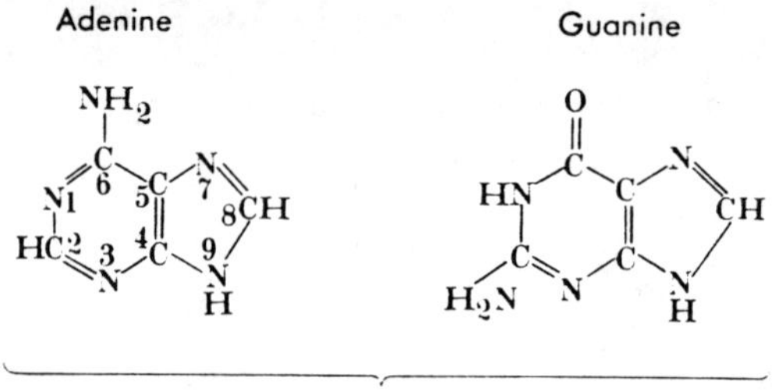

Adenine Guanine

Purines

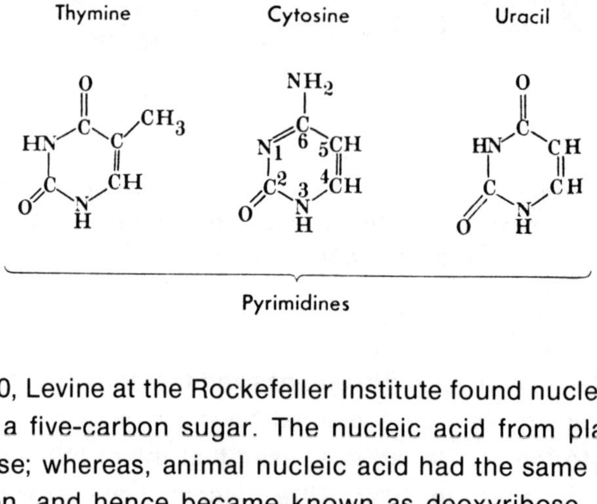

Thymine Cytosine Uracil

Pyrimidines

In 1910, Levine at the Rockefeller Institute found nucleic acids also contained a five-carbon sugar. The nucleic acid from plants had the sugar ribose; whereas, animal nucleic acid had the same sugar minus one oxygen, and hence became known as deoxyribose.

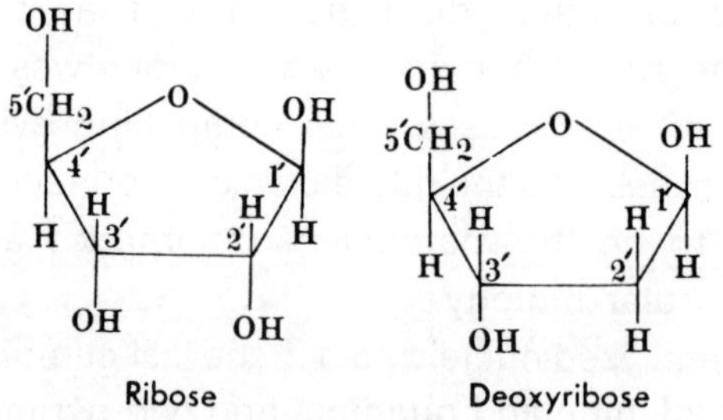

Ribose Deoxyribose

(RNA only) (DNA only)

The structural units of nucleic acid consist of the purine and pyrimidine base bonded to the terminal carbon atom (No. 1) of the sugar, and the sugar portion has a phosphate group attached. These three constituents together — bases, sugar, phosphate — form a nucleotide.

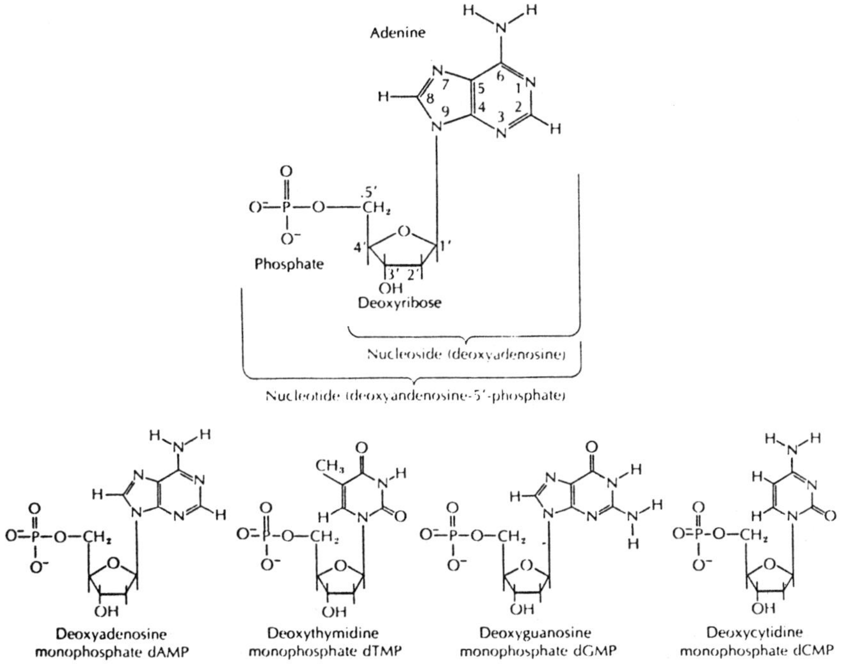

Nucleoside (deoxyadenosine)

Nucleotide (deoxyandenosine-5′-phosphate)

Deoxyadenosine monophosphate dAMP

Deoxythymidine monophosphate dTMP

Deoxyguanosine monophosphate dGMP

Deoxycytidine monophosphate dCMP

When nucleotides join through a phosphate diester by a 3′, 5′-linkage of their sugars, they create the long chains known as nucleic acids.

It soon became apparent there were two kinds of nucleic acids: one contained adenine, guanine, cytosine and thymine with deoxyribose and was called deoxyribonucleic acid (DNA); the other nucleic acid also consisted of four bases, but contained uracil in place of thymine. Since the sugar of the latter was ribose, it was called ribonucleic acid (RNA).

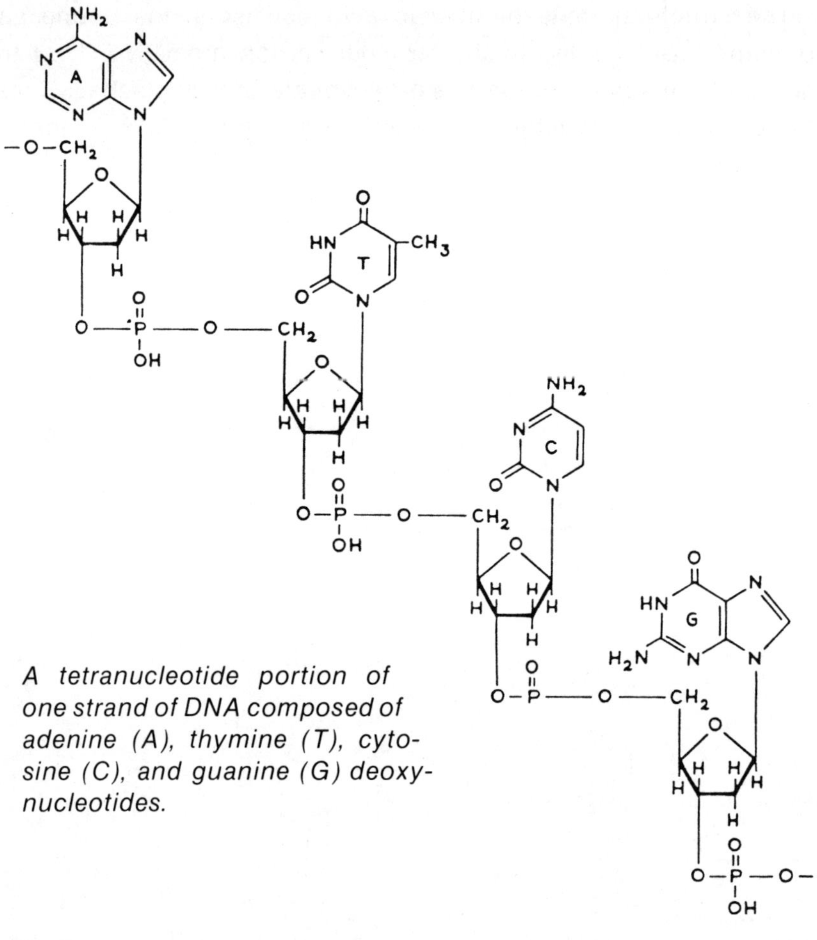

A tetranucleotide portion of one strand of DNA composed of adenine (A), thymine (T), cytosine (C), and guanine (G) deoxynucleotides.

Eventually, biologists realized the two kinds of nucleic acid did not distinguish plants and animals, but that all living things contained both types, DNA and RNA. Beneath life's immense diversity there was an astonishing unity. The principles of genetics were found to be coextensive with living matter in a general validity that covers all forms of life. The continuity of living substances through reproduction is based on the multiplicity of genes which are copied and passed on from generation to generation — the material of inheritance being the same for viruses and man alike. That substance is DNA.

Only four basic chemical units are used to create the blueprint in a coded sequence of the units in an informational molecule where the molecular weight can run into billions even for bacteria. A section of the DNA constitutes a gene that carries the information for the amino acid sequence for a particular protein. In bacteria the number of genes can be in thousands, but in mammals it runs as high as 100,000 to 1,000,000. In the procaryotic cell all the genetic information is carried in a single two-stranded DNA molecule looped in a circle. The DNA is arranged in the cell in either a compact whorl or in densely packed parallel pattern — but fully extended it would be 1 millimeter long.

Cellular reproduction is ultimately molecular reproduction, and the unique nature of the chemical structure of nucleic acids allows these biopolymers to be copied faithfully. In procaryotes with their circular DNA, cellular reproduction is replication of the nucleic acid followed by binary fission into two daughter cells with each carrying a full complement of cellular material. The chemistry is simple and direct, and must represent the mode of replication assumed soon after the origin of the first living systems.

Eucaryotic cells, on the other hand, have reproduction procedures so elaborate that they must have taken an extremely long time to evolve. Instead of a single DNA molecule, the nucleus became multiples of DNA linked together in groups as chromosomes. This served well for a cell to accumulate the volume of hereditary material necessary for advanced forms of life. Where procaryotes are restricted to what can be regarded as one chromosome, eucaryotes evolved a method whereby they have chromosomes joined together in long thread-like bodies, creating an open-end expansion for genetic material and development.

When a eucaryotic cell undergoes nuclear division it does so by one of two procedures: meiosis or mitosis. These involve replication of the DNA molecule and duplication of the chromosomes by complex nuclear changes. Instead of a simple replication as with procaryotes, eucaryotic cells fuse the genetic material from different individual cells, multiplying the spread of variety and bringing to the world sexual reproduction.

To be the informational reservoir of the cell, there had to be a chemical procedure for making duplicates of the molecule. Before understanding how this was accomplished, it was necessary to determine the complete structural arrangement of DNA. The nucleic acids were polynucleotides that existed as long, unbranched chains, but only the precise three-dimensional configuration would reveal the mode of action of their biological function. And thus began the search to learn the architecture of DNA.

In 1950, Erwin Chargaff and his students[5] at Columbia University made an odd observation. After carefully analyzing the purine and pyrimidine composition of various DNA's, they noticed the number of adenine bases always nearly equalled the number of thymines, and the number of guanine and cytosine bases were also nearly equal. To put

Chromosomes of the Drosophila (fruit fly) salivary gland. Magnification is 1,000X. (Carolina Biological Supply Company)

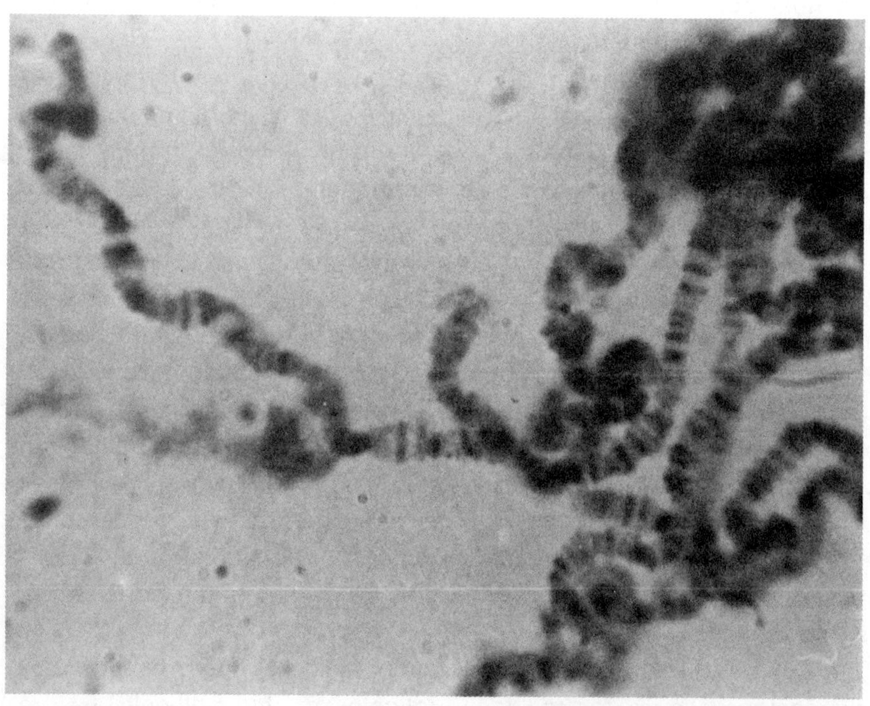

it more conveniently, they found A=T and G=C. This was despite large variations in the amounts of A=T to G=C in different DNA's.

While Chargaff's laboratory was analyzing the base composition of DNA, Rosalind Franklin and Maurice Wilkins at King's College, London, were using X-ray crystallography to obtain some precise measurements of DNA. And in California, Linus Pauling and his associates at the California Institute of Technology attacked the problem of DNA's structure by using the bond lengths and angles of the quantum theorists as guides to construct atomic models. Both the London group and the Cal Tech chemists were inclined to believe there were three polynucleotide chains in the DNA molecule.

The principal force of attraction that would hold the polynucleotide strands together was hydrogen bonding. Hydrogen bonds are weak compared to covalent bonds. To break a covalent bond requires between 50 and 100 kcal/mole, whereas the energy to break hydrogen bonds ranges from 0.5 to 12 kcal/mole. Nevertheless, hydrogen bonds are of enormous importance in biology by being primarily responsible for the specificity of interactions between macromolecules.

The number of possible combinations that can form hydrogen bonds among polynucleotide chains is large. A critical question was whether the bases pointed toward the outside or the center of the molecule. Pauling suggested the bases were on the outside, but Franklin felt she had evidence the phosphates were on the outside and the bases were toward the center.

This was the situation in 1951 when James Watson, a 22-year-old American postdoctoral fellow arrived in Cambridge and met Francis Crick, a physicist working on his Ph.D. in biophysics. Although ostensibly Crick was doing research on protein and Watson was interested in the structure of the Tobacco Mosaic Virus, they both had an abiding interest in DNA and decided to collaborate on solving its structure.

Franklin's X-ray diffraction patterns indicated a regular and compact configuration. The helical structure had been shown by Pauling to be a favored configuration of macromolecules and Crick became enamoured with helices. The question of prime importance was the chemical basis of the procedure organisms used to copy their DNA.

Presumably the purines and pyrimidines were important. Reasoning that nature has a penchant for doing things in pairs, Watson discarded the three-strand concept and felt it was more plausible to build a model with two strands twisting around each other with the bases directed toward the center. Using cardboard cutouts of the four bases, he attempted to build a model on hydrogen bonding with each base facing a like base as it could be imagined duplication of a strand to occur. Not only was the model not compact as shown by the X-ray studies, but Jerry Donahue, an American crystallographer working in the same laboratory, pointed out that Watson, like everyone else, was using the wrong tautomeric form of the bases. Donahue felt the bases existed in the keto rather than the enol form.

With new cutouts, Watson again attempted to combine base pairs for his model. At this point he discovered that the cutouts of adenine with thymine were the same size and shape of guanine with cytosine. The significance of Chargaff's A= T and G = C ratios suddenly became obvious.

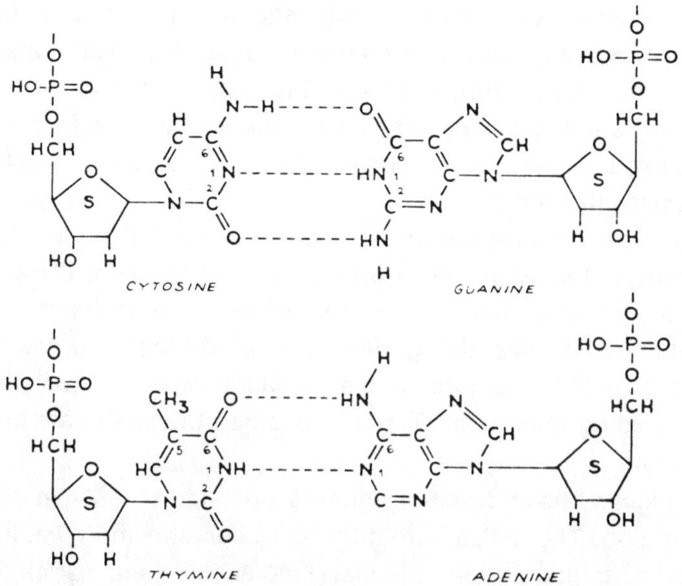

CYTOSINE GUANINE

THYMINE ADENINE

Since it was possible for the adenine-thymine and guanine-cytosine pairs to be held together by at least two hydrogen bonds to give nearly identical shapes, the model would be consistent with the compact arrangement indicated by the X-ray analysis. Instead of replicating through a like-like combination, the model showed the DNA molecule to be two strands of polynucleotide chains twisted in a double helix, held together by bonding between complementary bases with one strand acting as the "negative," and the other as the "positive." Replication was achieved upon unwinding, when each single strand became the template for the new complementary strand.[7]

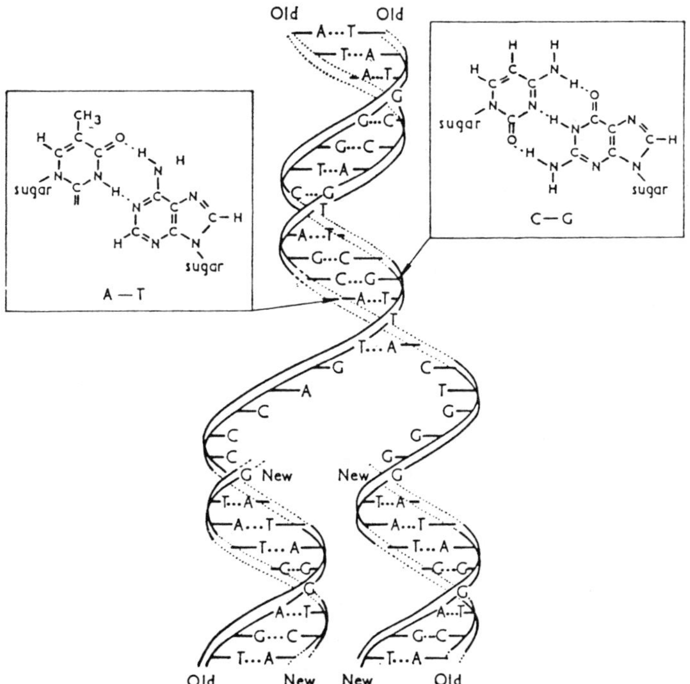

Within eighteen months, Watson and Crick had constructed a model of DNA consistent with the physical data that showed not only the three-dimensional shape of the DNA, but also the manner in which the molecule is duplicated. Since their results were first published in 1953,[8,9] a great deal of evidence has been accumulated supporting their proposed structure, the most spectacular being the synthesis of a biologically active DNA molecule in the test tube by Arthur Kornberg.[10]

References

1. O.T. Avery, C.M. MacLeod and M. McCarty, Studies on the chemical nature of the substance inducing transformation of pneumcoccal types, *J. Exptl. Med.* **79**, 137-157 (1944).
2. G. W. Beadle and E.L. Tatum Genetic control of biochemical reactions in Neurospora, *Proc. Nat. Acad. Sci.* **27**, 499-506 (1941).
3. W.M. Stanley, Isolation of a crystalline protein possessing the properties of Tobacco Mosaic virus, *Science* **81**, 644-645 (1935).
4. E. Schrödinger, **What is Life?** The MacMillan Co., 1945.
5. E. Chargaff, S. Zamenhof, G. Bravermian and L. Kerin, Bacterial deoxypentose nucleic acids of unusual composition, *J. Am Chem. Soc.* **72**, 3825 (1950).
6. L. Pauling and R.B. Corey, Structure of the nucleic acids, *Nature* **171**, 346 (1953); ------, A proposed structure for the nucleic acids, *Proc. Nat. Acad. Sci.* **39**, 84-97 (1953).
7. J.D. Watson, **Molecular Biology of the Gene**, 2nd ed., Benjamin, New York, 1970.
8. J.D. Watson and F.H.C. Crick, A structure for deoxyribose nucleic acid, *Nature* **171**, 737-738 (1953).
9. J.D. Watson and F.H.C. Crick, Genetic implications of the structure of deoxyribonucleic acid, *Nature* **171**, 964-967 (1953).
10. M. Goulian, A. Kornberg and R.L. Sinsheimer, Enzymatic synthesis of DNA. XXIV. Synthesis of infectious phase Ø x-174, *Proc. Nat. Acad. Sci.* **58**, 2321-2328 (1967).

13

From Blueprint to Organism

The Miller experiment opened the research to how life began by showing the manner in which the building blocks were formed before the first cells. Among the building blocks are the nucleotides that join together to form nucleic acids, and it is the nucleic acid, DNA, that is the molecular basis of life's reproductive capacity. But DNA is only an informational molecule --- like a computer tape. The proteins, in their immense variety and roles, are the chemicals most directly responsible for the shape, composition and functionality of an organism. Only after the information coded in the chemical structure of DNA is retrieved and translated to protein structure does it complete its biological purpose. How then are proteins created from the DNA structure?

As aforementioned, there are two kinds of nucleic acids: DNA and RNA. DNA is the molecule that is the store of hereditary information and is found only in the nucleus of the cell. RNA, on the other hand, is found in both the nucleus and in the cytoplasm. And too, protein synthesis takes place in the cytoplasm. Even in the 1940's, before DNA was known to be the material of genes, research by Torbjorn Caspersson[1] of Stockholm and Jean Bracht[2] of Brussels gave indications that the RNA was involved in protein synthesis.

In 1950, Henry Borzook and his group[3] at the California Institute of Technology and Tore Hultin of the Wenner-Gren Institute of Stockholm independently identified the microsomes, later known as ribosomes, in the cytoplasm as the site of protein synthesis. The DNA does not act directly as the template for the synthesis of protein, but instead the DNA sequence is transcribed to an RNA molecule which is copied from the DNA in the same manner DNA is replicated. The RNA copy of DNA is a messenger RNA (mRNA) that carries the hereditary information in its sequence to the ribosome to be translated into the amino acid sequence of a polypeptide.

$$\text{DNA} \xrightarrow{\text{(transcription)}} \text{mRNA} \xrightarrow[\text{ribosome}]{\text{(translation)}} \text{protein}$$

In the mid-1950's, biologists thought ribosomal RNA was literally a template for protein synthesis containing structural cavities that were complementary to the shape of amino acids from which the protein was constructed. But no one could construct a model of RNA with specified holes that could conceivably act as a template. It was Francis Crick who recognized that amino acids do not fit directly in the template molecule, but require an adapter molecule that is specific for the amino acid that recognizes the particular site on the template.

Mahlon Hoagland of Harvard University had discovered a type of RNA that could not be settled by centrifugation, but remained in solution, hence he called them soluble RNA's. It was not long before it was realized Hoagland's soluble RNA'S were Crick's adapter molecules. A specific soluble RNA was found for each of the twenty amino acids, and more in keeping with their role, they have become known as transfer RNA's (tRNA's).

It has been known that all tRNA molecules have a sequence of CCA at the end of the polynucleotide that has the sugar with a free hydroxyl on the 3'-carbon, the end to which the amino acid is attached. Also, it was known the A/U and G/C ratio approached equality, so that there was the possibility of considerable base pairing within the molecule. Robert Holley and his coworkers[4] at Cornell University observed that tRNA's contain a number of unusual bases that differ from A, G, C and U by having one or more methyl groups substituted in various positions in their structures.

A complete analysis of a tRNA for alanine was accomplished by Holley and others in 1965 and the nucleotide sequence of a yeast tRNA for tyrosine was reported by Madison and coworkers[5] the following year. The structures proposed by these two tRNA's was a "cloverleaf" configuration held together by hydrogen bonding and with the CCA bases at the 3′ end sticking out. Since then, sequences of some 75 different tRNA molecules have been determined and all can be organized in the same general cloverleaf folding.

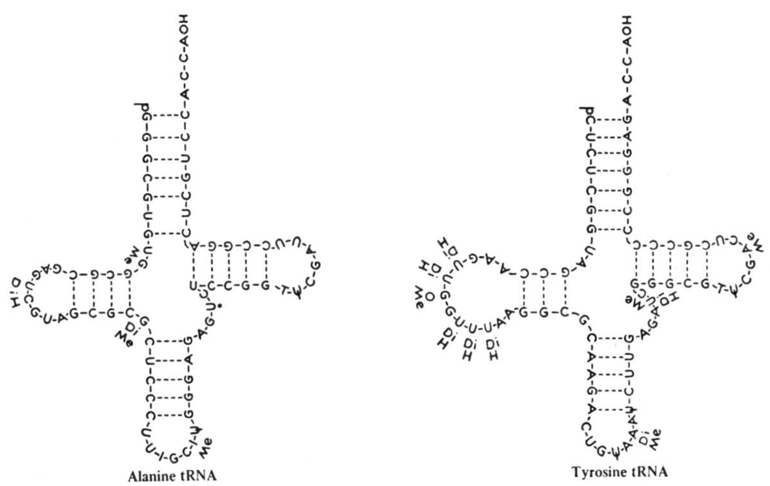

Proposed structure for alanine tRNA and tyrosine tRNA. (Madison et al., Science **153**, *531, 1966)*

The middle loop of the cloverleaf on the opposite end from the CCA contains a triplet of unpaired bases that form the anticodon, these three bases being complementary to the triplet of bases in the mRNA that represent a codon, or one word in the information in the mRNA that translates to one amino acid. The tRNA's range in number of nucleotides from 74 to 91, but of the various tRNA molecules, the overall distance from the CCA at one end to the anticodon at the other end appears to be constant, the difference in the nucleotide number being compensated for by the size of the little loop located between the right hand and bottom limbs. Also, the unusual bases are located in bases in regions not forming the hydrogen bonds. Transfer RNA's, unlike the other forms of nucleic acids, must have a highly specific three-dimensional structure, and in this respect they really resemble proteins.

Amino acids are prepared for use in protein synthesis by being activated in a reaction with ATP which requires the enzyme, aminoacyl RNA synthetase. The result is an activated complex of enzyme-AMP-amino acid in which the 5′-phosphate group of AMP is linked as a mixed anhydride to the carboxyl group of the amino acid. Pyrophosphate is split from the activating ATP in the process.

$$\underset{\text{Amino acid}}{\text{R-}\underset{\substack{|\\ \text{NH}_2}}{\text{CH}}\text{-COOH}} \xrightarrow[\text{Aminoacyl-RNA-Synthetase (E)}]{\text{ATP} \;\to\; \text{PP}_i \text{ (Pyrophosphate)}} \underset{\text{Activated amino acid}}{\text{E-adenine-ribose-O-}\underset{\substack{|\\ \text{OH}}}{\overset{\substack{\text{O}\\ \|}}{\text{P}}}\text{-O-}\overset{\substack{\text{O}\\ \|}}{\text{C}}\text{-}\underset{\substack{|\\ \text{NH}_2}}{\text{CH}}\text{-R}}$$

In the next step, the activated amino acid molecules are transferred to the corresponding tRNA by another enzyme. There is a particular tRNA for each amino acid, and a specific enxyme for each amino acid to be attached to the tRNA. The tRNA complex containing the amino acid then moves to a ribosome.

The mRNA having been formed from DNA and moved to the cytoplasm has ribosomes attached to it as the chain initiator codon (AUG) which binds, for example, N-formylmethionyl-tRNA. The ribosome moves down the chain of the mRNA one codon at a time, accepting the respective tRNA complex that corresponds to the codon and connecting the amino acid to the growing peptide chain. As the ribosome moves down the mRNA, the polypeptide chain grows. Other ribosomes attach themselves to the mRNA as the initiator codon is vacated. In this way a single mRNA can serve as many as six or eight ribosomes at the same time. There is only one specific site of the ribosome where peptide bond formation can occur, but from each ribosome moving along the mRNA, a polypeptide chain grows, each on an average between 125 to 400 amino acids long.

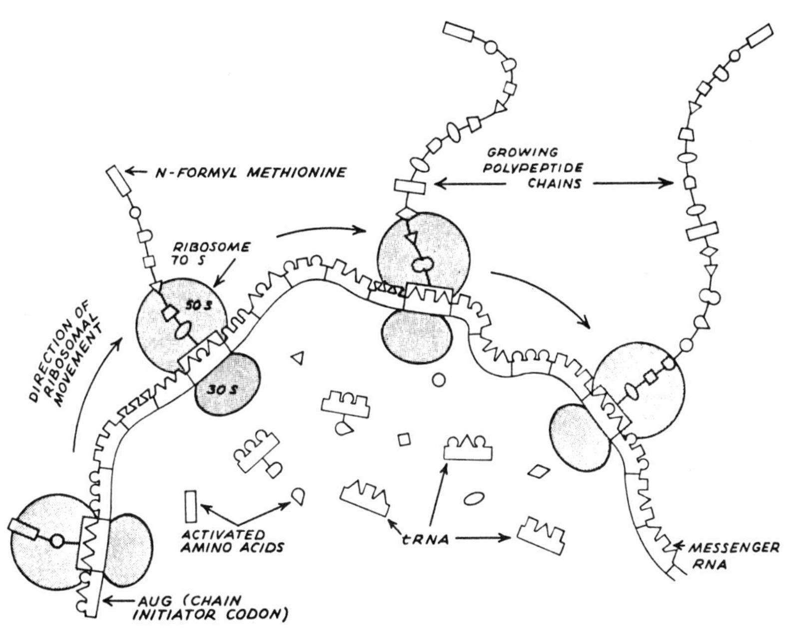

Illustration of ribosomes on a mRNA synthesizing polypeptides. (Watson, Science **140**, *17, 1963)*

The sequence of purine and pyrimidine bases on the mRNA strand, originally transcribed from the nuclear DNA, directs the arrangement of amino acids in the synthesis of proteins. This information carried on mRNA is not in single nucleotides, but resides in sequences of three nucleotides or triplets. The "genetic code," therefore, consists of nonoverlapping triplets in the mRNA chain, each triplet being a code word or codon.

After resolving the question of how hereditary information was stored in DNA, then transcribed to mRNA and translated to protein structure, there remained deciphering the code. What nucleotides corresponded to what amino acids?

Nirenberg and Matthael[6] in 1961 were the first to decipher a codon. They discovered a synthetic polynucleotide containing only uridylic acid (polyuridylic acid) could serve as a template for ribosomes isolated from the bacterium *E. coli.* When poly U was mixed with ribosome preparations and tRNA molecules were added, each bearing its own specific amino acid, a polypeptide was synthesized that contained only phenylalanine. From this they were able to conclude the codon for phenylalanine is UUU.

In similar experiments, GUU directed the synthesis for valine-containing polypeptides; UGU was the code word for cysteine, and UUG for leucine. Eventually, using "block copolymers," polynucleotides of repeating sequences of two or three bases, the entire genetic code was deciphered.

As the result of many additional studies, not only the triplets for all the amino acids were assigned, but codons for special instructions were found. When it was discovered all proteins synthesized by *E. coli* have N-formylmethionine as the N-terminal amino acid residue, it was recognized AUG was the initiator codon. All polypeptides begin with N-formylmethionine which may or may not be removed later. Three amino acids have six codons, five have four codons and ten have two codons. UAA, UAG and UGA are chain-terminating triplets that signal for the peptide to end at that point.

Unlike proteins, nucleic acids are robust molecules. They are stable in mild acids and alkalies and can be heated to almost 100° C, conditions that wreck the delicate protein structures. This is a property that facilitates the isolation of nucleic acids from other cellular components. Another feature that simplifies the purification of DNA is that, in contrast to proteins, there is only one kind of DNA in an organism.

Both DNA and proteins are biopolymers, built of subunits, that evolved for different purposes. Proteins required shape and a variety of functional groups to achieve specificity and chemical activities. To obtain these they needed a variety of subunits, and they found it in the

THE GENETIC CODE

FIRST LETTER	SECOND LETTER: U		C		A		G		THIRD LETTER
U	UUU	Phe	UCU	Ser	UAU	Tyr	UGU	Cys	U
	UUC		UCC		UAC		UGC		C
	UUA	Leu	UCA		UAA	OCHRE	UGA	UMBER	A
	UUG		UCG		UAG	AMBER	UGG	Tryp	G
C	CUU	Leu	CCU	Pro	CAU	His	CGU	Arg	U
	CUC		CCC		CAC		CGC		C
	CUA		CCA		CAA	GluN	CGA		A
	CUG		CCG		CAG		CGG		G
A	AUU	Ileu	ACU	Thr	AAU	AspN	AGU	Ser	U
	AUC		ACC		AAC		AGC		C
	AUA		ACA		AAA	Lys	AGA	Arg	A
	AUG	Met	ACG		AAG		AGG		G
G	GUU	Val	GCU	Ala	GAU	Asp	GGU	Gly	U
	GUC		GCC		GAC		GGC		C
	GUA		GCA		GAA	Glu	GGA		A
	GUG		GCG		GAG		GGG		G

[a] UAA (ochre), UAG (amber), and UGA (umber) are chain terminating codons. AUG is used as a chain initiating codon standing for formylmethionine in E. coli. In the middle of a protein chain it stands for methionine.

twenty or so amino acids. DNA, on the other hand, did not need a variety of shapes — it needed only to store information. For this purpose it had a choice. It could use a large alphabet (subunits) and be able to have a large vocabulary, or it could use just a few letters, but make the informational molecule extremely long. In the end, biological systems adopted a DNA of only four subunits used as three-letter words with a vocabulary of only 64 words, but the number of units in DNA molecules often runs into the billions.

It can be argued that this is all that DNA needed to accommodate twenty amino acids. But there are many more possible amino acids than twenty that could have been adopted for proteins. Certainly, a DNA constructed of four kinds of nucleotides seems adequate and could have been the type that proved superior to other more complex arrangements by being simpler, more stable and compact. And there may be no appreciable advantage in using more kinds of amino acids if twenty is enough.

The answer, however, may be for another reason. The emerging cell would have constructed its proteins and nucleic acids from the selection of amino acids and nucleotides in its primordial environment. Once committed to an efficient biological system, however, the primitive cells would have been unable to incorporate any additional building blocks. The amino acids and nucleotides adopted may have been the only ones available.

References

1. T. Caspersson, Studien über den Eiweissumsatz der Zelle, *Naturwiss.* **29**, 33-48 (1941).
2. J. Bracht, La localization des acides pentosenucleiques dans les tissus animaux et les oeufs d'Amphibiens en voie de developpement, *Arch. Biol. (Liege)* **53**, 207-257 (1942).
3. H. Borzook, C.L. Deasy, A.J. Hagen-Smit, G. Keighley and P.H. Lowry, Metabolism of C^{14}-labeled glycine, L-histidine, L-leucine and L-lysine, *J. Biol. Chem.* **187**, 839-848 (1950).
4. R.W. Holley, J. Apgar, G.A. Everett, J.T. Madison, M. Marquisse, S. H. Merrill, J.R. Penswick and A. Zamir, Structure of a ribonucleic acid, *Science* **147**, 1462-1465 (1965).
5. J.T. Madison, G.A. Everett and H. Kung, Nucleotide sequence of a yeast tyrosine transfer RNA, *Science* **153**, 531-534 (1966).
6. M.W. Nirenberg and J.H. Matthael, The dependence of cell-free protein synthesis in E. coli upon naturally occurring or synthetic polynucleotides, *Proc. Nat. Acad. Sci.* **47**, 1588-1602 (1961).

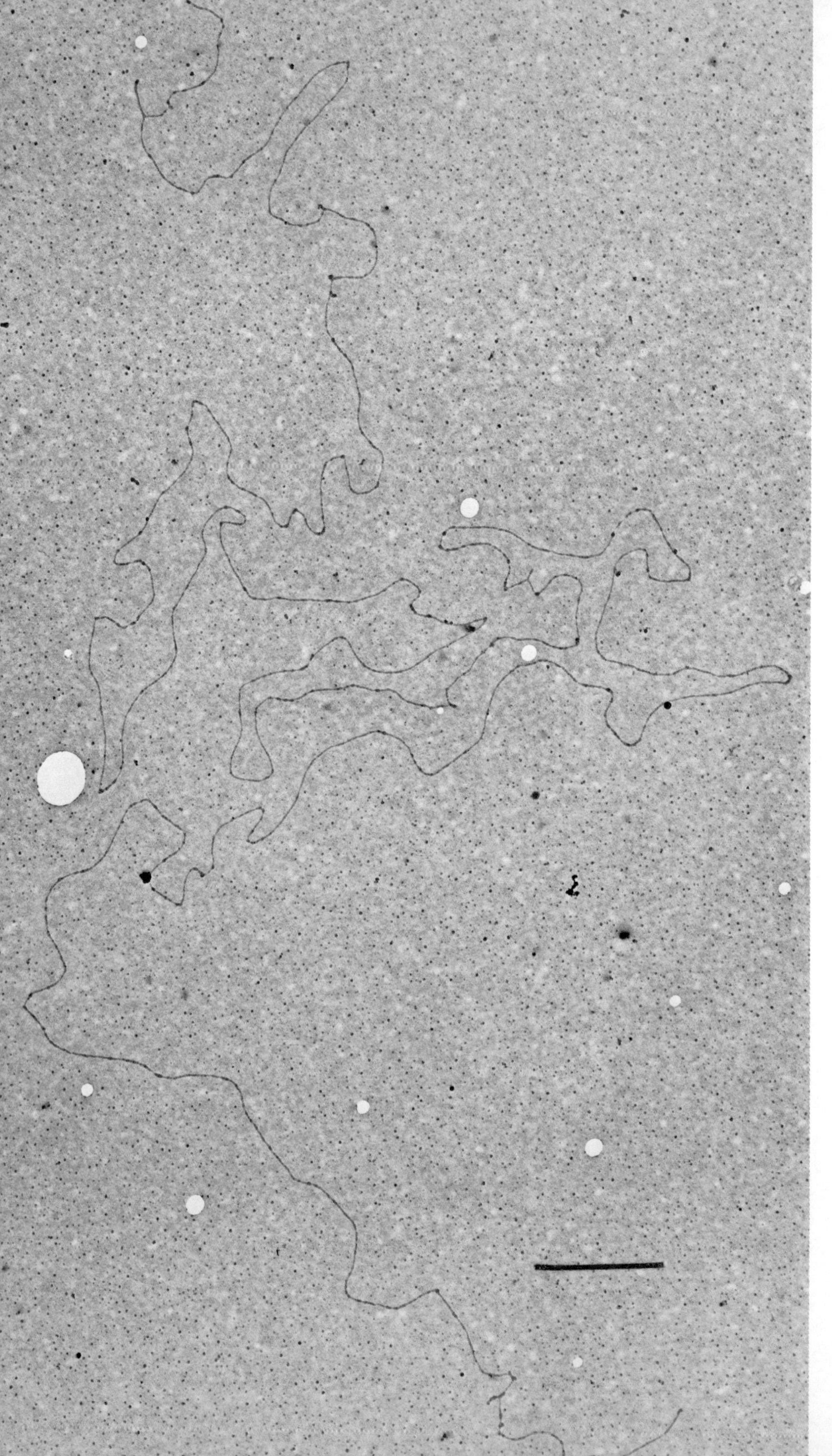

14
The Thread of Life

All living things on earth are tied to an invisible evolutionary thread that stretches back to the beginning of life. The thread is the DNA molecule that is in each of our cells and carries the genetic information for the construction of our very being. That molecule has existed, has been altered, lengthened and copied generation after generation from the moment the first living cells formed on earth over 3.4 billion years ago. The infrequent changes that occurred in the molecule were retained and passed down to the succeeding generations; and each change in

A molecule of linear double-stranded DNA. The bar represents 1,000 nm; magnification is 20,000 X. (Courtesy of Dennis O'Callaghan, University of Mississippi Medical Center. Photograph by Nan Mansfield)

DNA became reflected in a change in a protein translated from its structure.

There are many kinds of proteins in a functional cell, performing or monitoring essentially all biochemical reactions; a single cell can have 5,000 to 10,000, and man may have as many as a million. The metabolic processes, the matrix for bone and shell, the transport of reactants, the synthesis of constituents and even the shape and mechanical properties of biological systems are all governed by proteins, each protein delicately adapted to perform its specific role by its chemical structure, which in turn is a direct expression of the arrangement of different amino acids in its chain. When, therefore, a change in the amino acid composition of a protein occurs, it often has a profound effect on the entire cell or organism. Nevertheless, this is the basis of evolution and without it life could not have developed.

It is the mutability of the genetic apparatus that results in alteration of proteins. A gene is a segment of the DNA molecule and carries the coded message for the synthesis of a single polypeptide — a polypeptide that may itself be a protein or may be combined with other polypeptides to form a protein. If then, by mutation a nucleotide is changed in the gene, one of the coded messages is altered and is read for a different amino acid, so that when the protein is synthesized, a substitution occurs in the peptide chain. Mutation generally results from the low level of natural radioactivity radiation, but it can also result from certain chemicals.

This is mutation on the simplest level and for single polypeptides. When advanced plants and animals evolved, their DNA molecules became clustered in chromosomes and reproduction became more complex, allowing for greater variation of the genetic material. The diversity of genotypes can be attributed to different allele combinations, chromosomal interchange, inversion, recombination or polyploidy. As a result, except in the case of twins, no two individuals of advanced species are identical. This complexity of reproduction introduced a new set of mutations by errors that occur in the procedure, but the mutation of the DNA molecule resulting in an amino acid substitution in a single protein is the subject of interest to molecular evolutionists. Chemically, it is simpler and can be studied analytically and mathematically.

The rate of mutation, like radioactive disintegration, is a statistical factor that is impressively constant. Zuckerkandl and Pauling[3] estimated that each amino acid in hemoglobin undergoes substitution by genetic mutation at an average rate of once every 800 million years. Since hemoglobin has 140 amino acids, this averages to one substitution for the molecule every 5.07 million years.

The constancy of the rate of substitution was confirmed by Motoo Kimura[4] by comparing the number of amino acid substitutions that have occurred in hemoglobin chains of man and the carp. Hemoglobin consists of two chains each of polypeptides called alpha and beta chains that evolved from an ancient hemoglobin of only one chain. Man and carp with their two-chain hemoglobins had a common ancestor with the primitive globin that lived in the Devonian Period 350 to 400 million years ago and divergence of the separate evolutionary lines is taken to be around 375 million years ago. By comparing the alpha and beta chains of human hemoglobin which come from separate genes, Kimura found they differed in the total number of amino acid substitutions by 75. Then when he compared the number of substitutions of the human beta chain and the carp alpha chain he found the difference was 77, or essentially the same. In other words, after diverging from a common ancestor 375 million years ago, man and carp underwent virtually the same number of mutations in the alpha chain of their hemoglobins.

It was Vernon Ingram[5] of the Massachusetts Institute of Technology in 1961 who suggested that the substitution rate in proteins by mutation could be used as a molecular evolutionary clock. Various species have many of the same proteins in common which perform the same function, but differ slightly from species to species by amino acid composition. Such proteins are called hemologs, and the more closely related species are, the more similar are the homologous proteins in composition.

The degree of divergence in the composition of blood proteins in different animals is particularly evident in the study of blood serum. When human blood is injected into a rabbit, the rabbit's immune response produces antibodies to the human proteins. This antihuman serum in return, when mixed with human blood, causes clumping of 100 percent of the blood protein. The same antihuman serum mixed with blood of other species gives the following percent precipitation : gorilla, 64; orangutan, 42; baboon, 29; ox 10; deer, 7; and kangaroo, O. This is an extremely critical measure of chemical resemblance and affinity, and the order of relationship correlates with evidence from comparative anatomy, embryology and paleontology.

Molecular evolution can now compare this diveregence of amino acid composition of homologous proteins directly. Since 1965, the known sequences of proteins have been published periodically by Margaret Dayhoff and her colleagues of the National Biomedical Research Foundation in the **Atlas of Protein Sequence and Structure.** The Number of entries has grown from 50 protein sequences in the 1965 edition to 1,080 through 1974.[6] By the known sequence of homologous proteins from a number of species, a comparison can be made to assess to what extent each species has undergone amino acid substitution in the protein by mutation.

One of the earliest proteins to be studied was cytochrome c by Emanuel Margoliash of Abbott Laboratories and Walter M. Fitch of the University of Wisconsin Medical School.[7] This heme protein is easily extracted and purified and is found in every mitochondrion of eucaryotic cells, that is to say, of all living things above bacteria and blue-green algae. It therefore is the expression of a distinct recognizable gene that has existed for some 1.3 billion years.

Cytochrome c has 104 amino acids in vertebrates, a few more in others. Because the structural shape of cytochrome c is closely associated with its ability to perform by interacting with cytochrome oxidase and cytochrome reductase, the surface of the protein is conserved. Any mutation whose amino acid substitution changes the protein's shape is deleterious, and consequently, does not survive As a result, 50 percent of the molecule remains invariant. Within the variable amino acids, there are 19 particular ones that play a role in the conformation of the polypeptides, and 6 others that have remained the same for undetermined reasons. There is also a constancy of the hydrophobic and basic segments of the protein, and some classes of amino acids are mutably interchangeable.

Thus, in studying the mutation distance between cytochrome c's of 20 species ranging from yeast to man, Fitch and Margoliash found a connection between the taxonomic kinship of species and the number of residue differences. Proteins of closely related species showed few or no differences, whereas, the greatest differences in amino acids was with the most diverse species: the monkey and human lines are distinguished by a single mutation in the human line that resulted in the substitution of isoleucine for threonine at one position; and the horse differs from the tuna fish by 20 amino acids, but from Baker's yeast by 45. The average difference between primates and the other mammals is 10.1 residues. With the amino acids substitutions from mutation through the history of cytochrome c calculated, Fitch and Margoliash were able to reconstruct the phylogenetic tree. Although substitutions in cyto-

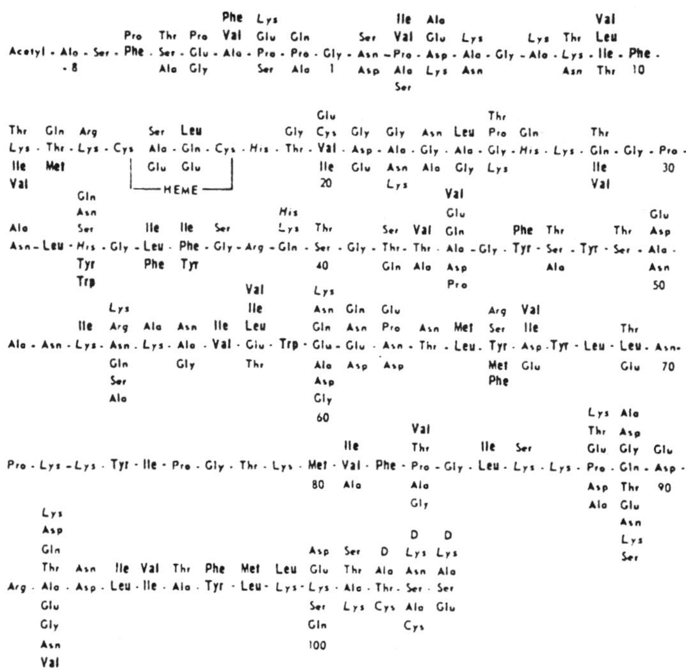

Composite of amino acid sequence of 30 eucaryotic cytochrome c's. The continuous sequence of 112 residues is that of wheat germ protein. All the other cytochrome c's are shorter with their various amino acids shown above and below the linear sequence. (Margoliash et al., *in* **Molecular Evolution 2**, *North Holland Publ. Co., 1971)*

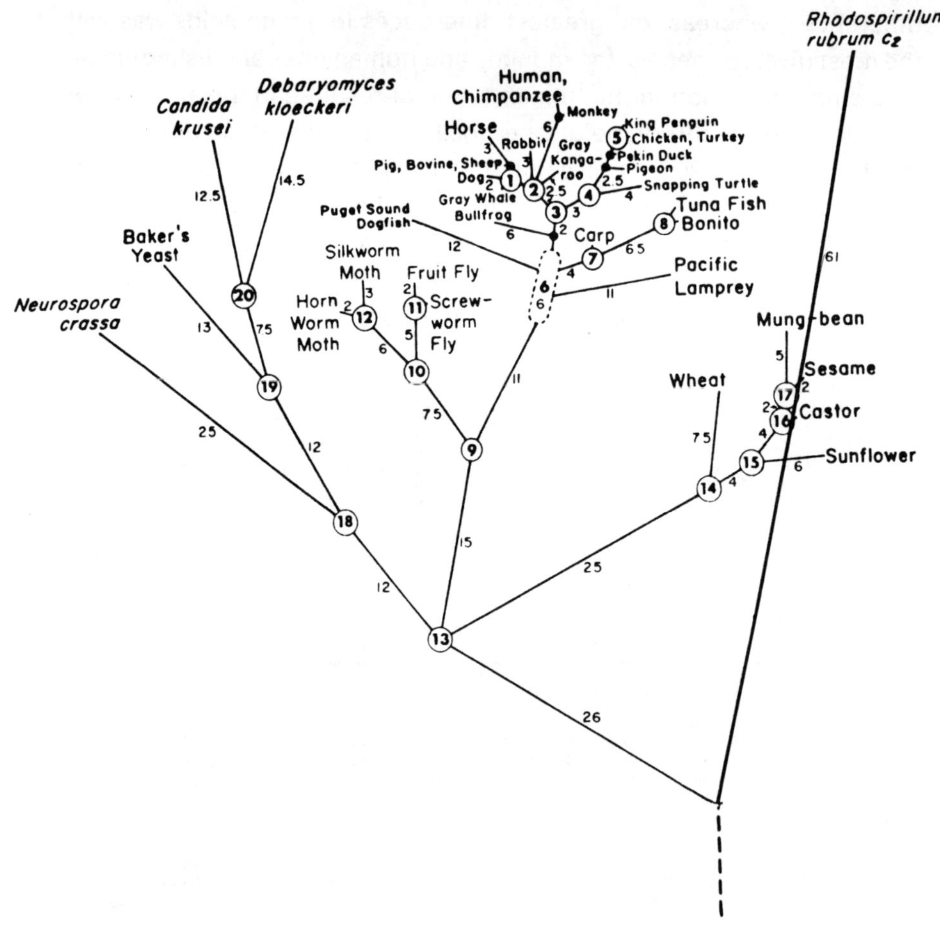

*Phylogenic tree based on cytochrome c. The numbers are the inferred amino acid changes per 100 links. (***Atlas of Protein Sequence and Structure***, 1972)*

chrome c may not have been the mutation most responsible for a particular divergence, its evolution coincides remarkably with the taxonomic development of the species.

To derive the topology of a phylogenetic tree, the amino acid sequences of homologous proteins are programmed in a computer. The computation is based on the premise that the least number of changes occurred in the ancestral organism. The computer then considers each amino acid along the polypeptide chain one at a time. Amino acids that have remained unchanged have been conserved and are considered invariant. For the others, the method involves a mathematical formula for each possible combination to take into account possible sequences for the ancestral structures. The detailed procedure is described in Chapter 2 of the **Atlas of Protein Sequences and Structure,** 1969.

Kimura and Ohta[8] have tabulated some of the principles governing molecular evolution. The rate of amino acid substitution is approximately constant if the change does not affect the function or tertiary structure of the protein. Therefore, those parts of the protein that are funtionally least important undergo the fastest change. And when a gene having a new function is evolved, it is preceded by gene duplication. In this way the organism has one copy to accumulate mutations and eventually emerge as a new gene, while the other copy retains the old function required for survival.

A study of the globins reveal species divergence coincidental with duplication of genetic material in the last billion years. The alpha and beta chains of hemoglobin, presently from separate genes on different chromosomes, were derived from a single ancestral gene by an ancient duplication of the genetic structure. The hemoglobin of the lamprey, a primitive fish, still retains a single chain. And too, myoglobin, a related heme protein found in muscle, evidently is the result of a divergence from hemoglobin by an ancient duplication that took place in the Precambrian approximately a billion years ago. In this way, as organisms evolved to more advanced levels, their genetic material and the associated proteins expanded in number and complexity.

A gene contains an average of 1,000 nucleotides; and in man, the total number of nucleotides making up a genome (the set of chromosomes and all their genes in an ovum or sperm cell) is about 4 billion. This is roughly the same for all mammals. In a study of seven proteins, King and Jukes[9] found in the evolutionary history of mammals the number of amino acid substitutions averaged 2 to 2.5 per year in a species. If the average generation time in the line to man was 10 years, there would have been 20 substitutions in each generation. This is much too rapid for a stable species; variants would be lost before natural selection would have time to derive potential advantages they might present. For this reason, the majority of changes in proteins have been neutral or almost neutral in natural selection.

The rate at which different proteins evolve depends upon the number of amino acids that are invariant for the protein to be functional. To study the rate of molecular evolution Doolittle and Blombäck[10] chose the fibrinopeptides. Unlike hemoglobin and cytochrome c, the fibrinopeptides do not have to conserve particular amino acids for their biological role. They are the peptide segments, 13 to 21 amino acids long, that are cut out of fibrinogen when it is converted to fibrin in a blood clot. Since fibrinopeptides can consist of virtually any amino acid, they are excellent for studying the unrestricted rate of mutations.

Application of the fibrinopeptides is essentially limited to the mammals, but their information is an outstanding contribution for hominoid evolution. Humans, chimpanzees and gorillas all have indentical fibrinopeptides; whereas, there are differences in the fibropeptides of such closely related pairs as the cat-lion, dog-fox, donkey-horse and the water buffalo-Cape buffalo. In studying the molecular evolution of the six hominoids by comparing their fibrinopeptides, Doolittle and coworkers[11] discovered that, although the gorilla is identical to man and the chimpanzee, he differs from the Asian apes, the orangutan and siamang. It appears this chemical evidence of man's relationship to the African apes supports Leaky's thesis that our early progenitors lived in Africa.

Paleontologists tend to place the emergence of man distinct from the other primates as early as 14 million years ago.[12] Molecular evolutionists, on the other hand, believe man and the African apes diverged as late as 4 to 5 million years ago.[13] For better or for worse, the chemical analysis and comparisons are less susceptible to subjectivity than taxonomy. Consequently, we learn the molecular relationship between man and the other primates is much closer than generally believed — and actually closer than between members of some other recognized species. Of 50 different proteins isolated from man and chimpanzee, the difference in amino acid sequences has been found to be less than 1 percent.

There are two forms of chromosomal organization: the single chromosome as a double-stranded DNA in a closed loop of bacteria and blue-green algae, and the bead-like chain of chromosomes of the higher organisms. Mutation can occur in errors in a number of ways in replication of the chromosome arrangement, but these chromosomal aberrations are almost always lethal. On the other hand, the effect of a mutation of the genes resulting in amino acid substitution depends upon the protein. If the substitution has no effect on the function of the protein, it is neutral; but if it alters the shape and efficiency of the protein, it will be deleterious and will not survive by loss of the individual from reproduction.

A species is an interbreeding pool, so that any surviving mutation can spread throughout a breeding range. New species arise when mutations accumulate in reproductively isolated groups. As the changes from mutations become prevalent, interbreeding with populations of the ancestral species is first rendered unusual, then eventually impossible.

Whereas substitutions of invariant amino acids in existing proteins is a mutation that is not retained, it is the means by which new proteins achieved their optimal amino acid sequence for functionality. In the early stages of life on earth the initial proteins were probably of low efficiency, but were continually improved upon by amino acid substitution until they attained maximum effectiveness. Since then the sequence responsible for their function has been rigorous conserved. But without mutation, life would have remained on the level of the first primitive cells on primordial earth.

It appears life began on earth with a few basic reactions to synthesize components, and hence, perpetuated itself by reproduction. The proteins for these fundamental reactions are conserved, and as the organisms evolved, they developed improvements by introducing new reactions to the old ones and refining the efficiency of biochemical conversions. Because of this conservative manner in which evolution proceeds, we all have within us "relics" of our progenitors, even of the ancient microscopic organisms that floated in Archean seas. Life does not discard what the survival of the species has depended upon, but retains the old alongside any new developments. For this reason, many of the basic biochemical reactions derived from extremely remote ancestors, little changed in billions of years, can still be seen in the biochemical architecture of contemporary plants and animals.

One such vestige of our origins in an anaerobic environment is a metabolic pathway for glycolysis. A main source of nutrition now and probably from the beginning is the metabolism of carbohydrates. In the simple process of fermentation, glucose is broken down to pyruvic acid yielding 47 kilocalories of chemical energy per mole of sugar. Contemporary anaerobic organisms carry out this conversion in 10 reactions. Since the development of this basic series of reactions, it has been extended by some organisms to metabolizing pyruvic acid farther to lactate, propionate, acetate, ethanol, acetone, butyric acid and higher fatty acids. Despite the fact decomposition of carbohydrates to pyruvic acid by fermentation has been supplanted by more evolved metabolic pathways in all except the anaerobic organisms, it is still preserved in the biochemistry of higher plants and animals as a relic from an age when it was the sole means of extracting chemical energy by our primitive anaerobic ancestors.

But the development of the whole biochemical structure has branched out from a few fundamental reactions. The result of this is that the original reactions can no longer be changed because too much of the overall biochemistry of the organisms stems from them and depends upon them. For example, acetate is involved in energy transfer systems, but is also the essential starting material of such diverse components as carbohydrates, amino acids and fats. Even if some other substance could be found that worked better than acetate, it could not be adopted without devastating consequences because so many reactions require it. A single change would pyramid into changing much of the metabolism of the organism.

This conservation of biochemical processes accounts for the close unity of all living things in the very fundamental steps that make life possible. This is where determining the amino acid sequences of many proteins and the application of computers has allowed biochemists to trace back the evolutionary development of today's plants and animals on a molecular level. Whereas the genetic complement of contemporary mammals is estimated to be 100,000 to 1,000,000 genes, the number of metabolic reactions that the various phyla have in common is quite small. From this it appears that all animals and man descended from an ancestral primordial cell that had only about 200 genes.[14]

The gene that transcribes cytochrome c dates back as early as the development of the eucaryotic cell 1.3 billion years ago, but a universal protein that may extend as early as the beginning of life on earth is ferredoxin, an iron-containing protein that is vital in photochemical reactions for electron transport to cellular energy storage. Ferredoxin has a reducing potential near that of molecular hydrogen making it the most highly reducing stable compound in a cell and suggesting it evolved at a time when the earth's atmosphere was still strongly reducing.

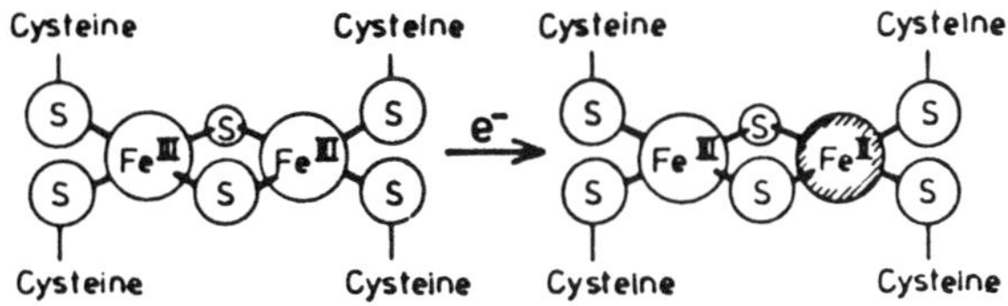

Model of the active site of ferredoxin. (Hall et al., in **Cosmochemical Evolution and the Origins of Life,** *D. Reidel Publ. Co., 1973)*

The various roles of ferredoxin in the cell are fundamental: it assists in the ATP formation by radiation,[15] it participates in the reduction of CO_2 to pyruvate, and it is used in the fixation of nitrogen.[16] Apparently ferredoxin is more ancient than nicotinamide adenine dinucleotide (NAD), a ubiquitous reducing agent in cells. In the primitive microbe, *C. pasteurianum* and the photosynthetic bacteria, *Chromatium* and *Chromatium thiosulfatophilium,* ferredoxin participates directly as a reductant of CO_2 with acetyl coenzyme A, instead of through NAD.[17]

Ferredoxin is an iron-sulfur protein of only 55 amino acids, consisting of an unusually high proportion of the smaller and thermodynamically stable amino acids, gylcine, alanine, serine, aspartic acid and cysteine. From a study of the sequence of amino acids of ferredoxin, Eck and Dayhoff[18] concluded the protein had an ancestral sequence of 29 units and the original molecule was based on a repeating sequence of alanine, serine, aspartic acid and glycine. It appears the original genetic mechanism was a sequence of 12 nucleotides that doubled, and then doubled itself, making a longer repetitive chain. Later, as the genetic code became more complex, other amino acids, including cysteine, were added and the sulfide bond of the cysteine became attached to the iron. Eventually, four cysteines were added by mutation and two identical chains combined to make an intricate protein-iron-sulfide complex of greatly increased efficiency.

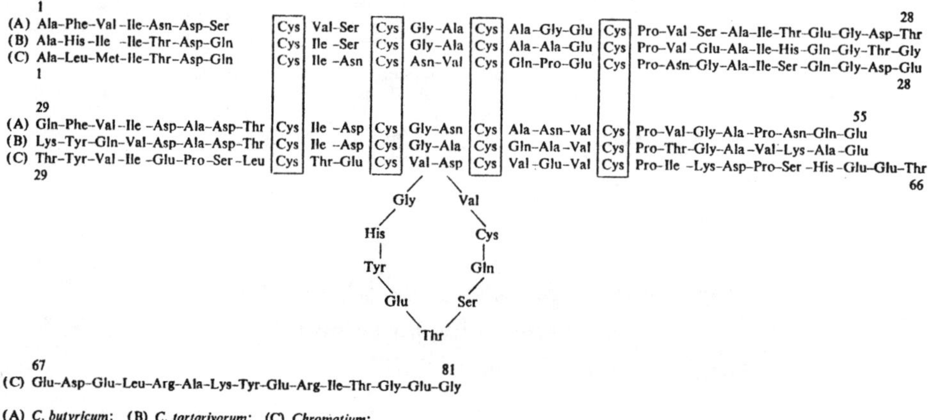

Comparison of sequences of ***Clostridium*** *and* ***Chromatium*** *ferredoxins. (Hall* et al., Nature **233**, *136, 1971)*

Ferredoxin occurs in the primitive anaerobic organisms, both photosynthetic and non-photosynthetic, and is basic to cell chemistry. The simplicity and evolutionary development of ferredoxin suggests that it may have been one of the earliest proteins formed by life on earth.[19]

Life extends uninterrupted from the first living cell on earth down through the ages to all its living descendants. The genetic information coded in the thread of DNA nucleotides has been passed on from generation to generation, slowly being improved upon, becoming more efficient, adding new genes and progressively moving toward the higher forms of plants and animals.

It needs to be borne in mind that all of today's descendants are equidistant genetically. There are the "living fossils"——plants and animals that exist little changed from their fossil ancestors. The shark has remained essentially the same for the last 70 million years, the horseshoe crab for 180, and the cockroach, scorpion, millipede and nautilus have changed little in several hundred million years. The ginkgo tree of China flourished during the age of the dinosaurs, and in 1958 off the coast of southwest Africa some fishermen caught in their nets a strange fish they had never seen before. There was ample reason. It was a coelacanth, a primitive fish paleontologists thought had become extinct aroung 150 million years ago.

But the "living fossils" extend to the most ancient forms of life. About 10 years ago, Sanford Siegel, a University of Hawaii botanist, on a chance visit to Harlech Castle in Wales, observed tourists honoring an established practice passed down from Medieval times. In the manner of the knights and sentries of old, they were relieving themselves at the base of the castle walls. Siegel, supported by the National Aeronautics and Space Administration, had worked for several years investigating microorganisms living under harsh environments likely to be encountered in space travel. Because ammonia is a major component of the atmosphere of Jupiter and may have been common on primitive earth, it was one of the environments studied. A natural condition high in ammonia would be soil saturated with urine.

Siegel returned home with soil samples he had collected from around the castle walls and attempted to culture them in concentrated ammonium hydroxide. Most organisms would have been killed or greatly inhibited by the medium, but Siegel observed one growing in microscopic clusters of star-shaped bodies attached to slender stalks. It did not fit a description of any known living organism, although it did closely resemble a Precambrian microfossil Barghoorn had discovered in 2 billion-year-old Gunflint chert at Kakabeka, Ontario, Canada, he had named *Kakabekia umbrellata.*[20]

Siegel hypothesized he had found a living microfossil that was an obligate ammonophile, an organism that requires ammonia to grow. Since he collected the first specimens at Harlech Castle, studies by

The Gate-house, Harlech Castle

Siegel and his wife, Barbara,[21] have shown the organism's need for ammonia is not absolute. The organism has also been found in soils from

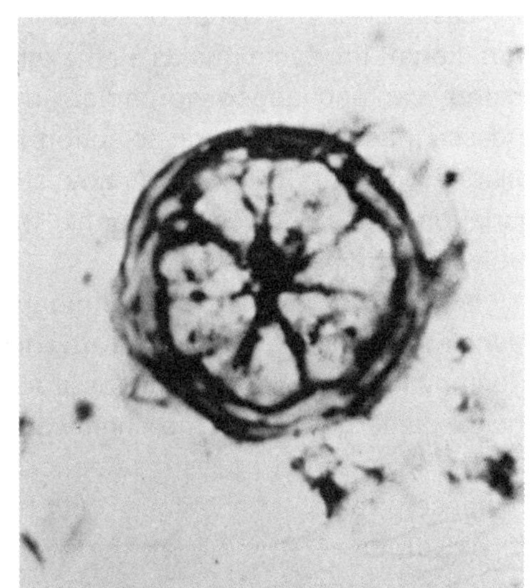

Kakabekia barghoorniana *from Wales. (Courtesy of Sanford Siegel, University of Hawaii)*

Alaska, Iceland and various alpine regions that are low in ammonia but high in alkalinity. It does not need oxygen, but, unlike most anaerobic bacteria, is not killed by it. Siegel's discovery, which may be a living relative of Barghoorn's fossil from the Middle Precambrian Period, he named *Kakabekia barghoorniana.*

The blue-green algae, although widely dispersed, have probably remained essentially the same for at least a billion years. And the anaerobic microbes that were dominant for the first 2 billion years of life before free oxygen existed in any significant amounts have managed to remain with us in sheltered niches and are represented today by the *Clostridia* that survive to give us tetanus, botulism and gas gangrene. The clostridia, which lack even cytochrome c, are listed as one of the most primitive forms of life. Even the photosynthetic bacteria, those primitive microbes that have the ability to synthesize organic matter from CO_2 in an anaerobic environment using H_2S as their source of hydrogen and requiring only acetic acid, light and some minerals, survive as one of the earliest life forms on earth.

But, although the "living fossils" appear to be frozen in time while other plants and animals are undergoing dynamic evolution, this is not the case. Even the genes of these relics of the past have undergone mutation at the same rate as all the other living descendants. In order to maintain an unchanged morphology they apparently have been under an incessant action of natural selection for hundreds of millions and even billions of years while a steady stream of almost neutral genetic variations has flowed through, transforming their informational molecules tremendously.

All living organisms have within their biochemical structures traces of the events that have led to the advancement of life for the last three and a half billion years. Unlike the fossil record that has left many branches that became deadends, the chemical relics within all living things are derived from direct ancestry. Application of molecular evolution is an immensely valuable technique. With it scientists can conceivably fulfill an old dream——trace back the evolution of the species to the very beginning of life itself.

References

1. F. Miescher, Über die chemische Zusammensetzung der Eierzellen, Hoppe-Seyler Med. Chem. Untersuch. 44a (1871).
2. O.T. Avery, C.M. MacLeod and M. McCarty, Studies on the chemical nature of the substance inducing transformation of pnemococoal types, *J. Exp-Med.* **79**, 137-157 (1944).
3. E. Zuckerkandl and L. Pauling, Evolutionary divergence and convergence in proteins, in **Evolving Genes and Proteins**, V. Bryson and H.J. Vogel, eds., Academic Press, New York, 1965, pp. 97-166.
4. Motoo Kimura, The rate of molecular evolution considered from the standpoint of populations genetics, *Proc. Nat. Acad. Sci.* **63**, 1181-1188 (1969).
5. Vernon M. Ingram, Gene evolution and hemoglobins, *Nature* **189**, 704-708 (1961).
6. **Atlas of Protein Sequence and Structure**, vol. 5, Suppl. I, II, M.O. Dayhoff, ed., National Biomedical Research Foundation, Silver Spring, Md., 1972.

7. W.M. Fitch and E. Margoliash, Construction of phylogenetic tress, *Science* **155**, 279-284 (1964).
8. Motoo Kimura and Tornoko Ohta, On some principles governing molecular evolution, *Proc. Nat. Acad. Sci.* **71**, 2848-2852 (1974).
9. J.L. King and T.H. Jukes, Non-Darwinian evolution, *Science* **164**, 788-798 (1969).
10. R.F. Doolittle and B. Blombäck, Amino-acid sequence investigations of fibrinopeptides from various mammals: evolutionary implications, *Nature* **202**, 147-152 (1964).
11. R.F. Doolittle, G.L. Wooding, Y. Lin and M. Riley, Hominoid evolution as judged by fibrinopeptide structures, *J. Mol. Evol.* **1**, 74-83 (1971).
12. L.S.B. Leaky, The relationship of African apes, man and the Old World monkeys, *Proc. Nat. Acad. Sci. U.S.* **67**, 1088-1093 (1969).
13. A.C. Wilson and V.M. Sarich, A molecular time scale for human evolution, *Proc. Nat. Acad. Sci.* **63**, 1088-1093 (1969).
14. M.O. Dayhoff and R.V. Eck, Paleobiochemistry, in **Organic Geochemistry**, G. Eglinton and M.T.J. Murphy, eds., Springer-Verlay, New York, Heidelberg and Berlin, 1969. p. 205.
15. D.I. Arnon, Ferredoxin and photosynthesis, *Science* **149**, 1460-1470 (1965).
16. L.E. Mortenson, Ferredoxin and ATP, requirements for nitrogen fixation in cell-free extracts of **Clostridium pasteurianum**, *Proc. Nat. Acad. Sci.* **52**, 272-279 (1964).
17. R. Bachofen, B.B. Buchanan and D.I. Arnon, Ferredoxin as a reductant in pyruvate synthesis by bacterial extract, *Proc. Nat. Acad. Sci.* **51**, 690-694 (1964).
18. R.V. Eck and M.O. Dayhoff, Evolution of the structure of ferredosin based on living relics of primitive amino acid sequences, *Science* **152**, 363-366 (1966).
19. D.O. Hall, R. Cammack and K.K. Rao, Role for ferredoxins in the origin of life and biological evolution, *Nature* **233**, 136-138 (1971).
20. S.M. Siegel, K. Roberts, H. Nathan and O. Daly, Living relative of the microfossil Kakabekia, *Science* **156**, 1231-1234 (1967).
21. Barbara Z. Siegel, Kakabekia, a review of its physiological and environmental features and their relation to its possible ancient affinities, in **Chemical Evolution of the Early Precambrian**, Academic Press, Inc., New York, 1977, pp. 143-154.

15

The Question of Genesis

All organisms on earth, from the simplest cell to man himself, are machines of extraordinary powers, effortlessly transforming complex organic molecules, displaying elaborate behavior patterns, and indefinitely producing from raw materials in the environment more or less identical copies of themselves. The life processes consist of exquisitely interlocked and controlled steps carried out in a marvelously architectual interior of the cell, with specialized regions where particular chemical reactions are performed. It has been estimated a single human cell contains 100,000 enzyme molecules to mediate 1,000 to 2,000 chemical reactions, an average of 50 to 100 molecules for each process; and the human body contains 100 trillion cells, each serving a particular role in the whole organism.

The ability of the enzymes to promote biochemical reactions is equally impressive. The rate of catalysis by most enzymes range from 1,000 to more than 500,000 molecules a minute. But the fastest rate observed seems to be by the enzyme catalase. One molecule of catalase can transform more than 5 million peroxide molecules a minute.

It is of small wonder then that men have sometimes looked upon life as a phenomenon that can be explained only in terms of non-physical laws. But as is the case with all phenomena, a living cell has appeared inexplicable only because there had not yet existed sufficient information about the biochemical processes to piece together a logical sequence of events in its function.

At one time it appeared that, because life created order from disorder by its synthesis and growth, it defied the Second Law of Thermodynamics that specifies that no processes can occur that increase the net order (or decrease the net entropy). This view, however, failed to take into consideration that the Second Law is valid only for closed systems. The universe as a whole, with no exchange of matter and energy from the outside, is steadily moving toward a state of complete randomness. Living systems, on the other hand, are open — not closed. It is the flow of sunlight from the outside the environment that drives the life machine.

The impressive powers of synthesis by enzymes have been confounding simply because our technology generally has not reached the level of efficiency of life processes. The laws of physics and chemistry are derived by the statistical probability of molecules to behave in a defined manner. The kinetics of a chemical reaction are computed upon the percentage of molecules of sufficient energy moving freely in a reaction mixture that collides with another appropriate molecule. The energy content of molecules in a population follows a distribution curve, and only those molecules with an energy above a particular level are likely to form a product. But biological systems have evolved a mechanism that is entirely different from the probability mechanism of chemistry and physics. As we shall see in Chapter 23, enzymes possess active sites where the donor and acceptor, attached to the same molecule, are positioned spatially so that the reaction occurs with near certainty when the substrate joins the enzyme. In this way the efficiency of the reaction is made maximal by dispensing with the inefficient procedure where the donor and acceptor molecules move independently in solution.

It is by this tack the living cell is capable of carrying out series of reactions with amazing efficiency. A single or small but highly organized group of molecules is held and oriented in regions of the cell so that a chemical conversion can be achieved through a chain of reactions with the probability of each reaction being essentially 100 percent. The collective behavior of molecules organized in this manner, except in living matter, was unprecedented in science until the recent development of solid-state physics.

Nonetheless, photosynthesis, metabolism, enzyme mechanics, the synthesis of proteins and the replication and translation of nucleic acids have all been found to follow established chemical and physical laws. There is no evidence of a vital force, nor is there any need to call upon the idea to understand the mechanics of life. Vitalism was never a principle that was ever thought out, anyhow, but was a sort of catchall concept to cover anything otherwise inexplicable.

Equally impressive has been life's complexity. There are approximately one million species of animals and a half million species of plants classified by biologists, with the number of undescribed living species estimated to range up to ten million. The number of extinct species represented by fossils is many times larger. Life has become enormously diverse, expanding into virtually every accessible ecological niche from oxygen-depleted oceanic oozes and ammonia-rich soils to mineral deposits with high radioactivity content. There are procaryotic bacteria that live in pools at Yellowstone National Park at temperatures of 80°C (176°F), and there are microflora in the Don Juan Pond in Antarctica that metabolize in calcium chloride water at temperatures as low as -23°C (-9°F). Other bacteria, algae and fungi can live in extremely acidic or alkaline environments, and much to the annoyance of nuclear physicists, the bacterium *Pseudomonas radiodurans* continues to thrive in the large neutron flux at the cores of swimming pool atomic reactors.

We tend to be amazed at this immense variety of life on earth, but beneath the diverse exterior there exists a great commonality. All living systems consist of cells; and although a baby weighing 3.4 kg (7½ lbs.) is 3 billion times the weight of the ovum, the individual cell remains the fundamental unit of life.

The advances of biochemistry have revealed that all biological systems use basically the same processes to function as self-sustaining organisms. The nucleic acids and proteins are absolutely central to living processes and the subunits for these biopolymers are the same for all organisms. Even the stereochemistry, the left- or right-handedness of biological molecules, is the same. There is also one principal class of compounds used by all forms of life to transfer chemical energy, and these agents are the nucleotide phosphates. And porphyrins, the cyclic compounds that form the active nucleus of hemoglobin, chlorophylls and cytochromes, are ubiquitous constituents. But the most impressive of all is the similarity in translating the nucleic acid information to protein structure. Since the genetic code was broken in the 1960's, it appears the language of heredity is the same for all living things. These commonalities and many others, particularly where no obvious selective advantage exists, strongly imply that all forms of life on earth are descendents of a single common ancestor.

Since life evolved from a primitive microscopic predecessor, it has become immensely complex. The weight of the cellular DNA in mammals has been found to be 6.5×10^{-12} gram. If then, one nucleotide pair weighs 1.03×10^{-21} gram, the amount of DNA in each mammalian cell is equivalent to 3.2 billion nucleotide pairs. Considering an average protein to be 500 amino acids long, which is equal to a gene of 1,500 nucleotide pairs, then each mammal has 2.1 million genes.[1] Britten and Kohne[2] have suggested that 40 percent of the DNA consists of sequences repeated between 10,000 and 1,000,000 times. After subtracting these repetitions, there remain 1,250,000 different genes in the chromosomes of each species of mammal. In what manner could such complexity have evolved in 3.5 billion years?

A parallel complexity followed the rise of multicellular systems. When unicellular organisms evolved to become multicellular, a single cell was able to give rise to an astronomical number of duplicates. The cells that form the human body are derived from a single fertilized egg that divided into 2, then 4, 8, 16 ... and on by geometric progression to form the whole person. As incredible as it may seem, it takes only 45 divisions for a single cell to become 100 trillion.

Geometric progression is an extremely effective means of attaining large numbers, and molecular evolutionists have discovered that the principal mechanism in evolution is the doubling of the gene through mutation. With each doubling, a single amino acid substitution in one copy could add a new protein. In this way proteins as variant in function as lactalbumin from milk and the enzyme lysozyme have evolved from the same gene. The doubling of the genetic material would have been a rare event; nevertheless, for a single gene to become 1.6 million through geometric progression would have required doubling only 21 times since the beginning of life on earth, or at an average interval of 188 million years.

The path to complexity was not as straight forward as the geometric progression of a single gene. There have been other factors involved in mutation and evolution, and presumably the primal cell consisted of a multitude of small polymeric substances rather than a single gene. The time scale is uncertain because genes evolved, not to maximum size, but to the optimal size for the enzymes. The duplication of a large genome (all the combined genes) would signify extensive duplication of cellular material by multiple copies of similar proteins, introducing conditions that may have been more advantageous to early life than to later forms. Nonetheless, the doubling of genes with subsequent accumulation of point mutations apparently was the most influential and effective means of attaining size and diversity, and certainly some ancient duplications have involved the whole genome.

The amount of DNA measured from each of a large variety of mammals has been found to be nearly the same. Within mammalian lines there has been duplication of some small segments of chromosomes as indicated by the beta and delta chains of hemoglobin, but no duplication of the entire DNA. Although mammals may all have closely the same amount of DNA, as a class, however, they have about four times the amount found in protochordates and some fishes. It appears there was duplication of the whole genome twice in the course of evolution from protochordates to mammals. The first occurred sometime around 465 million years age when early vertebrates evolved from the primitive chordates. The second genome duplication occurred during early reptilian or prereptilian evolution about 320 million years ago.

The case of ferredoxins clearly illustrates the manner in which an enzyme evolved from a simpler structure. Ferredoxins are non-heme

HYPOTHETICAL DOUBLING OF A GENE
AT 188-MILLION YEAR INTERVALS

N^2	Time (millions of years)	Number of genes
21	0	2,097,152
20	188	1,048,576
19	376	524,288
18	564	262,144
17	752	131,072
16	940	65,536
15	1,128	37,768
14	1,316	16,348
13	1,504	8,192
12	1,692	4,096
11	1,880	2,048
10	2,068	1,024
9	2,256	512
8	2,444	256
7	2,632	128
6	2,820	64
5	3,008	32
4	3,196	16
3	3,384	8
2	3,572	4
1	3,760	2
		1

iron-containing proteins found in anaerobic and photosynthetic bacteria, blue-green and green algae, as well as the higher plants. They participate in a wide variety of biochemical processes, including photosynthesis, nitrogen fixation, sulfate reduction, hydrogenase reactions and other oxidation-reduction reactions as electron carriers.

The polypeptide chains of plant ferredoxins at 55 amino acid residues are nearly twice as long as those from anaerobic bacteria; whereas, the ferredoxin of *Chromatium,* a photosynthetic bacterium, is intermediate. Furthermore, two halves of bacterial ferredoxins are clearly related. It appears that all ferredoxins are derived from the repeated duplication of a primordial sequence of four amino acids, combined with deletions and amino acid substitutions. There was a doubling of the gene length in the bacterial line which occured just before the divergence of *Chromatium,* then an additional doubling independent of the bacterial doubling that led to the plant ferredoxins.[3]

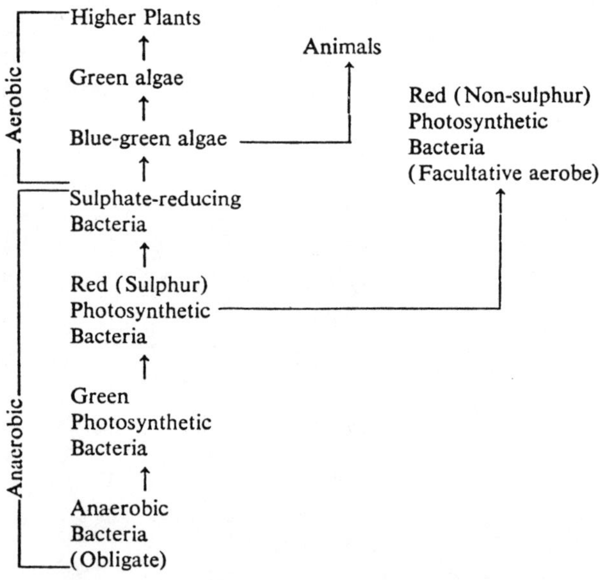

Evolutionary development of ferredoxins. (Hall et al., *in* **Cosmochemical Evolution and the Origins of Life***, D. Reidel Publ. Co., 1973)*

Life has evolved from the simple to the complex, pulled by the competitive advantage of the most efficient organism or biochemical procedure to appear through mutation. For this reason, we are tempted to look to the simplest organisms as models of early life. There is value in this approach because, as we saw in Chapter 9, there exist today living representatives of many of the stages of evolution throughout life's long advance. This approach must be taken with caution, however, for all contemporary life has an equally long ancestry. Although microorganisms appear to be simpler forms of life, they are not a primitive form of life. The enzyme structures and metabolic processes that bacteria share with us are no less sophisticated and efficient than our own. We differ because we have each evolved to exploit different ecological niches.

Though their polymeric constituents may be of equal refinement, the cellular architecture of procaryotes is considerably simpler than that of eucaryotic cells, and there are other features that give sufficient grounds to believe procaryotes preceded the latter. To put things into perspective, we should examine the composition of a procaryote. The bacterium, *Dialister pneumosintes,* as an example, has the dimensions of 0.4-0.6 × 0.5-1.0 micron. Since a micron equals 1/1,000 millimeter, or 1/20,000 inch, the *D. pneumosintes* is so small that 250,000 of them could be placed under this period. Nevertheless, it is a simple matter to measure its chemical composition.

From its composition, much can be deduced about the organism.

COMPOSITION OF *Dialister pneumosintes*[4]

	(Grams × 10^{-14})	**(Daltons × 10^{8})**	**Percent**
Dry Weight	2.80	160	
DNA	0.13	7.8	4.66
RNA	0.30	18	10.33
Protein	1.20	72	43.00
Carbohydrate	0.47	28	16.45
Lipid	0.16	37	21.70

A weight of o.13 × 10^{4} grams of DNA is equivalent to 6.5 × 10^{8} daltons (one dalton is the molecular weight of one, or 1 gram is approximately 6 × 10^{23} daltons.

Since a double-stranded DNA must have approximately 20 times the weight of protein for which it is supplying the information, 6.5×10^8 daltons of DNA will carry the information for 3.3×10^7 daltons of protein. Assuming an average molecular weight for protein to be 40,000, then there must be 800 molecules of different proteins in a cell of *D. pneumosintes.* If all the proteins are enzymes, for a single molecule per reaction, the cell uses 800 reactions to be an autonomous functional system. The bacterium, therefore, is probably using several hundred reactions, which seems like a reasonable figure since in the larger *E. coli,* the microorganism most extensively studied, there are already 500 known biochemical reactions.

Small as they may seem, these are not the smallest autonomous cells. The smallest free-living cells known are the pleuropneumonia-like organisms (PPLO) called mycoplasmas. These organisms cause serious diseases in sheep, goats, chickens and turkeys, and are found as harmless saprophytes on the mucous membranes of animals and man, as well as in sewage and the soil. While an amoeba has a mass of 5×10^{-7} gram, a PPLO weighs 5×10^{-16} gram and is only about 0.1 millimicron across. It can be seen only with an electron microscope.

Because of its size, a PPLO has room for only about 100 enzymes. These organisms grow very slowly. Apparently they live in an environment where they receive free many necessary constituents that larger organisms have to synthesize. Nevertheless, the PPLO are fully functional reproducing organisms that survive on no more, and probably considerably fewer, than 100 biochemical reactions. Were there an environment in which all the necessary building blocks and such energy sources as ATP were provided, a functional organism could be substantially smaller and simpler than even the PPLO. In fact, the inside of a cell is such an environment and that is why viruses are smaller.

Viruses, however, are not self-sustaining organisms and cannot be regarded as a form of life. They should not be considered primitive, but rather a sophisticated form of parasitism, for they too are products of 3.5 billion years of evolution. In the case of viruses, they do not appear to be the end-product of evolution from a simpler structure, but are either an aberrant derivation of a cell or a degenerate product from a higher form of life.

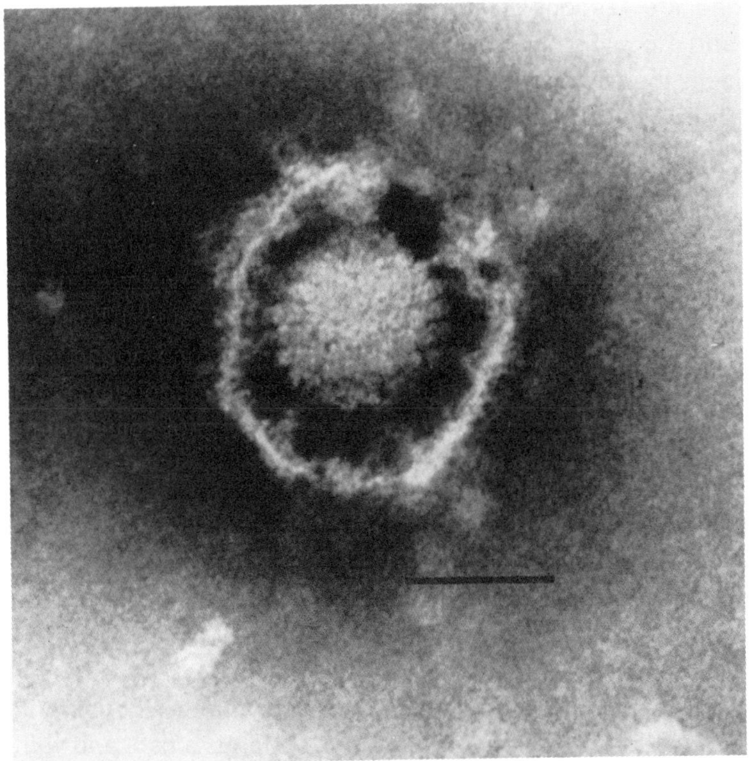

Electron photomicrograph of a herpes virus particle (virion). The virus envelope surrounds the nucleocapsid that has the shape of an icosahedron. The capsomeres (morphological) subunits of the capsid are apparent. The bar represents 100 nm; magnification is 200,000 X. (Courtesy of Dennis O'Callaghan, University of Mississippi Medical Center. Photograph by R. Abodeely. J. Virology **5**, *514, 1970)*

Viruses are the simplest, but there is another type of organism that exists in the realm between bacteria and viruses. These are the rickettsiae which, like the viruses, are parasites that multiply only in a host cell, but are nearer to bacteria in size, complexity and metabolic capacity. Rickettsiae are responsible for several diseases, including epidemic typhus and Rocky Mountain spotted fever. An interesting feature of rickettsiae is their similarity to mitochondria. Both have the components for the Krebs cycle of reactions, both use NADP, and both cannot carry on their usual oxidations after having been frozen in a salt medium, but can be protected against the loss of activity by the addition of sucrose.

One theory is that viruses originated as degenerate genes that broke from the cell, a concept prompted by the extreme specificity of the viruses. A more attractive hypothesis is that first the rickettsiae, and then the viruses, evolved from bacteria, and as they developed a parasitic mode of existence, they lost as superfluous the capability of synthesizing some enzymes necessary for a free-living organism.

Men have marveled at the beauty and efficiency of plants and animals and expressed the idea that such developments must be singular events that could never have arisen through natural processes alone. But nature is not based on the improbable. Various life forms, their structures and functional parts, evolved as the most advantageous of a large number of possibilities, which means that the selective process made their development probable under the circumstances. The streamlined shape for high-speed marine motion appeared with the *Stenopterygius* and other Mesozoic reptiles, with the tuna which is a fish, and with the dolphin, a mammal. That this shape evolved independently three times in unrelated life forms does not indicate a rare coincidence, but rather that hydrodynamics has a narrow range of solutions to the problem. The eye, which has been regarded as a wondrous organ, developed independently several times, indicating that such a structure is the best solution to visual recording.

Calculations that show a chance assembly of the base triplets of a nucleic acid would be of 10^{87} different ways,[5] or that the probability of a protein of MW 60,000 to form by mass action is 1 in 10^{603}, are meaningless.[6] The formation of life was neither by chance nor improbable. Such calculations are designed to prove that life could not have happened through natural circumstances, but they are based on the incongruous premise that life sprouted in full bloom with all the complexity and refinement of contemporary organisms. Life began simply and slowly and evolved as the result of a systematic survival of combinations of substances that worked and the rejection of all that did not.

Complex systems, from empires to biological structures, do not appear already in their full stages of development. Instead, they have to grow by stages with each level established as a stable platform before the next higher tier is undertaken. Life developed by tiers of chemical structures, each tier progressively larger and more complex than the previous, the units of each tier having within their chemical nature the means of creating the succeeding stage of development.

Nucleotides condensed to polynucleotides; amino acids condensed to polypeptides; and we know that these macromolecules eventually assembled into a functional cell; and the tier of cells in turn became associated into multicellular plants and animals. At each level of this pyramid the units had to undergo self-assembly to form the next higher stage. But here lies a crucial feature of genesis. If one dissociates a contemporary living cell and then recombines all the biological constituents, they do not reassemble into a functional cell. Nor can one dissociate an advanced multicellular plant or animal into its constituent cells and reconstruct the original organism. At this stage of development, the feature responsible for self-assembly appears to have been lost.

At first glance this seems to refute the basic principle just when it applies to the level at which life formed. But we saw that multicellular organisms at the early stages of evolution — sponges, coelenterates and embryos in their initial development — do possess the powers of self-assembly. It was only after multicellular organisms had evolved further that the organization and control of these various cells became built into the overall genetic blueprint and the cells became too specific for self-assembly.

What is happening is that the more complex a unit becomes, the more specific are its intra- and intermolecular associations, and hence, the less probable for the unit to reassemble correctly, once dissociated. The denaturation of enzymes is an excellent example. Small polypeptides, like non-polymeric chemicals, have a relatively stable and uniform spatial arrangement. Proteins, on the other hand, occupy space as complex and often fragile structural configurations dictated by the amino acid sequences and a multiplicity of internal interactions.

In the biosynthesis of a protein, as the polypeptide chain grows from the ribosome, it coils, twists and bends into its shape and is held by internal interactions as they form with the emerging protein. Under the chemical environment of the cell, the three-dimensional configuration remains. If, however, the protein is isolated and subjected to even modest changes in the pH or salt concentration, as well as elevated temperatures, the weak forces holding the protein in its configuration rupture. The polypeptide chains reform intra- and intermolecular bonding, but they have lost their uniformity because now a completed chain has many possible ways of interacting. The probability of the protein assuming its original configuration is generally quite small and the protein is said to be denatured. When the protein is an enzyme whose activity is dependent upon its specific configuration, denaturation results in the loss of enzymic activity.

When the components and the architecture of a biological system are small and simple, the probability of self-assembly is the greatest. For instance, ribosomes have the capability of self-assembly, and some viruses have been dissociated and recombined to yield several percent of reconstituted organisms.[7] The chemical nature of many biological compounds is to aggregate in fairly specific supramolecular combinations — the base pairing of complementary nucleotides as an example. There are, nevertheless, additional interactions, including other base pairings, that are possible but not used by biological systems. Some of these may have been part of primal cells that were dropped as being less useful than those adopted by organisms. But the most dramatic form of self-assembly is the spontaneous impulse of lipids toward structure formations.

The minimum requirement for the formation of the primal cell was that the associating components had to be chemically adequate and appropriately organized to carry on regeneration of the cell. Probability would have favored cells that had the smallest and the least number of components, and still were functional. The biochemical transformations would have been slow and inefficient, but there was no competition and the only enemy was dissolution. The threshold the initial living systems had to cross was to be able to grow and reproduce at a rate faster than hydrolysis and dissolution. Once across the hump, the cell accelerated by mutating to ever greater efficiency, and the descendants of this first successful form of life inherited the earth.

As testimony to life's simple beginning, the complexity of advanced organisms is based on a surprisingly few number of substances. Of the billions of possible organic compounds, less than 1,500 are employed by contemporary life on earth, and these 1,500 are constructed from less than 50 simple molecular building blocks.

References

1. **Atlas of Protein Sequence and Structure**, vol. 5, M.O. Dayhoff, ed., National Biomedical Research Foundation, Silver Spring, Md., 1972, p. 50.
2. R.J. Britten and D.E. Kohne, Repeated sequences of DNA, *Science* **161**, 529-540 (1968).
3. **Atlas of Protein Sequence and Structure**, vol. 5, M.O. Dayhoff, ed., National Biomedical Research Foundation, Silver Spring, Md., 1972, pp. D35-D36.
4. H.J. Morowitz and M.E. Tourtellotte, **The Smallest Living Cells**, Scientific American offprints, W.H. Freeman and Co., San Francisco, 1962.
5. Wayne F. Frair, Life in a Test Tube? *Quart. J. Creation Res. Soc.* **5**, 34-41 (1968).
6. M. Dixon and E.C. Webb, **Enzymes**, Academic Press, Inc., New York, 1958, pp. 667-670.
7. H. Fraenkel-Conrat and R.C. Williams, Reconstitution of active tobacco mosaic virus from the inactive protein and nucleic acid components, *Proc. Nat. Acad. Sci.* **41**, 690-698 (1955).

16
Priming the Pump

We all have an ancestry that extends in an uninterrupted line back more than 3.4 billion years. It was at some moment in that incredibly distant past that substances on primordial earth came together to form an entity that was able to absorb energy and use it to grow and assemble ever more complex units. Unlike the inanimate world that absorbs energy only to become more disordered, the biological systems that formed had a capacity to direct energy toward greater organization and expansion. That capability that we inherited from the first living cells characterizes all living things.

A living cell performs the synthesis of all its organic constituents by a series of biochemical reactions catalyzed by enzymes. How an enzyme possessed such impressive catalytic powers remained a mystery for decades; but there persisted a more fundamental problem. A biological system synthesizes its components by building complex molecules from simple chemicals. They grow and multiply, reproducing not one or two types of chemicals, but literally thousands, all meshed together in a highly organized manner. These are all functions that require energy. In effect, life creates order from disorder.

By this century it was realized that plants absorbed and used sunlight in a process called photosynthesis, and animals breathed oxygen in the air to burn sugar and other foodstuffs to obtain their energy. Combustion was a straightforward reaction, and animals oxidizing sugar to generate heat was understandable. The mechanics of photosynthesis was not well understood, but was accepted as a fact of life. It was obvious biological systems were being fueled by chemical energy from oxidation and photosynthesis, but the result was they appeared to be moving uphill in contradiction to the natural response of matter.

The physical behavior of matter and energy was formulated long before the life processes were understood. The First Law of Thermodynamics, recognizing the conservation of energy, was enunciated by Julius Robert von Mayer in 1841. It points out that, aside from the interconversion of matter and energy by nuclear processes, the content of energy in the universe remains constant. Since energy can exist in many forms as light, forces of attraction and repulsion, motion or heat (motion on the molecular level), this means that when energy changes from one form to another, no energy is gained or lost in the procedure.

Kinetic energy, the force of matter in motion, is the dynamic side and most familiar to us. On the other hand, matter can also possess or store potential energy by virtue of its position to move to a lower energy level. The classic example of something with potential energy is a rock on the side of a hill. The rock's position leaves the possibility of its taking on kinetic energy by rolling down the hill, and as it goes down the hill, it sacrifices its potential energy to give it movement and momentum.

Just as objects have a capacity for physical energy, so too do chemical compounds have a capacity for energy. Gravity is the force of attraction that pulls matter together and is responsible for the potential kinetic energy of objects, but chemical energy is the force that holds atoms and molecules together. The energy that binds atoms, the energy that causes molecules to adhere as solids and liquids, and even the different spatial configurations and vibrations of molecules contribute to the internal energy of substances. For this reason, any transformation of matter, be it a change in its physical state or change in its chemical composition, involves going to a different level of internal energy and is invariably accompanied by a loss or gain of heat.

This then brings us to the Second Law of Thermodynamics. The Second Law states that heat can flow only to something of a lower temperature. In effect, this is the same as saying that energy, like water, cannot flow uphill. The principle is simple and direct, but ramifications of it can become quite abstruse.

Since heat flows from a hot object to a cold one, it will continue to do so until the temperature level is the same for both objects, or in other words, they reach equilibrium. Any substance above absolute zero (-273° C, -523° F) has thermal motion, hence it has energy. Entropy is its name. As heat flows from high to lower temperatures, it raises the average temperature level toward the medium, and toward an equilibrium. High temperature is associated with randomness, and when there is a flow of heat from one system to another, the randomness of the two systems considered together increases. Consequently, in classic physics the overall entropy of the universe can only increase, which is to say, the motion or order of matter can only become more random. The universe is running down.

Any process concentrating matter to build order, therefore, is going against the energy tide. It requires an input of energy to go in the direction from random to non-random. Nevertheless, this is exactly what biological systems do. To see how it is possible, the biological system can be regarded as a localized phenomenon and best understood by looking at the analogous behavior of water. Despite the fact that water tends to seek a level, there are waves that rise above the level to an unstable position at the expense of the downward trough. So too does the randomness of the universe tend to seek a common level of thermodynamic equilibrium, but waves of order rise above the equilibrium level at the expense of the energy of other substances.

The Laws of Thermodynamics were derived before it was known there existed interconversion of matter and energy. It can now be seen that the conversion of matter to energy in one location of the universe can furnish energy to fuel the formation of order in another part above the thermodynamic equilibrium level. This has happened with the thermonuclear fires of the sun giving energy for the birth and sustaining of life on earth.

The overall procedure for this does not controvert the Second Law. Plants, the initial collectors of solar energy, absorb more energy from the sun than they store as chemical energy, so the result is a downhill procedure. Animals, on the other hand, consume plants to build their components, and it is the stored chemical energy of plants that supply the energy used by animals. The manner in which they are able to do this takes us into a review of chemistry.

In non-nuclear physics, energy is never lost, but is defined in relation to matter. Apply energy to matter and it generally becomes thermal energy by increasing the motion of the molecules; withdraw energy and the matter slows down and becomes more compact. There exists then a state of equilibrium between the attractive forces of matter and the thermal motion from the energy content. Accordingly, the arrangement that atoms and molecules assume is one which is most stable for equilibrium with the energy level. This then is the thermodynamic equilibrium.

Because of energy barriers restricting the flow of chemical reactions, there exists a narrow temperature range where durable configurations can be rather complex molecules. Molecules can form under short-lived conditions of high energy and freeze into chemical structures with potential energies out of equilibrium with the surrounding temperature. Some of these molecules can interact through chemical forces so that the energy absorbed is no longer converted to thermal motion, but is directed to elevate the chemical energy of the complex structure and its components. It creates a thermodynamically unstable arrangement of matter that can be maintained only by a continual input of energy. Once the special arrangement is lost, the unstable configuration cannot be held and the matter falls back again toward the thermodynamic equilibrium. This is the principle of physics upon which life arose, using the energy of the sun to maintain itself.

All biological reactions are spontaneous reactions. This means the reactions are uphill from equilibrium and are energetically favored to move toward thermodynamic equilibrium, although it does not tell anything about the rates of the reactions. Like the rock on the hillside, biological reactions are slow to move until given a push. As indication of this, gasoline or sugar can stand in air almost indefinitely with no perceptible signs of combustion, despite the fact their oxidation is a vigorous exothermic reaction (gives off heat). For the reaction to proceed, the weaker C-H bonds need to break before the stronger C-O and O-H bonds can form. At room temperature, these C-H bonds are quite stable. If the reaction is to go quickly, sufficient energy, called the activation energy, must be added to break the C-H bonds. Once this is accomplished, the energy from the reaction is sufficient to fuel the process in a chain reaction.

Spontaneous reactions have the potential energy for continuing on their own, but do so only if the activation energy barrier is overcome. The energy content of the reactants in a large statistical number follows a bell-shaped distribution curve. The hydrolysis of urea where water and

$$H_2N\text{-}\overset{\overset{\displaystyle O}{\|}}{C}\text{-}NH_2 + H_2O = CO_2 + 2\ NH_3 \qquad \Delta G = -\ 13.8\ \text{kcal}$$

urea must have sufficient energy to form an activated complex as shown illustrates the role of an activation energy. At room temperature only a few of the reactant molecules have sufficient energy to breach the barrier, so the rate of reaction remains slow. If the temperature is elevated, however, a greater proportion of the reactant molecules have enough energy and the rate is accelerated.

The rate of hydrolysis of urea increases immensely by the enzyme urease by lowering of the activation energy barrier. This is achieved through a transient intermediate complex between the catalyst and the reactants that weakens the bond constituting the barrier. The enzyme catalysis is much more effective than H+ catalysis because the energy of activation in the enzymatic reaction is much lower. The result of this is that chemical reactions necessary for life processes can be rigidly controlled by enzymes. If spontaneous reactions did not have energy

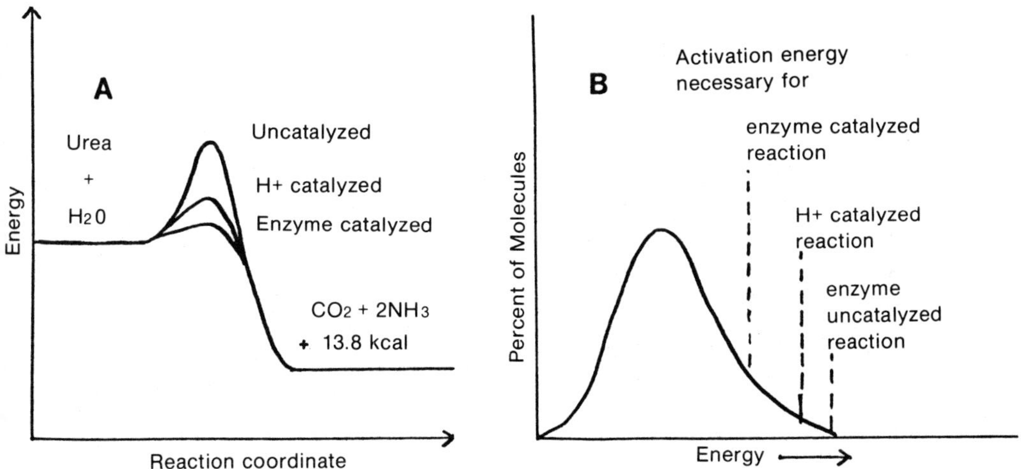

A. Energy diagram showing the effect of catalysis on the activation energy in the hydrolysis of urea. B. Diagram showing the effect of lowering the activation energy on the percent of molecules having sufficient energy for reaction.

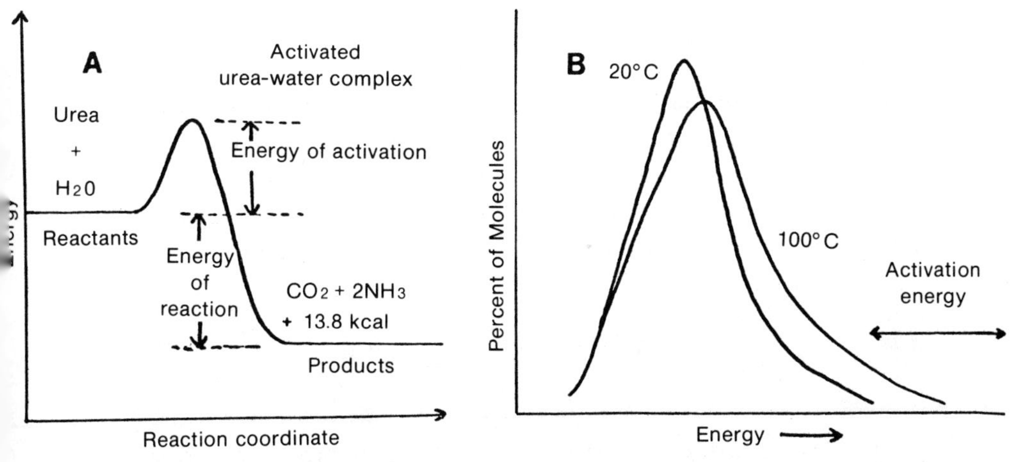

A. Energy diagram of the hydrolysis of urea. Although the formation of products liberates 13.8 kcal/mole, the reaction cannot take place without overcoming an activation energy. B. Distribution curves of activation energy at 20⁰ and 100⁰.

barriers, but proceeded instantaneously, life would not have been possible.

Yet, the principal activity of biological systems and the basis of growth and reproduction is synthesizing large complex molecules from small compounds. These syntheses are not spontaneous reactions, but require an input of energy. They are on the downhill side of equilibrium. The products have more energy than the reactants, so they must be pushed up to a higher energy content. This, therefore, is not a reaction that goes spontaneously with the liberation of heat, and consequently, cannot be promoted by a catalyst. Nonetheless, to a casual observer it appears that a biological system does just that. How then is it possible?

The manner in which a cell carries out chemical conversions began to become evident between 1930 and 1940 when the chemical details to the biochemical degradations of glucose were discovered. Biochemists realized there had to be some method in which the cell accepted chemical energy and transferred it from one compound to another. The biochemical agents that play this role were found to be the phosphate compounds, adenosine triphosphate (ATP) and adenosine diphosphate (ADP).

In 1941, Fritz Lipmann[1] introduced the concept of the high-energy phosphate bond and the role of these compounds in bioenergetics began to be clearly appreciated. ATP is a compound of high potential energy. When it loses a phosphate group by hydrolysis to form ADP and inorganic phosphate, a rather large amount of energy is liberated. Under standard conditions at pH 7 and 25°C, the standard free energy change, ΔG, for the hydrolysis of ATP is -7.3 kilocalories.

$$\text{ATP} + H_2O \longrightarrow \text{ADP} + P_i \quad \Delta G = -7.3 \text{ kcal}$$

The free energy change of ΔG is the energy that drives the reaction by giving off heat to the surroundings. The value of energy change is minus when heat is liberated because it represents a reduction in the overall energy content. For a system in equilibrium at constant temperature and pressure, ΔG = O. A spontaneous reaction will have a

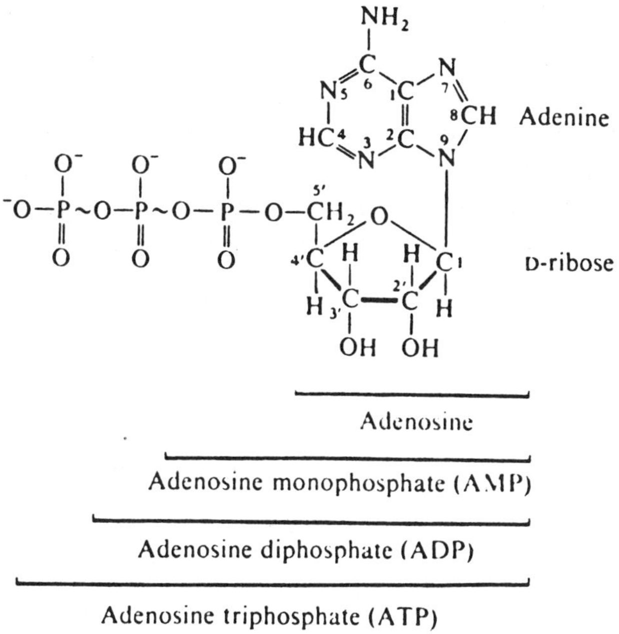

Adenine

D-ribose

Adenosine

Adenosine monophosphate (AMP)

Adenosine diphosphate (ADP)

Adenosine triphosphate (ATP)

The structure of adenosine phosphate derivatives

negative free energy change, and the higher the negative value, the greater is the driving force of the reaction.

Actually, under cellular conditions, Mg^{++} forms complexes of differing affinity with ATP, ADP and phosphate. This, and other factors that affect the equilibrium of the reaction, tend to increase the free energy of hydrolysis of ATP to an even higher value.

If then, the cell wants to carry out a synthesis in which the product has an energy level higher than the reactants, that is, it is an uphill reaction, the reaction is changed to a spontaneous reaction by making an activated derivative of the reactant. This is achieved by transferring a phosphate to a reactant through phosphorylation by ATP. An example is the biosynthesis of glutamine, an important amino acid in proteins. To form the amide bond from glutamic acid and ammonia requires an input of 3.4 kilocalories of energy. Onthe other hand, glutamic acid can be converted to the mixed anhydride by reacting with ATP. This derivative, glutamyl phosphate, now is of higher energy level than glutamine, so the reaction with ammonia is to form glutamine becomes a downhill reaction that goes spontaneously, catalyzed by the enzyme, glutamine synthetase. The combined effect of converting glutamic acid to glutamine of a higher energy through the use of ATP of an even higher level gave a net release of 3.9 kilocalories of energy, enough to drive the reaction well toward the product.

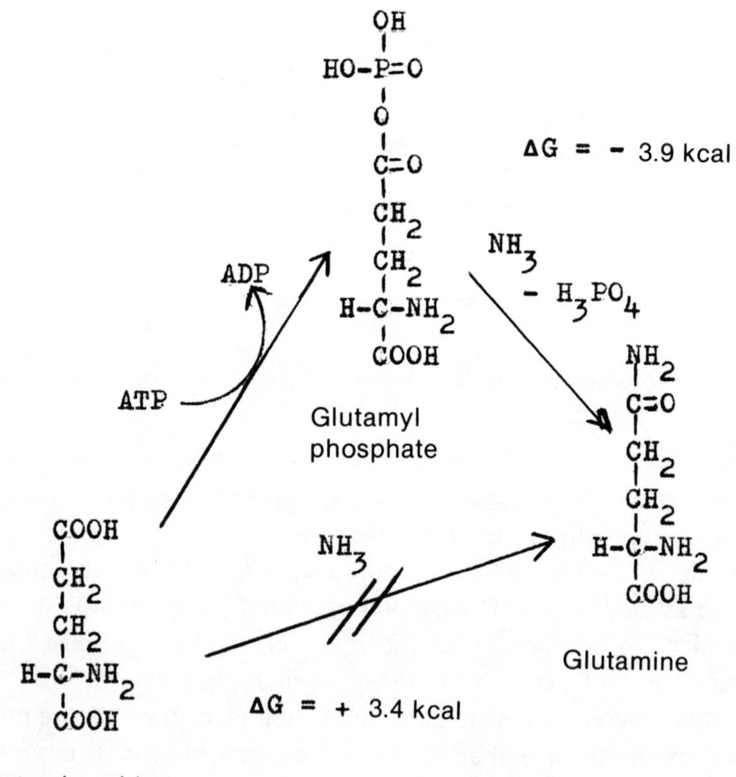

The biosynthesis of glutamine

This is the basic procedure the cell uses to synthesize ester linkages, peptide bonds and glycosidic couplings — all endothermic reactions that require energy. It is the chemical energy of the phosphate bond of ATP, far in excess of energy added to the products, that is the source of energy for these syntheses.

To carry out its many syntheses, a cell needs to continually generate ATP. Plants with their photosynthesis mechanism produce their ATP through a complex procedure using the energy of absorbed sunlight, which in turn, they utilize to reduce CO_2 to carbohydrates as stored chemical energy. Plants also contain mitochondria that permit them to generate ATP through the breakdown of their carbohydrate reserves.

The amount of energy in a mole* of glucose is 686 kilocalories, the quantity of heat liberated when glucose is oxidized by oxygen to CO_2 and water.

$$C_6H_{12}O_6 + 6\ O_2 \rightarrow 6\ CO_2 + 6\ H_2O \qquad \Delta G = -\ 686\ \text{kcal}$$

Animals, using plants as food, draw from this potential energy stored in the chemical bonds of sugar to generate their ATP and to use the heat to maintain their body temperature. To do so, they do not want all the energy liberated as heat, but instead, as much as possible to be collected in high energy chemical bonds of compounds like ATP which they can use in their syntheses.

One reason ATP was adopted by living systems as the agent for the transfer of the phosphate group is not that it is a phosphate derivative of the highest potential energy, but because it is of an intermediate level among phosphate compounds. To function as a phosphate transfer agent, ATP must be able to accept phosphate groups from some compounds and donate them to others. There then exists in organisms a group of phosphate compounds comprising a scale of free energy. In biological processes, when ATP is generated it receives its phosphate from a phosphate derivative more energetic than itself in order for the reaction to be spontaneous.

One mole is the numerical value of the molecular weight expressed as grams.

STANDARD FREE ENERGY OF HYDROLYSIS OF PHOSPHATE COMPOUNDS[2]

	ΔG (kcal/mole)	Direction of phosphate transfer
Phosphoenolpyruvate	-14.8	↓
1,3-Diphosphoglycerate	-11.8	
Phosphocreatine	-10.3	
Acetyl phosphate	-10.1	
ATP	-7.3	
Glucose 1-phosphate	-5.0	
Fructose 6-phosphate	-3.8	
Glucose 6-phosphate	-3.3	
3-Phosphoglycerate	-2.4	
Glycerol 3-phosphate	-2.2	

References

1. F. Lipmann, Metabolic generation and utilization of phosphate bond energy, *Adv. Enzymol.* **1**, 99-162 (1941).
2. Albert L. Lehninger, **Bioenergetics**, 2nd ed., W.A. Benjamin, Inc., Reading, Mass., 1971, p. 42.

17
The Driving Force

A biological system is more than an assembly of organic substances. It is a mechanism that can take up energy and use it to elevate simple chemicals to more complex arrangements. The success then in life's creation was the coming together of prebiotic materials that could act in concert to harness available energy in the environment. All the energy — ultimately derived from the sun — was present in two forms. It existed as chemical energy sealed in the structure of organic substances produced by the various forms of energy acting on the atmosphere, and it was as the sunlight that bathed the earth's surface each day. Eventually, both sources of energy were used by organisms.

Of all the biological processes studied by chemists, few have elicited more wonder or given greater resistance to being unraveled than photosynthesis. With fermentation, all the enzymes and other components in the breakdown of glucose to pyruvic acid have been isolated, and each step, as well as the complete series of reactions, has been reproduced in the laboratory. The case with photosynthesis is quite different. When extracts are made of plant cells to collect chlorophyll and other components, the extracts are no longer capable of photosynthesis. In the view of biologists, this is like smashing a watch and looking at the pieces, rather than observing the complete mechanism, to see how it work.

But considerable research has been devoted to studying photosynthesis and much of it is now well understood. Since light is a form of energy, plants have, in effect, developed a biochemical means of trapping the energy of sunlight and converting it directly to chemical energy. They have succeeded in channeling it to the synthesis of ATP and the reduction of CO_2 for the production of carbohydrates. To reduce CO_2 to the reduction level of sugar takes an input of 112 kcal/mole of carbon dioxide.

$$CO_2 + 4\,H \longrightarrow CH_2O + H_2O \quad \Delta G = +112\ \text{kcal}$$

Light travels in waves of particles known as photons. Rather than continuous, the energy is in discrete packets called quanta, the energy of each quantum varying inversely with the length of the photon wave (λ). That is to say, as the wavelengths become longer going from ultraviolet to visible to infrared, the energy of a quantum of light becomes less. In the mathematical expression of a light quantum, v is the frequency, η is Planck's constant, and c is the velocity of light.

$$q = \eta v = \eta c/\lambda$$

Red light with its wavelength of 0.68 micron can stimulate green plant photosynthesis by a light quantum corresponding to 2.9×10^{-12} ergs. When this quantity of energy is converted to units of chemical reactions, the energy compares to 40 kcal/mole. This means it takes at least three quanta of light to reduce a mole of CO_2. In actuality it seems to take ten.

Generally, when light is absorbed by dark or colored objects, they

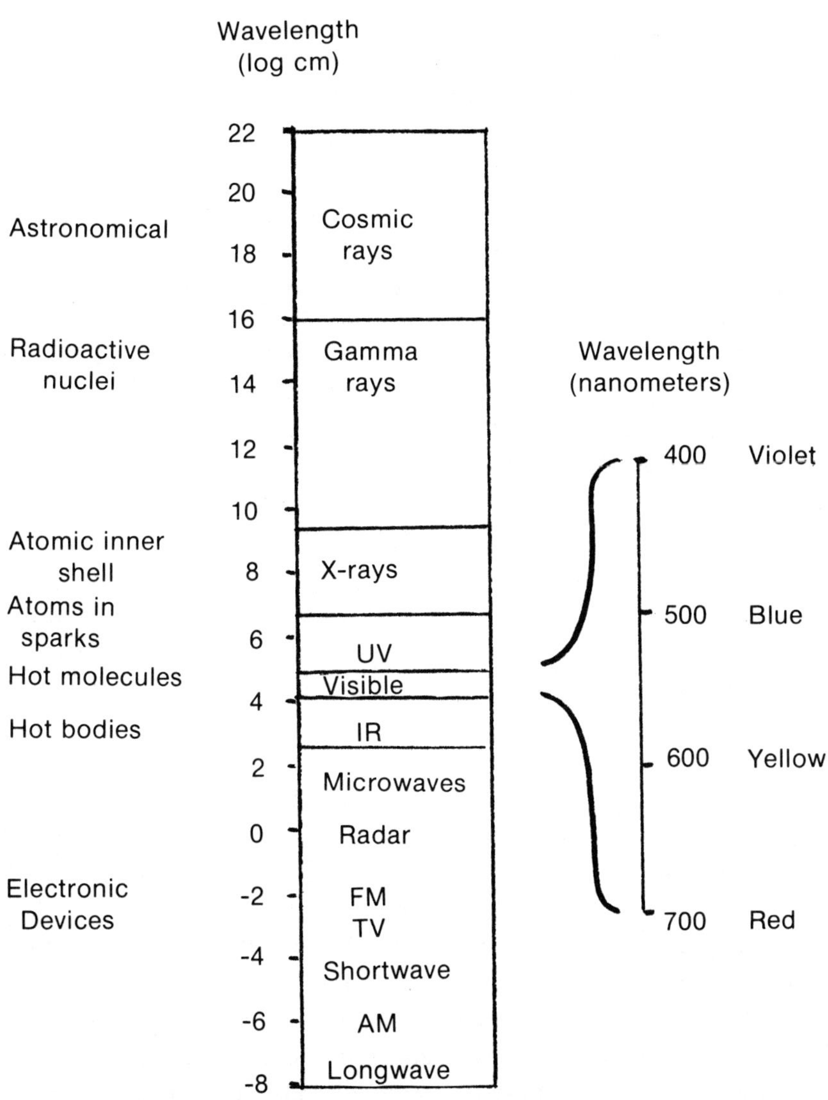

The electromagnetic spectrum

become warm as energy is converted to heat. But just as biological systems have developed means of tapping the energy from the oxidation of organic substances, so too, have they succeeded in draining off part of absorbed light energy before it is lost as heat.

If the photons are of short wavelengths, and consequently of high energy, such as for ultraviolet light, they are destructive to many organic compounds by cleaving covalent bonds. On the other hand, if the wavelengths are too long and of low energy, they are of too low a frequency to be absorbed. In order for energy in the form of a wave such as light to be transferred, it can pass only to something that is vibrating at the same frequency. Electrons, like all matter in motion, travel in a wave pattern of a definite frequency that depends on the mass in velocity. The frequencies of most electrons around atoms are extremely short of the order of X-rays, but in molecules with alternating single and double bonds, the electrons that resonate the length of a series can be of long wavelengths. These compounds are the colored organic substances that absorb the blue, red or yellow light and reflect the complementary color.

The orbits of electrons are not fixed, but are divided into suborbits or orbitals that represent a range of energy levels within an orbit. When, therefore, a molecule absorbs a light quantum, the energy is passed to an electron which is elevated to an orbital of a higher energy level. At this point, it is said to be in an excited state. Excited states, however, are unstable configurations and the electron quickly drops back to the lower level or ground state, dispensing with the energy by emission of light (fluorescence), or through collisions, generating heat.

In order to harness energy to do work, it must not escape as heat or light but must be funneled to a useable energy form which, for biological systems, means chemical energy. When electrons are energized sufficiently, they can often be induced to leave the orbit of the excited molecule and transfer to an acceptor substance. This then becomes the oxidation-reduction chemical reaction where an oxidant accepts electrons from a donor and is reduced by it. It is the mainspring of photosynthesis and the manner in which sunlight is converted directly to chemical energy.

Plants contain a number of pigments such as carotenes and carotenoids (which give the yellow-orange color to carrots) that absorb light, although the chlorophylls are the main light-absorbing molecules in green plants. When chlorophyll absorbs a quantum of sunlight, the energy of an energized chlorophyll will be quickly re-emitted through fluorescence unless the electron is transferred to a more stable state.

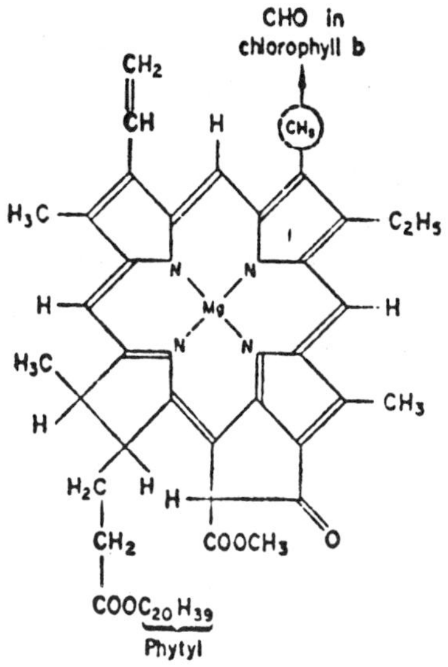

The structure of chlorophyll a. The phytyl group is a long unbranched chain.

In 1937, Robert Hill[1] of Cambridge University made a discovery that led to the identification of a number of electron carriers that function to transport electrons away from excited chlorophyll. Hill found that dried or powdered leaves, suspended in water with ferric oxalate or some other ferric salt and illuminated, released oxygen for an hour or longer, much longer than without a ferric salt. Later studies showed the ferric salts could be replaced by quinone or by certain dyes. The added substances had one thing in common — they were all strong oxidants. Ferric salts were acceptors of electrons, and the

$$Fe^{+++} + e^{-} \longrightarrow Fe^{++}$$

particular organic dyes were acceptors of hydrogen atoms. This observation sparked a search for naturally occurring electron carriers in plants that may be connected with photosynthesis.

It was found that ultimately the electron acceptors were two coenzymes chemically related to the building blocks of the nucleic acids. These were nicotinamide adenine dinucleotide (NAD) and its phosphorylated derivative (NADP).

It is the nicotinamide portion of the molecule that can accept and give up electrons. Just as ATP is a phosphate carrier, so too are NAD and NADP carriers of electrons. In man and other vertebrates, the nicotinamide part of the compound must be supplied through the diet as niacin, one of the B vitamins. A deficiency of the vitamin results in pellagra.

Although similar in chemical composition, NAD and NADP each play a specific role different from the other. NAD accepts electrons that are directed toward oxygen in respiration; whereas, NADP directs its electrons for the reduction of organic compounds. It then is NADP that is more immediate in the reduction of CO_2 to sugar.

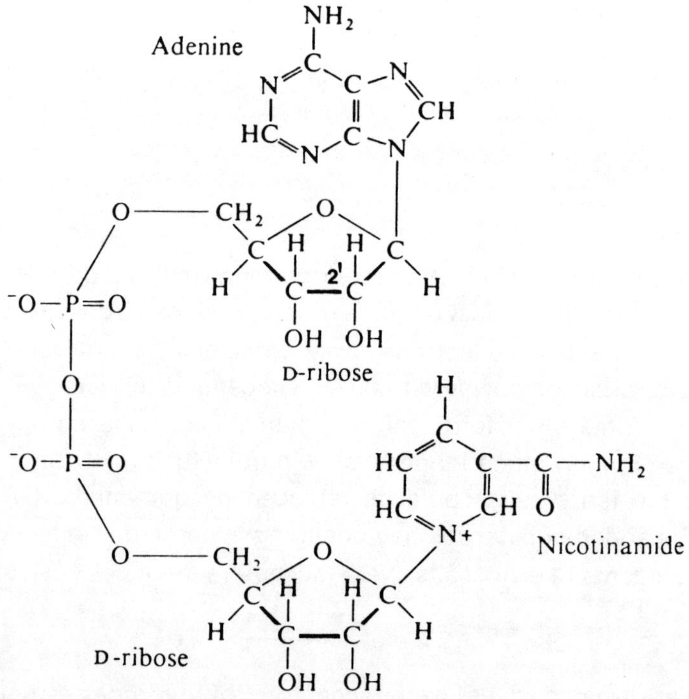

Nicotinamide adenine dinucleotide (NAD). NADP has a phosphate group attached to the 2′-hydroxyl of the ribose next to the adenine ring.

Oxidized form (NAD_{ox})	$+ 2H \rightleftharpoons$	Reduced form (NAD_{red})	$+ H^+$

NADP does not receive electrons from energized chlorophyll directly, but instead, the electron is transported by a series of specialized compounds. It is at this point that ferredoxin, the iron sulfide protein that may have been the first protein used by living cells, becomes important. When an electron is energized in a chlorophyll molecule, it leaves this compound and passes to another type of chlorophyll molecule designated as P700. The energized electron is pulled away from P700 by Z, a strong electron acceptor. Z then passes the electron to ferredoxin whose iron is reduced from Fe+++ to Fe++ in the process. From ferredoxin the electron is passed by an electron carrier,

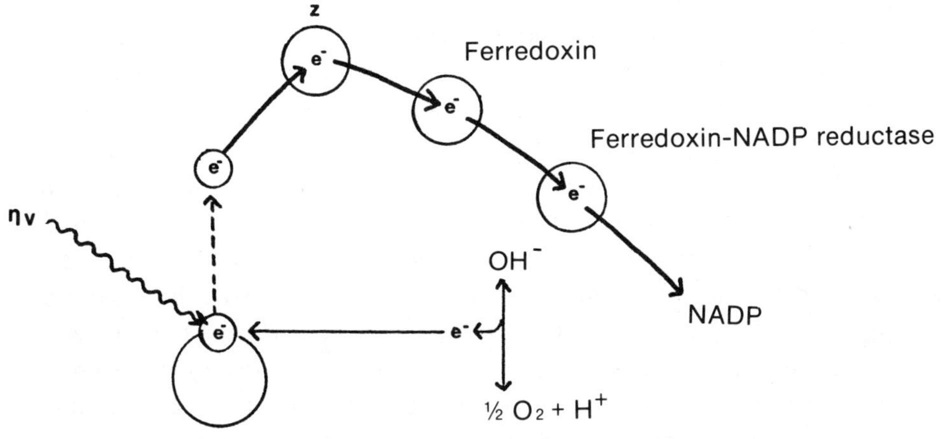

The high-energy electrons from energized chlorophyll are used to reduce $NADP_{ox}$ to $NADP_{red}$.

ferredoxin-NADP oxido-reductase, to $NADP_{red}$. As ferredoxin-NADP gives up the electron, its iron is oxidized from Fe^{++} back to Fe^{+++}. Thus there is a light-induced flow of electrons from chlorophyll to NADP until all the available NADP is reduced.

Once NAD or NADP are reduced, this completes the link from the absorption of sunlight to enzymatic synthesis, for these reduced coenzymes can then participate in the various biochemical conversions, including carboxylations, which are dependent upon reduced pyridine nucleotides.

It was generally assumed that photosynthetic organisms obtained all their ATP from the breakdown of glucose, an implication that glycolysis or similar degradations would have preceded the biosynthesis of ATP in the origin of life. But in 1954, Daniel Arnon with Mary Belle Allen and Frederick Whatley[2] at Berkeley discovered what has become called photophosphorylation. They observed that chloroplasts, unaided by other cellular particles, have the ability for CO_2 fixation and for the direct conversion of light energy into ATP.

This is the simplest, and possibly the original, harnessing of the sun's radiant energy to produce ATP. The ATP formation was in complete absence of organic substrates or oxygen. When isolated chloroplasts were illuminated in the presence of ADP and inorganic phosphate, ATP formed at a high rate. The longer the chloroplasts were illuminated, the greater the amount of ATP formed.

In photophosphorylation, an external electron donor is not needed and the generation of ATP is due to a cyclic flow of electrons from the excited chlorophyll to ferredoxin, then through an enzymatic mechanism, and back again to chlorophyll by a chain of carriers. In order for this process to occur, the first electron donor has to be separated or insulated from the last electron acceptor, otherwise, the circuit of electron flow would be shorted. It is the insulating barrier of the lipid membrane that creates this separation. This is why photosynthesis, unlike an extract for anaerobic glycolysis, cannot occur in isolated solutions. The structural integrity is an absolute requirement for photophosphorylation, and life would not have been possible without the unique properties of the lipid membrane.

The photosynthetic organisms are able to generate ATP by

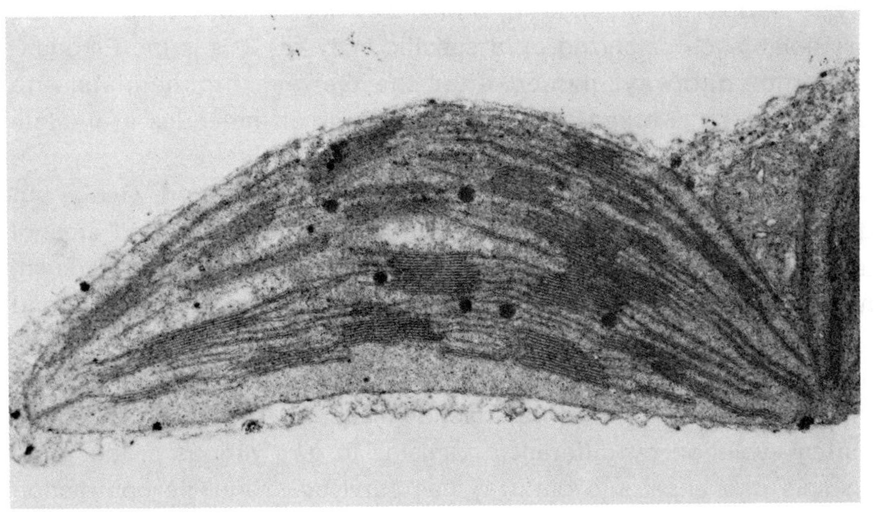

A tomato chloroplast as viewed through the electron microscope. The striated sections are the lamellar vesicles with membranes that serve as the essential insulating barriers for photosynthesis. Magnification is 32,000 X. (Courtesy of Randall S. Beaubien, Michigan State University)

capturing and using the energy of sunlight directly. This may well have been the initial manner of the primitive cells in producing their ATP. The degradation of glucose, however, is also of early origin and a model of simplicity. In photosynthesis, organisms convert solar energy to chemical energy by building organic compounds of a higher energy level. In glycolysis, organisms take glucose containing that chemical energy and degrade it to derivatives of lower energy, using the energy difference to produce ATP and to drive the reaction steps.

When Büchner, in 1897, found that chemical components from yeast were able to break down glucose to ethanol and carbon dioxide outside the cell structure, he discovered the original procedure of biological systems for extracting chemical energy from organic compounds. At the time, Büchner believed fermentation was a single chemical reaction catalyzed by an enzyme he called zymase, but when the mechanism of the conversion was eventually solved in its entirety, it was learned the breakdown of glucose consisted of eleven separate reactions, each catalyzed by a specific enzyme. This is the Embden-Meyerhof pathway, named after the German biochemists who postulated and worked out the critical steps of the series in the late 1920's and early 1930's.

Brewer's yeast ferments glucose to ethanol and CO_2, but different bacteria generate acetone, butanol, acetic acid and ethanol as their end products of fermentation. The principal breakdown, however, is the anaerobic degradation of glucose to pyruvic acid and lactic acid. This is the initial degradation of glucose that exists in all living things, inherited from the primitive anaerobes that were the first forms of life on earth. The reaction sequence has been extended during evolution by different organisms to give various products. In animals, the anaerobic pathway has survived in muscle contraction where pyruvic and lactic acids appear as primary end products before oxygen is admitted for further oxidation to CO_2 and water.

$$\underset{\text{Glucose}}{C_6H_{12}O_6} \xrightarrow[\text{steps}]{11} 2\ \underset{\text{Lactic acid}}{HO-\overset{\displaystyle COOH}{\underset{\displaystyle CH_3}{C}}-H} \qquad \Delta G = -47 \text{ kcal}$$

As Bŭchner discovered, the entire process of fermentation proceeds merely by having all the reactants together in solution. Since the conversion has been found to be a series of separate reactions, each reaction capable of being conducted independently in the laboratory, the products of each step serve as the reactants or substrate for the enzyme of the succeeding reaction. With all the components present, the breakdown of glucose, therefore, proceeds nonstop through each step to the final product.

To carry out gylcolysis, glucose is phosphorylated with ATP so that in the breakdown two derivatives are produced that are of a higher energy level than ATP. Consequently, these high-energy derivatives are able to generate ATP by passing their phosphate group to ADP. The overall result of the degradation of glucose to lactic acid is that two ATP molecules used to phosphorylate glucose result in the formation of four ATP's from the ADP for a net yield of two ATP's. In the process, NAD_{ox} is reduced to NAD_{red} , but is regenerated in the end when it converts pyruvic acid to lactic acid. The combined equation of all the reactions becomes

$$\text{Glucose} + 2\ P_i + 2\ \text{ADP} \longrightarrow 2\ \text{Lactic acids} + 2\ \text{ATP} + 2\ H_2O$$

When glucose is broken down stepwise to yield chemical energy for the production of ATP, there is one chemical reaction that is the key to the energy transfer. It is the oxidation of glyceraldehyde 3-phosphate by NAD_{ox} with the simultaneous phosphorylation, elevating the intermediate to 1,3-diphosphoglycerate, a high-energy phosphate compound whose energy is higher than ATP. In the final reaction of the pathway, NAD_{ox} is regenerated in the reduction of pyruvic acid to lactic acid by NAD_{red} thus completing the cycle of an oxidation-reduction reaction. It was at this step of oxidation by NAD_{red} that some of the chemical energy invested in glucose by the reduction of CO_2 through phosphorylation was recovered by the reverse reaction of oxidation.

What then is the basis of oxidation-reduction that permits it to play a central role in bioenergetics? Except for fluorine, oxygen is the most electronegative element; whereas, hydrogen is electropositive. This electrochemical opposition of the two elements makes a reaction between oxygen and hydrogen one of the most vigorous, and the O-H bond, one of the strongest. An oxidation reaction, typically characterized by the addition of oxygen, is simultaneously accompanied by the reduction of the oxygen. With the formation of water, the reductant is hydrogen. In a broader sense, the reductant is anything that is being oxidized. Since a hydrogen atom consists simply of an electron and a proton (H+), the addition of an electron is a reduction; its removal, an oxidation.

Through photosynthesis, plants use the energy of sunlight to reduce CO_2 to glucose with an imput of 686 kcal/mole of glucose. It then is this reservoir of chemical energy that organisms draw upon to produce ATP.

To liberate 686 kilocalories, the glucose would have to be oxidized completely with oxygen to regenerate the CO_2 and water. This procedure, however, was not accessible to the Archean procaryotes when little or no free oxygen existed in their environment.

Nonetheless, some of the energy can be withdrawn because atoms can exist also at various states of oxidation, depending upon the composition of the compound. For carbon, CO_2 is the fully oxidized state and CH_4 is the fully reduced; all other carbon compounds represent intermediate levels of oxidation. By converting one compound to another where the carbon is less reduced represents an oxidation, and the difference in free energy between the compounds is liberated. Accordingly, when glucose is broken down to lactic acid by the anaerobic pathway, it liberates by oxidation 47 kilocalories of the 686 kilocalories in each mole of glucose. In the process, two molecules of ATP are produced from one of glucose, each with an energy of 7.3 kilocalories. The pathway, therefore, captures a total of 14.6 kilocalories of the 47 kilocalories of energy, using the remaining 32.4 kilocalories as the driving force to assure completion of the reactions. Of the total of 686 kilocalories in the structure of glucose, the anaerobic organisms were able to recover only 14.6, or about 2 percent.

The anaerobic breakdown of glucose to pyruvic acid provided an extractable source of chemical energy for producing ATP. The supply of abiotic carbohydrates eventually proved exhaustible and organisms developed a series of reactions to reverse the process to synthesize glucose from pyruvic acid. Seven of the steps in glycolysis are reversible; the remaining three reactions are by-passed by enzyme-catalyzed conversions that are made spontaneous in the direction of synthesis by an input of six high-energy phosphate bonds, four from ATP and two from GTP (guanosine triphosphate).

Just as biological systems developed means of using ATP to rebuild their stocks of glucose, so also did they use CO_2 as the source of carbon to synthesize glucose. Early organisms were able to derive ATP by photophosphorylation where they harnessed the energy of sunlight, and using ATP as an activator, they were able to degrade glucose and other organic compounds to tap their potential chemical energy. Glucose was a store of chemical energy and could be rebuilt from pyruvic acid with an input of ATP. But for continuing their growth, biological systems needed to draw from a supply of carbon and nitrogen when the available organic compounds became exhausted. They found a virtually inexhaustible reservoir in the atmosphere.

The CO_2 in the atmosphere was readily accessible, but chemically it was fully oxidized and needed to be partially reduced before it could be assimilated as organic material. In order to do this, photosynthetic organisms developed a means of "CO_2 fixation" by using the reducing power of photosynthesis. They had $NADP_{red}$ for a reductant and ATP for supplying the driving force; a pathway of spontaneous reactions that was needed was evolved to incorporate CO_2 into organic compounds. The overall reaction as it exists in contemporary photosynthetic organisms is

$$6\ NADP_{red} + 12\ H_2O + 12\ ATP + 6\ CO_2 \longrightarrow C_6H_{12}O_6 + 6\ NADP_{ox} + 12\ ADP + 12\ P_i$$

The reducing power of photosynthesis that is used to convert CO_2 to glucose produces at the same time an extremely strong oxidizing potential (oxidant) that extracts hydrogen from an external donor. The earliest forms of life, with a photosynthetic mechanism less evolved than the oxygen-liberating blue-green algae, would have extracted their hydrogen from available sources that required the least amount of energy to give up their hydrogens. The external source of electrons may be organic or inorganic. When isopropanol is the donor, it is subsequently oxidized to acetone; similarly succinate becomes fumarate. Inorganic electron donors used by some bacteria are the sulfides.

Ultimately, the substance never used by bacteria which became the electron source for blue-green algae and all plant life is water.

$$2\ H_2O \longrightarrow 4\ H^+ + O_2 + 2\ e^-$$

It takes ten times as much energy to extract hydrogen from water than from H_2S, but either because of a dwindling supply of the early donors or perhaps due to the sheer abundance of water, photosynthetic organisms evolved that were capable of wresting hydrogen from oxygen in water molecules. This became a momentous event in the evolution of life on earth — for the result was the discharge of oxygen as a byproduct into the environment.

It was the release of oxygen into the atmosphere that eventually led to the development of the third means of producing ATP. All biological systems were able to degrade glucose to pyruvic acid by the anaerobic pathway to extract some of the chemical energy, but most of the energy still remained in the structure of pyruvic acid. Some yeast and bacteria evolved procedures for converting pyruvic acid into other organic compounds. A large proportion, however, became acetyl coenzyme A which was used to synthesize lipids and other components. As long as the environment remained free of oxygen, there was no means of oxidizing pyruvic acid farther to extract the great store of energy still bound in its chemical bonds.

Then between 1.8 and 0.6 billion years ago, the oxygen liberated from water by photosynthetic organisms continued to oxidize the earth's surface and atmosphere until the environment began to accumulate free oxygen. During this interim of 1.2 billion years, some microorganisms evolved enzymes and components that became a series of reactions for the complete oxidation of pyruvic acid. It must have taken an extremely long time over countless generations for the genetic apparatus to mutate and evolve the developed pathway — but the selective advantage of the gain in energy was overwhelming.

We see today the aerobic breakdown of pyruvic acid in its most evolved state and know little of the various stages it must have gone through in its development. At least some of the reactions existed already as side reactions of fermentation to provide amino acids. These reactions were apparently modified and extended to create the aerobic pathway. Although it is a biochemical procedure that could not have been possible until atmospheric oxygen reached the Pasteur point of 1 percent of today's level, it probably was preceded by a long period of evolution. The pathway has come down in the plants and animals through the mitochondria, the sausage-shaped subcellular particles that are the suppliers of ATP in all eucaryotic cells.

The detailed chemistry of respiration was not discovered until the late 1930's when Hans Krebs[4] pieced together a series of enzymic reactions involving tricarboxylic acids used to oxidize pyruvic acid to CO_2 and water. In the sequence, acetyl coenzyme A for the oxidative decarboxylation of pyruvic acid enters a mitochondrion where the acetate group couples with oxaloacetic acid to form the six-carbon compound, citric acid.

In the succeeding seven reactions, citric acid is degraded back to oxaloacetic acid through a procedure whereby the two-carbon acetyl unit is oxidized to two molecules of CO_2 by molecular oxygen. In the series the di- and tricarboxylic acids containing four, five and six carbons are continually consumed and regenerated in the cyclic process. As a result, a single molecule of oxaloacetic acid can bring about the oxidation of an indefinite number of acetyl groups because it is generated at the end of each cycle.

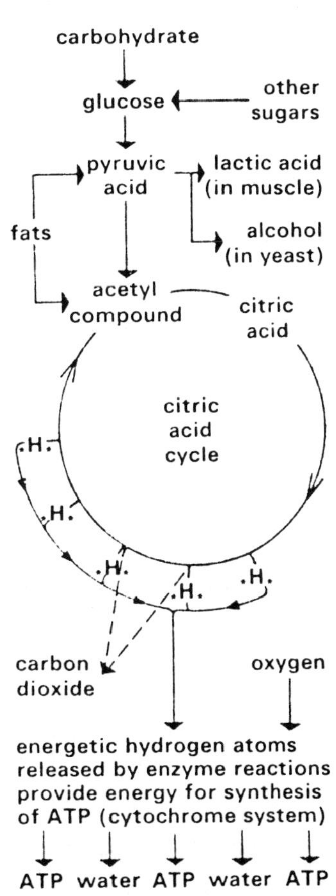

The metabolism of carbohydrates through respiration to produce ATP.

It is in the membrane complex of the mitochondria, one of the most sophisticated structures ever evolved by biological systems, that the aerobic degradation of pyruvic acid takes place. The molecular mechanisms of respiratory energy transformations are still not fully clarified, but mitochondria appear to be able to draw on it for ATP synthesis, transhydrogenation, ion transport and other fundamental processes through a highly coordinated procedure. What is known is that structure and function are inextricably intertwined where the enzyme complexes carry out the oxidation of pyruvic acid and fatty acids within the mitochondrial membrane.

For something as complex as the mitochondrion to have evolved, the selective advantage had to have been large. In examining the return of energy through respiration, it is easy to see what the mitochondria gained. All organisms contain the anaerobic pathway for glycolysis, inherited from our common procaryotic ancestors, but the eucaryotes with their mitochondria extended the degradation of glucose by oxidizing the pyruvic acid completely to CO_2 and water.

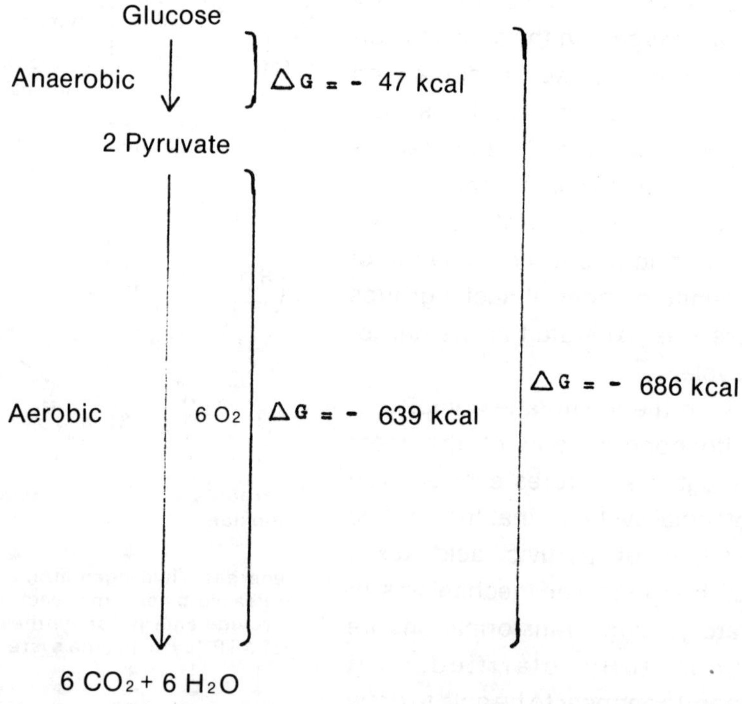

Comparison of energy yields of anaerobic degradation of glucose to pyruvic acid versus the oxidation of pyruvate to CO_2 and water.

As long as biological systems were restricted to the anaerobic breakdown of glucose, they derived just two molecules of ATP for each molecule of glucose. This represented a yield of only 14.6 kilocalories of energy from a total potential of 686 kilocalories sealed in the chemical structure. The change of the earth's atmosphere to an oxidized state with free oxygen permitted the degradation of glucose through respiration to draw from the untapped reserve. When the overall equation for the complete oxidation of glucose to CO_2 and water by aerobic organisms is written, it becomes

$$\text{Glucose} + 36\ P_i + 36\ \text{ADP} + 6\ O_2 \longrightarrow 6\ CO_2 + 42\ H_2O + 36\ \text{ATP}$$

For nearly 3 billion years life remained on the microscopic level, but the breakout was slowly being evolved by the mitochondria, or rather their direct predecessors that developed the enzymatic pathway for the complete oxidation of glucose. Evolution of the mechanism may have taken hundreds of millions of years, but the reward was immense. Instead of obtaining two molecules of ATP for each glucose as in fermentation, the organisms capable of oxidative phosphorylation obtained 36. It was this 18-fold bonus of energy that catapulted microbes to multicellular structure and the advanced forms of life.

References

1. R. Hill, Oxygen produced by isolated chloroplasts, *Proc. Roy. Soc. B* **127**, 192-210 (1939).

2. D.I. Arnon and F.R. Whatley, Photosynthesis by isolated chloroplasts, *Nature* **174**, 394-396 (1954).
3. H.A. Krebs and W.A. Johnson, The role of citric acid in intermediate metabolism in animal tissues, *Enzymologia* **4**, 148-156 (1937).

18

The Essentials of Life

Does life have a unique chemistry that was met by singular circumstances over three and a half billion years ago on primordial earth, or was life the inevitable consequence of ordinary geologic conditions? In order to answer this question, we need to delineate the components that would have been necessary for a functional living cell to have formed. By establishing the absolute requirements for a biological system, we can then understand what specific conditions were necessary for the origin of life on earth.

An examination of the chemical composition of living things shows only common elements. Of the 92 naturally occurring elements, 40 are found in plants and animals, but only 18 are commonly required. Of 36 elements found in protoplasm, four actually make up 98 percent of the total composition. These four are carbon, hydrogen, nitrogen and oxygen. There are small quantities of phosphorus, sulfur, sodium, chlorine, calcium, magnesium and potassium; and the trace metals, iron, boron, molybdenum, copper, cobalt, zinc and manganese represent less than 1 percent. There are no rare or unusual elements among them.

Carbon, hydrogen, nitrogen and oxygen, which predominate in biological systems are, except for helium, the four most abundant elements in the universe. Not only are carbon, hydrogen, nitrogen and oxygen among those elements with the highest cosmic appearance, they have chemical properties so distinct from any others that they are unique in their roles as essential elements. They are of low atomic weights and form a number of common stable and volatile compounds. For this reason, these four elements became concentrated in the gaseous and watery envelope that sheaths the earth's surface.

VOLCANIC GASES

Gas	Formula	
Steam	H_2O	↓ Decreasing Amounts
Carbon dioxide	CO_2	
Nitrogen	N_2	
Sulfur dioxide	SO_2	
Hydrogen	H_2	
Carbon monoxide	CO	
Sulfur	S	
Chlorine	Cl_2	
Hydrogen sulfide	H_2S	
Hydrochloric acid and other acids	HCl	
Volatile chlorides of iron, potassium and other metals		

Life arose from the mass of volatiles outgassed from the earth's interior that condensed and accumulated to form the atmosphere and the oceans. Without the geological evolution of the earth, life could never have formed on its surface. Not only does the earth revolve around the sun in a narrow zone with margins of only a few percent to permit the conditions that allowed life to develop, but if the earth had been appreciably smaller like the moon, any atmosphere would have escaped from the smaller gravity; but most of all, with its greater surface to volume ratio, the heat from the trapped nucleoclides would have been dissipated to outer space without the buildup to volcanism. The zone of magma would not have formed, the earth's interior would not have differentiated into concentric layers, and the excessive volatiles would not have been outgassed to the surface to create the atmosphere and oceans. Without these, the earth would never have spawned life.

Carbon has the indispensable property of being able to form valence bonds, not only with a large number of other elements, but also with other carbon atoms. Some other elements share this feature of concatenation, but only to a limited extent. Because of carbon's valence symmetry, it can link into long sequences with single, double and triple bonds, and can form ring compounds or enter into a vast number of combinations with other elements. The number of known carbon compounds is now estimated to be over one and a half million. It is this immense variety of carbon architecture that has furnished the complexity necessary for the interplay of chemical and physical properties that makes a self-sustaining biochemical entity.

One of the features of living systems that distinguishes them from the inanimate is their ability to reproduce. With the fundamental nature of a cell being chemical and physical structuring of the constituents, we are dealing primarily with molecules that are capable of being replicated. In Chapters 12 and 13, the manner in which nucleic acids are duplicated and how the sequence of the four nucleotides represents a coded message that can be translated to a chain of amino acids in the synthesis of proteins were given in detail. It is the uniqueness of a nucleic acid to be copied that is the basis of life.

The primary role of nucleic acids is to act as a relatively stable blueprint to the organism's construction. For this role its maximum size has to be large enough to carry the code for the structure of a peptide. Since three nucleotides are needed for each amino acid, the size of the postulated elementary proteins would dictate the nucleic acid requirement. It appears that ferredoxin began with a peptide four amino acids long; the corresponding nucleic acid would have been at least 12 subunits in length.

But a second role of nucleic acids is as transfer RNA's. In order to copy the coded nucleic acid and translate its composition to a sequence of amino acids, a series of tRNA molecules would be required. In contemporary organisms, there is a tRNA for each of the 20 amino acids.

In 1965, Robert Holley and coworkers[1] determined the nucleotide sequence for alanine tRNA and found it to be a polynucleotide of 75 subunits that could fold back upon itself and be held in a cloverleaf arrangement by hydrogen bonding between opposing complementary bases. Since then, the sequence of some 75 different tRNA molecules has been determined. The number of subunits ranges from 74 to 91 and they all form the same general cloverleaf configuration.[2]

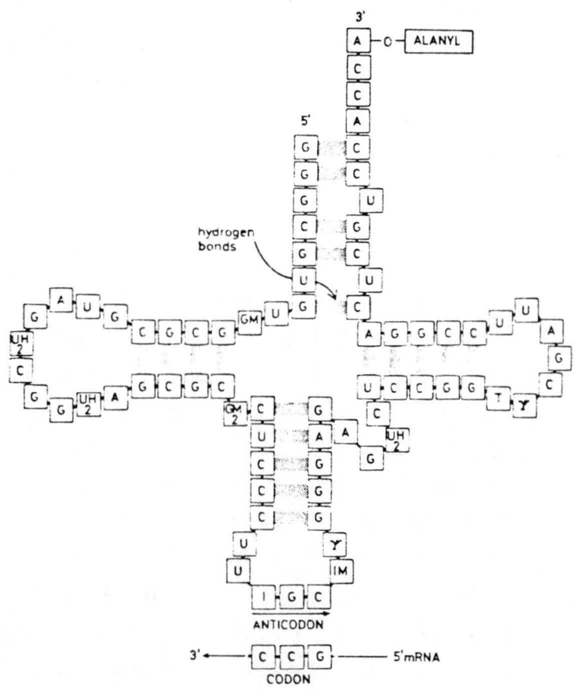

The cloverleaf configuration of transfer RNA's. (Alanine tRNA)

The minimum size requirement for polymerized nucleotides to function as tRNA's would appear to be, not the full cloverleaf arrangement, but at least the chain folded back on itself to form the hairpin loop to allow for the anticodon triplet at the bend. Since the amino acid specificity of the tRNA's would have evolved early, the stem of the initial tRNA's requiring the side-loop of the cloverleaf was probably nearly as long as they are now, which would place a minimum size for the nucleotide chain at about 40 units.

Replication of nucleic acids would have preceded protein biosynthesis in the development of life, and because of the high specificity and striking closeness in the structure of tRNA's, they are probably all derived from a single ancestral molecule.

That macromolecules had to precede the first living cell is easy to see. But if one looks at the mechanism by which nucleic acids and enzymes are formed in contemporary organisms, he faces a dilemma: nucleic acids carry the information and mechanism for synthesizing both themselves and the enzymes, but enzymes are the catalysts for the reactions to prepare both. How could either have been formed without the presence of both?

This is a question that has puzzled and divided scientists between those who believe nucleic acids came first[3] and those who contend enzymes or enzyme-like macromolecules would have been the more likely original components.[4] In order to reconstruct a rational origin of a biological system, one needs to either show that enzymes (or suitable substitutes) could have been produced abiotically, or be able to explain how a biological system could begin without them.

The fundamental basis of living things is to grow and maintain themselves by building molecules. They synthesize and compact large macromolecules from smaller units — a process that requires an input of energy. The free energy liberated in the hydrolysis of a peptide link of a protein molecule is between 2 and 4 kilocalories per mole; that is to say, to join each amino acid to the peptide chain in synthesizing the protein requires 2 to 4 kilocalories. A similar requirement exists for polymerizing nucleotides.

One way of meeting this energy demand to form chemical bonds would be to raise the temperature above the boiling point of water and high enough that the thermal energy of the reactants exceeds the energy needed to form the peptide linkage. But as molecules become more complex for a biological system, weaker interactions play a major role in maintaining the ascending architecture, and the structure becomes more susceptible to the disruptive action of thermal energy as it exceeds the chemical energy of these bonds.

For this reason, organisms have developed a highly selective and controlled input of energy to fuel their processes. In order to convert the uphill reactions of synthesis into spontaneous downhill reactions, biological systems activate one of the reactants to a high-energy derivative. To do this requires a third reactant of an even higher energy potential to pass some of the energy down to the reactant for activation.

The bioenergetics of a living cell is essentially analogous to the use of an electric power plant. Heat energy from burning coal is converted to electricity by a generator and carried to the homes where it is converted to heat and motion. In the process, more energy is required to generate the electricity than is ever recovered. In the same manner, a plant cell traps energy of sunlight, transfers it in special compounds to other parts of the cell, and recovers the energy to build chemical bonds.

Phosphoric acid derivatives are particularly feasible for this role of holding in their structure the energy collected from sunlight. It is the stored chemical energy of the pyrophosphate bond that fuels biological syntheses. Consequently, these high-energy compounds are essential components of all biological systems. Although other pyrophosphate derivatives could have played an initial role, the stability advantage of ATP suggests that it may have been the original constituent of life.

The requirement of pyrophosphate derivatives makes phosphorus an essential element. But of the six most common elements required for a biological system — carbon, hydrogen, nitrogen, oxygen, sulfur and phosphorus — only phosphorus does not have a stable volatile derivative — and there is no substitute. Arsenic is more closely related to phosphorus than any other element, but the acid anhydrides of arsenic are not stable in water, and it is the aqueous stability of high-energy ATP that makes it possible to be used in the synthesis of nucleic acids, proteins and the other cellular components.

This introduces an interesting inconsistency. The presence of phosphates in seawater is in only micromolecular quantitites, making it one of the scarcest elements in the ocean. Asimov[5] compared the composition of seawater to the required elements to determine what factor restricts the growth of life. Taking the tiny crustacean, copepod, as representative of ocean animal life, he compared the percent of essential elements in the copepod's composition to that of seawater. Any higher occurrence in the copepod indicated concentrating of the element by the animal. Four elements — carbon, nitrogen, phosphorus and iron — had large concentration factors. Carbon and nitrogen are available from the atmosphere through the food chain; but for the other two, the concentration factor was four times greater for phosphorus than for iron. Asimov concluded the limiting factor to the growth of life in the ocean is the supply of phosphorus. This is evident in inland waters where phosphorus pollution from detergents and fertilizers sets off a rapid growth of algae.

But as critical as phosphorus may be for life, it is not a rare element. Certain rocks, particularly granite permagtites, frequently contain large deposits of the tricalcium phosphate minerals, apatite, $Ca_3(PO_4)_2 \cdot CaCl_2$, and fluorapatite, $3Ca_3(PO_4)_2 \cdot CaF_2$. The difficulty is that the calcium salts of phosphoric acid are extremely insoluble, effectively removing phosphorus from any medium in which the calcium concentration exceeds that of phosphorus. It is quite possible life may have originated in close association with phosphorus-bearing rocks or in sedimentary deposits of secondary phosphates washed from such rocks.

John McClendon[6] of the University of Nebraska made a comparison of the abundances and the requirements of the elements found in biological systems. He found nine elements, because of their unique requirements, would have been essential for the origin of life. These are carbon, hydrogen, nitrogen, oxygen, phosphorus, sulfur, magnesium, potassium and iron. Carbon, hydrogen, nitrogen and oxygen would have been abundant in the gaseous components of the atmosphere, phosphorus was concentrated in rock deposits, and the remaining required elements would have been in seawater under the reducing conditions of primordial earth.

The heavy metals, iron, manganese, zinc, copper, cobalt and molybdenum are predominantly in the earth's crust——the oceans are nearly depleted of them. Nevertheless, they are essential elements for most plants and animals. McClendon found the concentration of essential heavy metals in plants did not correlate with oceanic concentrations, but did correlate with their occurrences in the crust. This would be consistent with plants, which colonized the earth's land areas before animals, adjusting their biochemical composition to the available crustal constituents, the incorporation of metals suitable for particular enzymes being affected by the abundance of the metal.

CONCENTRATIONS OF FREQUENTLY REQUIRED HEAVY METALS (mM)

	Plant Requirement	**Crust**	**Sea & Air**
Iron	0.400	900	0.0001
Manganese	0.200	17	0.000036
Zinc	0.060	1.1	0.000075
Copper	0.020	0.87	0.000050
Cobalt	0.0003	0.43	0.000002
Molybdenum	0.0002	0.015	0.0001

Adapted from J.H. McClendon, J. Mol. Evol. **8,** 175-195 (1976)

But did the heavy metals have any role in the biochemistry of the early forms of life on earth? The answer depends upon the order of events in the development of primal life. The primary function of iron, copper and manganese is as components of proteins used in photosynthesis. It has been suggested by D. O. Hall[7] that ferredoxin, the iron-containing protein involved in the transfer of electrons in the photosynthesis series, may have been the earliest protein formed, so it is quite conceivable a means of harnessing the energy of sunlight arose early in the development of biological systems. If this is so, in order to explain the evolvement of photosynthesis by organisms in the ocean we must account for a greater availability of these elements than there is presently in seawater. We now can see that when photosynthetic organisms arose over 3 billion years ago, the chemistry of these elements under the reducing conditions of Archean Earth would have been different than it is today.

Many of the heavy metals, being more abundant in the crust than in seawater, even under reducing conditions, probably became incorporated into enzymes of advanced biological systems after evolutionary development created a need. Cobalt and molybdenum appear to be of this category. Cobalt as a part of vitamin B_{12} and molybdenum in xanthine oxidase for vertebrates are clearly of late development. But cobalt is also associated with nitrogen fixation, as is molybdenum with nitrogenase. Nevertheless, legumes with their symbiotic bacteria for fixing nitrogen no longer need molybdenum if ammonia is available.[6] Margulis[8] has supported the contrary view that nitrogenase was a requirement of primitive organisms; and molybdenum, being an essential element that is in low abundance, has even brought the suggestion of an extraterrestrial origin of life.[9-13] It seems more probable neither cobalt nor molybdenum were essential when the first biological system began on primordial earth, but became incorporated after considerable evolution had taken place.

The role of magnesium as a part of chlorophyll would have developed with the advent of the blue-green algae at a later time. Because vanadium and nickel porphyrins are found in petroleum is not an indication these metals were used by early plants in photosynthesis. A more plausible explanation is that they resulted from the magnesium being displaced to form the more stable vanadium and nickel complexes during the formation of petroleum.

Calcium, on the other hand, which is so essential in contemporary animals for many physiological reactions, as well as for skeletal structure, may not have been a primitive essential element. It appears it became a derived requirement when plants and animals evolved extracellular structures.

in his examination, McClendon found there is an absolute limit below which an element may not fall and still be available in adequate amounts for biological systems. The minimum concentration is 1 to 2 nanomolar in the ocean and 10 to 21 micromoles per kilogram in the earth's crust. The elements that are indispensable for life are in abundance. Only cobalt and molybdenum are near the lower level of occurrence, but their dependence was apparently acquired late and isn't absolute. Some elements, like rubidium and strontium, are sufficiently abundant and chemically suitable for biotic processes, but are not used because of a greater supply of a similar element.

There are two additional substances indispensable for the formation of biological systems: water and lipids. Each has unique properties different from the other, and it is the opposing behavior of their respective properties that make them necessary for life.

Water is more than a solvent for biochemical reactions: it is generally a reactant. Most cellular chemistry involves the formation or hydrolysis of acid derivatives: phosphorylation and the coupling of nucleotides are esterification reactions; the synthesis of proteins, amidation. Since these condensations involve the elimination of water between the two reactants, and hydrolysis is the addition of a water molecule, water is directly a part of the reactions. When these reactions are carried out in an aqueous environment, the concentration of water is 55 molar. At such a high concentration, it plays as important role in establishing the position of equilibrium of the reaction.

Because water is amphoteric, it can act as an acid or a base; and it participates in both roles in biological processes. It serves as a weak base in the ionization of carboxylic acids;

$$\underset{\text{acid}}{\text{R-COOH}} + \underset{\text{base}}{H_2O} \rightleftharpoons \underset{\text{base}}{\text{R-COO}^-} + \underset{\text{acid}}{H_3O^+}$$

and as an acid in the protonation of ammonia;

$$\underset{\text{base}}{NH_3} + \underset{\text{acid}}{H_2O} \rightleftharpoons \underset{\text{acid}}{NH_4^+} + \underset{\text{base}}{OH^-}$$

and in the catalysts of mutarotation it acts as both an acid and a base.

But the fact that water is a liquid at all in an ordinary temperature range is due to one of its most outstanding features. Water does not exist as single molecules under normal circumstances but rather, it is an intermolecular array of molecules held together by hydrogen bonds. A molecule of water can participate in the formation of a maximum of four hydrogen

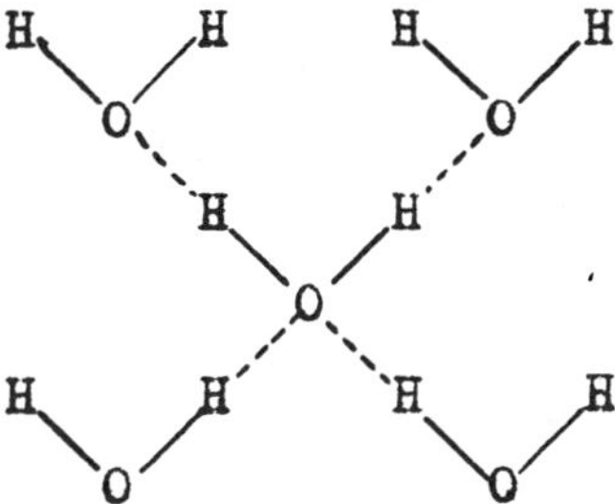

bonds. It is this network of binding that gives water a high boiling point for so simple a molecule. If H_2O had the properties more like the hydrides of the other elements of Group VIa of the Periodic Table, H_2S, H_2Se and H_2Te, its boiling point would not be 100°C — it would be -81°C (-112°F).

Water is one of the few substances that expands when it freezes, making its solid less dense than the liquid. If it behaved like most materials, then ice, instead of floating, would sink, lakes would freeze solid during winter, and as ice accumulated on the bottom of the oceans, the volume of water would become smaller and increasingly saltier. Another character of water is its unusually high heat capacity which acts as a stabilizer for the internal biochemical environment. It is conceivable that life could have existed without these special features of water, although being without them would have created a whole new set of problems.

But these features are related to the one property of water that is indispensable for life. The ability of water to form an array of strong hydrogen bonds with itself is a property that has great influence on biological systems. Much of the support holding complex proteins in their tertiary arrangement is from the associated structure of water around them. It is a particular relationship between water and lipids, however, that has created the familiar features of cells. By being immiscible, water and lipids have an interface that permits a zone of contact for reaction between dissimilar substances which would not be able ordinarily to interact in a single phase system and makes surface catalysis possible.

Lipids form a class of organic compounds that are insoluble or sparingly soluble in water, but are soluble in lipophilic organic solvents.

Fatty acids, triglycerides, phospholipids and glycolipids belong to this class of compounds. Lipids that contain paraffinic chains such as fatty acids or their derivatives become insoluble when the aliphatic chain exceeds about four methylene units. At this point, the water lattice extending from the polar end of the lipid molecule can no longer encapsulate the hydrocarbon tail and the lipid is insoluble. And since they are hydrophobic, the lipids are excluded from the water structure and they coalesce. It is this physical behavior that is vital for the formation of a cell.

A cell is a compact arrangement of biochemical molecules enveloped in a semipermeable membrane. The membrane is a bilayer of phospholipids with proteins closely associated with it in various arrangements including attachment to the polar ends of the lipids at the water-lipid interface. But because cells exist in aqueous environments, they have several features that are satisfied only by lipids.

A cell is insoluble. Even substances that are extremely insoluble will dissolve until they saturate their surrounding medium. For a cell with a membrane short of being completely insoluble, it would be continually faced with dissolution. In addition to being insoluble, the membrane has to be hydrophobic, for it is the exclusion from water that causes lipids to come together to create a bilayer that can act as the plane of contact between separate aqueous compartments. Moreover, lipids are lighter than water, whereas, other biological compounds are slightly denser. When lipids are combined with other compounds, the density of the aggregate can be near that of water.

Phospholipids are fundamental and universal with biological systems. Having a polar end which interacts with water molecules and hydrocarbon chains that are excluded from water, phospholipids in water automatically orient in a definite configuration. When a mixture of phospholipids and water is agitated, liposomes — small spherical particles — are formed in which the phospholipid molecules are aligned in double layers with the hydrocarbon chains coalesced and the polar phosphate groups extended outward in association with the water. Liposomes may be formed in a series of concentric bilayers, each oriented in this fashion. It is a form of self-assembly that creates an encapsulation of substances inside the sphere and restricts diffusion of ions and molecules across a lipid barrier. It forms spontaneously with phospholipids in water — it is a feature of all biological systems.

$$
\begin{array}{l}
CH_3CH_2CH_2CH_2CH_2CH_2CH_2CH_2CH_2CH_2CH_2CH_2CH_2CH_2CH_2CH_2CH_2\text{-O-CO-}CH_2 \\
CH_3CH_2CH_2CH_2CH_2CH_2CH_2CH_2CH{=}CHCH_2CH_2CH_2CH_2CH_2CH_2CH_2\text{-O-CO-}CH \\
\qquad\qquad\qquad\qquad\qquad\qquad\qquad\qquad\qquad\qquad\qquad\quad CH_2\text{-O-}\overset{O}{\underset{O^-}{P}}\text{-O-}CH_2CH_2\text{-}\overset{+}{N}(CH_3)_3
\end{array}
$$

Phosphatidyl choline (a phospholipid)

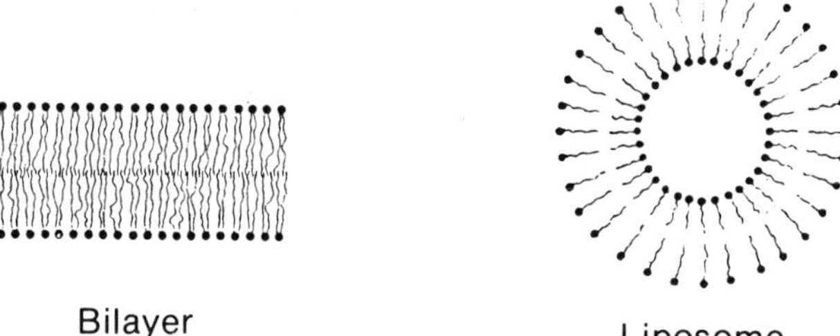

Bilayer

Liposome

The minimum requirements for a functional cell appear to be nine essential elements, a proper aqueous environment, and the formation of small nucleic acids, ATP, peptides and phospholipids. Nucleic acids are composed of purines, pyrimidines and ribose moieties; amino acids are needed for peptides; and phospholipids need fatty acids, glycerol and several other small subunits. These are the building blocks of the macromolecules and structures of a living organism.

But the problem is, as one looks around he discovers that all these building blocks for the development of a living organism come from one source — other living organisms. We find ourselves back to the beginning. If the building blocks for constructing a living system come only from living systems, how did the first cells come into being?

References

1. R.W. Holley, J. Apgar, G.A. Everett, J.T. Madison, M. Marquisse, S.H. Merrill, J.R. Penwick and A. Zamir, Structure of a ribonucleic acid, *Science* **147**, 1462-1465 (1965).
2. B.G. Barrell and B.F.C. Clark, **Handbook of Nucleic Acid Sequences**, Joynson-Bruvvers, Oxford, 1974.
3. L.E. Orgel, Evolution of the genetic apparatus, *J. Mol. Biol.* **38**, 381-393 (1968).
4. Sidney W. Fox, The proteinoid theory of the origin of life and competing ideas, *Am. Biol. Teacher* **36**, No. 3, 161-172 (1974).
5. I. Asimov, **Fact and Fancy**, Avon Books, New York, 1972, pp. 11-20.
6. J.B. McClendon, Elemental abundances as a factor in the origins of mineral nutrient requirements, *J. Mol. Evol.* **8**, 175-195 (1976).
7. D.O. Hall, R. Cammack and K.K. Rao, Role for ferredoxin in the origin of life and biological evolution, *Nature* **233**, 136-138 (1971).
8. L. Margulis, **Origin of Eukaryotic Cells**, Yale University Press, New Haven, Conn., 1970, pp. 7,8.
9. F.H.C. Crick and L.E. Orgel, Directed panspermia, *Icarus* **19**, 341-346 (1973).
10. W.R. Chappell, R.R. Meglen and D.D. Runnelis, Comments on "Directed panspermia," *Icarus* **21**, 513-515 (1974).
11. T.H. Jukes, Seawater and the origins of life, *Icarus* **21**, 516-517 (1974).
12. L.E. Orgel, Reply: "Comments on 'Directed panspermia'" and "Seawater and the origin of life," *Icarus* **21**, 518 (1974).
13. A. Banin and J. Navrot, Origin of life: clues from relations between chemical composition of living organisms and natural environments, *Science* **189**, 550-551 (1975).

19

Searching for the Building Blocks

In 1807 when Berzelius defined organic compounds as the exclusive products of biological systems, he was more correct than not. The synthesis of urea from ammonium cyanate by his student, Friedrich Wöhler, in 1828, only demonstrated that organic compounds could be synthesized from inorganic compounds, but without the directing hand of man, organic compounds still remained within the domain of biology. Organic chemistry developed as a branch separate from the inorganic, in no way disputing the fact that biological compounds are produced in nature only by living organisms.

But then the principle of spontaneous generation, the concept that bacterial life arose spontaneously, was finally put to rest by Pasteur in 1867 by a few simple experiments. Even the belief that life was due to a vital force that set it apart from the inanimate was losing adherents as the chemistry of biological systems became elucidated. This discrediting of the old principles before they were replaced by new created a severe gap in science's understanding of the physical world. The origin of a primal cell remained an unsolved mystery. If all living things can be defined in terms of a biological cell, and the cell is a functional unit of biochemical compounds and processes, how then did the first cells come into being on primordial earth?

In particular, how could the first living cells have obtained amino acids to make their proteins? Once they synthesized proteins they could produce enzymes which were the key to the entire biological machinery, but all amino acids found in nature come from a plant, animal or microbe at some time or other. Even for plants to use CO_2, minerals and water to produce amino acids, sugars and lipids, they need a complex array of enzymes and cellular structures. With the barren geological conditions of prebiological earth, it was inconceivable how even the simplest type of primitive cell began. It was a problem that was to perplex scientists for over a century.

One of the first attempts to formulate an answer to the enigma was by the eminent German physiologist, Eduard Pflüger. In a remarkable paper published in 1875, Pflüger[1] postulated that simple organic compounds may have formed from inorganic minerals by natural conditions of early earth. Drawing from chemical knowledge of a century ago, he pointed out that potassium and carbon heated to a high temperature together in air gave potassium cyanide. He reasoned that thunderstorms may have done the same thing. Several other reactions were listed showing how organic compounds could be produced from inorganic substances: heating carbon disulfide and hydrogen sulfide gave ethylene; and as Berthelot had found, methane, carbon and hydrogen reacted under an electric discharge to give acetylene which could be oxidized to oxalic acid. Heating carbon monoxide with potassium hydroxide gave potassium formate; and from the distillation of formate he obtained methane, ethylene, butylene, amylene and higher analogs. When ammonium formate was heated, hydrogen cyanide was formed, and ammonia passed over glowing carbon gave ammonium cyanide. Cyanides were known to be reactive compounds, so Pflüger postulated that from them proteins could be formed. He visualized an intermediary period when lifeless organic compounds polymerized to become proteins of living nature.

Unfortunately, Pflüger lived at a time when the primary structure of proteins was still speculative. He proposed a theory for protoplasm in which the nitrogen was thought as being largely in the form of cyanogen. When Pflüger's cyan-protein theory failed to survive, so did his theory on the origin of life. It was to be nearly another fifty years before any other significant proposals on the origin of life were to come to light.

In 1922, the Russian biochemist, A.I. Oparin, submitted a theory to the Botanical Society of Moscow on the self-assembly of abiogenetically formed organic compounds as precursors of the first cells. These precursors were to have developed by feeding on the abiotic organic compounds until they evolved to the point of being able to synthesize their own biochemicals. Oparin suggested that hydrocarbons were the initial organic compounds formed by the interaction of water and metal carbides found in the iron core of the earth. When the carbides and steam met at the surface of the earth, the hydrocarbons resulted. He felt they would have been burnt by the oxygen of the air, but the reaction would not have been complete, so that carbon monoxide and oxygen derivatives of hydrocarbons, the alcohols, aldehydes, ketones and carboxylic acids would have been formed. The nitrogen compounds, he believed, were derived from cyanogen formed by metal nitrites reacting with the hydrocarbons. The theory was published in 1924[2] followed by a revised edition in 1936.[3]

Oparin was influenced by the views of the time that held that the earth had been molten in its early stage and the atmosphere remained essentially the same throughout its history. When the British geneticist, J.B.S. Haldane,[4] gave support to the concept of chemical evolution in 1928, he expressed the idea of an atmosphere devoid of oxygen. To Haldane, the agency of ultraviolet light acting on water, carbon dioxide and ammonia created a variety of organic substances which accumulated in primitive oceans until there was the consistency of a "hot dilute soup."

Haldane's realization that it was an atmosphere without oxygen that was the key to the abiotic synthesis of organic compounds was a show of outstanding insight to the origin of life. But a curious flaw of human nature is to permit the imagery of a catchy phrase to shape one's reasoning. Haldane's hot dilute soup became "primordial soup," a feature that has been popularized for nearly fifty years without geologic evidence that it ever existed.

That life originated in a reduced environment was not generally considered before Haldane. It had been the concensus that the oxygenated conditions of today were necessary for life, and it was under these conditions that life began. But Pasteur, while studying fermentation, discovered that life without oxygen was possible and showed a host of anaerobic organisms that metabolized substances without it. In 1928, seeing that fermentative metabolic processes of living organisms are all similar but the oxidative reactions are often quite different, Haldane concluded the anaerobic metabolism as being the more primitive. He postulated that the first living organisms were anaerobes whose source of energy for metabolism was metastable molecules produced by the ultraviolet light from the sun.

Not until 1929 was it discovered that the most abundant element in the universe is hydrogen.[5] In a universe predominantly hydrogen, it was apparent the earth's oxygenated atmosphere could not have been its original gaseous envelope. There were two ways, therefore, that free oxygen could have been produced: photodissociation of water in the upper atmosphere; and photosynthesis by green plants. The significance of the oxygen-generating photosynthetic organisms in the evolution of the earth's environment began to be realized — Oparin, in his revised edition, included the anaerobic origin of life — and it is now generally accepted that the development of life on earth created the oxidized state of the atmosphere and oceans.

Following the end of the Second World War, the idea that the origin of life could be explained by the chemistry of the primordial earth began to draw a following. The speculations were that life originated in some prebiotic organic milieu; the crux of the problem was to find a plausible explanation of how organic substances could be produced from inorganic gases, salts and minerals before any biological system existed. Since plants construct compounds by reducing CO_2, one of the approaches was to attempt to accomplish this by some physical means. But even if small compounds were obtained, they had to be condensed into long chains before a functional cell could develop. J.D. Bernal,[6] crystallographer and physicist at the University of London, wrote **The**

Physical Basis of Life in 1951 in which he suggested that adsorption to clay surface would be a means to bring about the concentration and polymerization of simple prebiotic compounds.

At this time the analytical technology had not yet reached the level to allow the unraveling of the complex chemistry of the cell. Nucleic acids were known, but their exact significance was still uncertain; and proteins were considered the primary substance of life. The ultra-centrifuge enabled biochemists to establish that proteins had definite molecular weights, but whether they could ever be regarded as uniform compounds like giant chemicals was regarded as doubtful — they had properties more like colloids.[7] The first complete primary structure of a protein was not to be reported until Sanger[8] worked out the sequence of insulin in 1953 — an achievement many biochemists up to that time would have considered not possible.

Although the concept of life originating by a combination of chemical processes on early earth appealed to scientific logic, there was no experimental data to substantiate how this could have been possible. At the time when the biosynthesis of proteins was still explained in terms of some vague and hypothetical template, understanding how something as complicated as a living cell could have arisen from inorganic minerals on primordial earth seemed remote indeed.

A group at Berkeley in 1951 led by Melvin Calvin[9] attempted to reduce CO_2 by using the cyclotron, the instrument developed for accelerating atomic particles to study the nucleus of the atom. It was an experiment to simulate the effects of radioactivity from the earth's crust on constituents of primordial earth to demonstrate an abiotic origin of organic substances. When a mixture of CO_2 in water with a catalytic amount of a ferrous salt was bombarded with 40-meV helium ions from the 60-inch cyclotron, the chemists obtained a 4 percent conversion of the CO_2 to formic acid and a 0.1 percent to formaldehyde. The experiment showed some reduction had occurred, but the results were so small that the gulf between inorganic earth and proteins remained depressingly wide.

It was two years later in May of 1953 that Stanley Miller[10] published the results of his electric discharge experiment. Within a year, Frederick Sanger announced the primary structure of insulin,[8] the first protein whose amino acid sequence was ever determined, and James Watson and Francis Crick[11] showed that the chemical basis of life's reproductive nature was the double-helical nucleic acid.

Miller followed the first experiment with variations in the composition of the gas mixture and with detailed analysis of the material produced by the reaction.[12-14] A substantial amount of the product was non-descript tarry substance. Glycine was the amino acid produced in

YIELDS FROM SPARKING A MIXTURE OF CH_4, NH_4, H_2O AND H_2 [15]

Compound	Yield (pM)	Yield (%)
Glycine	630	2.1
Glycolic acid	560	1.9
Sarcosine	50	0.25
Alanine	340	1.7
Lactic acid	310	1.6
N-Methyl alanine	10	0.07
α -Amino-n-butyric acid	50	0.34
α -Aminoisobutyric acid	1	0.007
α -Hydroxybutryic acid	50	0.37
β -Alanine	150	0.76
Succinic acid	40	0.27
Aspartic acid	4	0.024
Glutamic acid	6	0.051
Iminodiacetic	55	0.37
Iminoaceticpropionic acid	15	0.13
Formic acid	2,330	4.0
Acetic acid	150	0.51
Propionic acid	130	0.66
Urea	20	0.034
N-Methyl urea	15	0.051

59 moles (710) of carbon were added as CH_4. The percent yields are based on carbon.

the highest yield — 2.1 percent based on carbon. Of the long list of products generated by the reaction, only four are amino acids that occur in proteins.

Miller studied the mechanism of the electric discharge experiment and discovered hydrogen cyanide (HCN) and aldehydes ($R\text{-}C{=O \atop -H}$) were the active intermediates formed by the reaction. From this he deduced that the products were made by the Strecker reaction, the oldest known method of synthesizing amino acids. In order to test this hypothesis, a mixture of HCN, aldehydes, hydrogen and ammonia was boiled in water for one week. Products similar to those formed by the sparking experiment were obtained in respectable yields.

BOILING OF H_2, NH_3, HCN, HCHO, CH_3CHO, C_2H_5CHO and H_2O FOR ONE WEEK

Reaction Product	**Yield** Moles × 10^5	**Percent**
Glycine	98	16
Alanine	129	35
α -Aminobutyric acid	27	23
Glycolic acid	72	12
Lactic acit	42	12
α -Hydroxybutyric acid	15	13
Iminodiacetic acid	56	18
Iminoaceticpropionic acid	45	

There would have been a number of energy sources on primordial earth that could have contributed to the synthesis of organic compounds. Among the most significant were ultraviolet light from the sun, electric discharges, radioactivity and thermal energy. From these, ultraviolet radiation from the sun would have been in overwhelming predominance.

PRESENT SOURCES OF ENERGY
AVERAGED OVER THE EARTH[18]

Source	**Energy (Calories/cm²/year)**
Total radiation from the sun	260,000
Ultraviolet light	
< 3000 Å	3,400
< 2500 Å	563
< 2000 Å	41
< 1500 Å	1.7
Electric discharges	4
Cosmic rays	0.0015
Radioactivity (to 1.0 km depth)	0.8
Volcanoes	0.13
Shock waves	1.1
Solar wind	0.2

Today the ozone layer screens out virtually all radiation below 3150 Å, but on primordial earth the solar flux would have streamed down with fierce intensity to have profound effects on the primitive atmosphere. Since the absorption of methane extends to 1450 Å, water to 1650 Å, and ammonia to 2200 Å, the photodissociation of these molecules would have taken place at these shortwave ultraviolet emissions, creating highly reactive chemical radicals. Unfortunately, there are technical difficulties in using shortwave ultraviolet light in the laboratory to simulate the synthesis of organic compounds in a primitive atmosphere and only some experiments at available wavelengths have been attempted.[16,17]

Philip Abelson[19] at the Carnegie Institute of Washington was the first to determine whether amino acids could be synthesized by photochemical reactions. When he radiated a solution of ammonium formate, ammonium hydroxide, sodium cyanide and ferrous sulfate with the 2536 Å wavelength, he obtrained glycinonitrile which hydrolyzed to glycine.

Experiments were carried out by others using gaseous mixtures and several ultraviolet wavelengths in which other amino acids were formed.[20] Glycine, alanine, valine and leucine were identified as products from irradiated methane, ammonia, water and carbon monoxide in the region between 1450 Å.[21] The amino acids formed by ultraviolet light were generally those found from electric discharge experiments.

Although ultraviolet light may have been a predominant source of energy for the synthesis of prebiological organic compounds, most of it is of long wavelengths that do not react with the gases used to simulate the primordial atmosphere. Carl Sagan and Bishun Khare, however, observed that hydrogen, methane, ammonia, water, ethane, and perhaps carbon monoxide and nitrogen are all entirely transparent to ultraviolet light above 2400 Å, but that hydrogen sulfide has a broad absorption continuum beginning at about 2700 Å. Hydrogen sulfide then could have served as the initial photon acceptor to capture energy of the long wavelength ultraviolet light and initiate chemical reactions. In simulation experiments, Sagen and Khare[22] found the presence of hydrogen sulfide and ethane with the gases irradiated by ultraviolet light at 2537 Å did produce amino acids, thus showing that the abundance of ultraviolet light in the longer wavelength region of the spectrum may have been one of the principal sources of energy for the synthesis of prebiotic compounds.

Ionizing radiation can also serve as an energy source. When a mixture of gases simulating the primitive atmosphere was exposed to X-rays and gamma rays, amino acids were formed.[23] This energy source is not viewed as having been a significant contributor to the synthesis of prebiotic compounds, however, since most of the ionization would have taken place in silicate rocks and not the atmosphere.

The importance of volcanic activity in the synthesis of amino acids has been disputed. When a mixture of gases simulating a primordial atmosphere is heated continuously at 1,200° C, no organic compounds will form and only an equilibrium of the gases results. If, however, the gases are passed over molten lava slowly and then rapidly quenched, a variety of hydrocarbons are synthesized. In this way phenylacetylene, a precursor to phenylalanine and tyrosine,[24] and indole, the precursor of tryptophan[25] are formed. This reaction presents a manner in which the aromatic amino acids could have occurred prebiologically, but these amino acids may not have become a part of biological systems until they were synthesized biochemically.

As curious as it may seem, it is conceivable that a principal producer of amino acids was shock waves. Bar-Nun and colleagues[26] have demonstrated with gases simulating a primitive atmosphere that in a shock tube the shock front temperature rises to 1,000 to 2,000° K within 10^{-8} seconds with rapid quenching, giving a high conversion of the gases to amino acids. The authors calculated the annual shock flux from cometary meteors, micrometeorites and thunder to be approximately 1 calorie per cm^2; in contrast, the energy from ultraviolet light below 3000 Å would have been about 1,000 calories per cm^2. But shock waves are a million times more efficient in producing amino acids than ultraviolet light. In this context, there should have been 1,000 times more amino acids generated by shock waves than by the most abundant energy source, the ultraviolet light.

These various experiments suggested a scenario in which organic compounds or their precursors were produced in the primordial atmosphere and rained down to accumulate in the juvenile oceans. With many reactive compounds washed into catchbasins, interactions would have generated additional substances. It was an exciting new image of the chemistry that took place on earth before life existed. The origin of life was no longer thought of in terms of strange inorganic substances in a geologic setting giving rise to a non-biological structure that had to undergo an undetermined evolution before a living cell could be formed; the prebiotic compounds to construct a biological system were the amino acids familiar to every biochemistry student.

After two decades it is possible to put the Miller experiment in a better perspective in respect to the origin of life. Urey's methane-ammonia atmosphere was calculated as the primary atmosphere of the earth acquired when the solar system was formed. But there is ample evidence to indicate the original atmosphere was lost and replaced by outgassing of the earth's interior. The question then remains: In what way did the second atmosphere differ from the first?

Studies have shown the composition of volcanic gases to be principally water and CO_2 with a significant amount of hydrogen.[27]

Chloride, as the substance third-most in abundance, issues as the acid, as does sulfur; nitrogen is principally as the element. Ammonia could not have been in the atmosphere in any significant quantity. Abelson[28] pointed out that a quantity of ammonia equivalent to the present atmospheric nitrogen would have been degraded by ultraviolet radiation in approximately 30,000 years. Similarly, its high solubility in water would have created an equilibrium with essentially all of it in solution in the oceans. The early earth's atmosphere, therefore, consisted of residual volcanic gases after they equilibrated between the atmosphere-ocean system. Abelson contends its composition would have been principally CO, CO_2, N_2 and H_2.

The fundamental nature of the Miller experiment allows the atmosphere of precursor gases to be apparently of any composition provided it is reducing and the components contain C, H, O and N. Nevertheless, the chemistry for the outgassed atmosphere may have been similar to that for the methane-ammonia mixture, but not the same. When a mixture of CO, N_2 and H_2 is subjected to an electric discharge, HCN is the major product with little else except carbon suboxide (O=C=C=C=O), CO_2 and H_2O.[28] One does not obtain the series of aldehydes that was intermediate to the amino acids by the Strecker reaction. As a result, the prebiological chemistry becomes one, not of a "soup" as envisioned resulting from a methane-ammonia atmosphere, but the chemistry of HCN.

Hydrogen cyanide undergoes two important reactions: it hydrolyzes to ammonium hydroxide and formic acid; and in slightly alkaline solutions it condenses with itself to yield a variety of compounds of biological interest. The major product from the condensation of HCN is the tetramer.

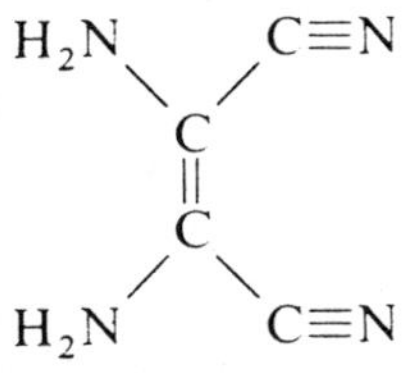

$$
\begin{array}{ccc}
H_2N & & C\equiv N \\
& \diagdown \;\; \diagup & \\
& C & \\
& \| & \\
& C & \\
& \diagup \;\; \diagdown & \\
H_2N & & C\equiv N
\end{array}
$$

Diaminomaleonitrile
(HCN tetramer)

Hydrolysis of the tetramer yields glycine; and Oró and Kamat[29] reported small amounts of alanine and aspartic acid when 2.2 M ammonium cyanide solutions were heated at 70° C for 25 days. But this is a high concentration. And in order for the tetramer formation to exceed the hydrolysis reaction, the concentration of HCN needs to be greater than around 0.1 M. This is unrealistic under natural conditions for HCN, but could have been commonplace with NH_4OH from HCN hydrolysis combining with additional HCN to give ammonium cyanide (NH_4CN), which could be concentrated by partial evaporation of the solution.

It is possible the concentration factor may have been circumvented by the action of ultraviolet light. Abelson found 0.002-0.10 M solutions of HCN at pH 8-9 irradiated with 2536-Å light gave a product mixture that hydrolyzed to glycine, serine, aspartic acid and glutamic acid.

The research by the various laboratories in the wake of Miller's experiment was actively pursued in an effort to show the abiotic synthesis of as many of the 20 biological amino acids as possible. As a result, all but histidine and arginine have been reported to have been produced in simulation experiments.[30] In addition to these the Miller experiment yields many amino acids that are not used in proteins.

Life may have begun with much less. In one respect the prebiological chemistry based on HCN is simpler and perhaps more coincidental with the origin of life. When one looks at the process of contemporary biosynthesis, he is impressed by how few basic building blocks there really are.[28] Pyruvate, acetate and carbonate in some microorganisms can furnish all the carbon for:

serine	leucine	methionine
glycine	isoleucine	glutamic acid
cysteine	lysine	proline
alanine	aspartic acid	arginine
valine	threonine	

Pyruvate and acetate can result from the degradation of serine; and from pyruvate and from malonic acid, acetate can be obtained. Furthermore, ferredoxin which is believed to have been one of the earliest proteins was apparently formed from a repeating sequence of alanine, serine, aspartic acid and glycine — amino acids that are produced most readily from HCN.

The Miller experiment illustrated the ease of formation and the probability of the abiotic presence of life's building blocks; and a number of energy sources were available on primordial earth for the production of biological compounds. A requisite was a mixture of reduced gases. It is interesting that if the atmosphere had originally contained oxygen as had long been believed necessary for the origin of life, it would never have happened. Oxygen would have quenched the reaction before it could have made the building blocks.

Abelson has pointed out that an atmosphere containing appreciable amounts of methane would have resulted in the production of a large deposit of hydrophobic organic material, but unusually large amounts of carbon or organic material have not been found in rocks predating the earliest organisms. Nevertheless, there are indications a considerable amount of organic compounds apparently was synthesized in a methane-ammonia atmosphere, not on primordial earth, but in the gaseous nebula before the earth's formation.

Hydrocarbon gases have been found near Lake Huron in Canada and as the Ukhtinsk deposit in the U.S.S.R. in crystalline rock formations having no connections with sedimentary rocks.[31] The great reservoirs of petroleum are definitely of biological origin, but findings in the Soviet Union clearly indicate some petroleum deposits to be of an abiogenic derivation. Gas emissions in the Khibinsk massif on the Kola paninsula show methane and heavier hydrocarbons that apparently are of magmatic origin. Although such sources rarely have commercial importance, they now number in the hundreds.[32] It appears that this organic matter is not a vestige of the "primordial soup," but has survived from a time even before the earth was formed. This hypothesis stems from and is supported by the discovery of organic compounds in objects that were there when it happened — meteorites.

References

1. E. Pflüger, Ueber die physiologische Verbrennung in den ledendigen Organismen, *Arch. gesam. Physiol.,* **10**, (1875).
2. A.I. Oparin, **Proiskhozhdenie zhizni (The Origin of Life)**, Ixd. Moskovskiy Rabochiy, Moscow, 1924.
3. A. Oparin, **Vozniknovnie zhizni na Zemle**, Biomedgiz, 1936; **Origin of Life** (Trans. by S. Morgulis), Macmillan Company, New York, 1938.
4. J.B.S. Haldane, The origin of life, Rationalist Annual, 148-153 (1928), reprinted in **Science and Human Life**, Harper Brothers, New York, 1933.
5. H.N. Russell, *Astrophys. J.* **70**, 11 (1929), cited in Virginia Trimble, The origin and abundances of the chemical elements, *Rev. Mod. Phys.***47**, 877-986 (1975).
6. J.D. Bernal, **The Physical Basis of Life**, Routledge and Kegan Paul, London, 1951.
7. J.W. Williams, Problems in protein chemistry, in Colloid Chemistry, *Ann. Rev. Phys. Chem.* **2**, 403-424 (1951).
8. F. Sanger and E.O.P. Thompson, The amino-acid sequence in the glycyl chain of insulin, *Biochem. J.* **53**, 366-374 (1953).
9. W.M. Garrison, D.C. Morrison, J.G. Hamilton, A.A. Benson and M. Calvin, Reduction of carbon dioxide in aqueous solution by ionizing radiation, *Science* **114**, 416-418 (1951).
10. S.L. Miller, A production of amino acids under possible primitive earth conditions, *Science* **117**, 528-529 (1953).
11. J.D. Watson and F.H.C. Crick, A structure for deoxyribose nucleic acid, *Nature* **171**, 737-738 (1953).
12. S.L. Miller, Production of some organic compounds under possible primitive earth conditions, *J. Am. Chem. Soc.* **77**, 2351-2361 (1955).
13. S.L. Miller, The mechanism of synthesis of amino acids by electric discharge, *Biochem. Biophys. Acta* **23**, 480-489 (1957).
14. S.L. Miller, The formation of organic compounds on the primitive earth, *Ann. N.Y. Acad. Sci.* **69**, 260-275 (1957).
15. Stanley L. Miller and Leslie E. Orgel, **The Origin of Life on Earth**, Prentice—Hall, Inc., Englewood Cliffs, N.J., 1974, p. 85.
16. T.E. Pavlovskaya and A.G. Pasynskii, The original formation of amino acids under action of ultraviolet rays and electric discharges, in **The Origin of Life on the Earth**, F. Clark and R.L.M. Synge, eds., Pergamon Press, New York, 1959, pp. 151-157.
17. A.N. Terenin, Photosynthesis in the shortest ultraviolet, in **The Origin of Life on the Earth**, F. Clark and R.L.M. Synge, eds., Pergamon Press, New York, 1959, pp. 136-139.
18. S.L. Miller, H.C. Urey and J. Oró, Origin of organic compounds on the primitive earth and in meteorites, *J. Mol. Evol.* **9**, 59-72 (1976).
19. P.H. Abelson, Paleobiochemistry, Carnegie Inst. of Washington Yearbook, No. 53, 1955-6.
20. W. Groth and H. v. Weyssenhof, Photochemical formation of organic compounds from mixtures of simple gases, *Planet. Space Sci.* **2**, 79-85 (1960).

21. M. Ya. Dodonova and A.I. Sidorova, Photosynthesis of amino acids from a mixture of simple gases under the action of short-wave ultraviolet radiation, *Biophys.* **6**, 164-175 (1961).
22. Carl Sagan and Bishun N. Khare, Long-wavelength untraviolet photoproduction of amino acids on the primitive Earth, *Science* **173**, 417-420 (1971).
23. K. Dose and B. Rajewsky, Strahlenchemische Bildung von Aminen und Aminocarbonsauren, *Biochim. Biophys. Acta* **25**, 225-226 (1957).
24. N. Friedman and S.L. Miller, Phenylalanine and tyrosine synthesis under primitive earth conditions, *Science* **166**, 766-767 (1969).
25. N. Friedmann, W.J. Haverland and S.L. Miller, Prebiotic synthesis of the aromatic and other amino acids, in **Molecular Evolution I. Chemical Evolution and the Origin of Life**, R. Buver and C. Ponnamperuma, eds., North Holland Publ. Co., Amsterdam, 1971, pp. 123-135.
26. A. Bar-Nun, N. Bar-Nun, S.H. Bauer and C. Sagan, Shock synthesis of amino acids in simulated primitive environments, *Science* **168**, 470-473 (1970).
27. W.W. Rubey, Geologic history of sea water, *Bull. Geol. Soc. Am.* **62**, 1111-1148 (1951).
28. Phillip H. Abelson, Chemical events on the primitive earth, *Proc. Nat. Acad. Sci.* **55**, 1365-1372 (1966).
29. J. Oro′ and S.S. Kamat, Amino acid synthesis from hydrogen cyanide under possible primitive earth conditions, *Nature* **190**, 442-443 (1961).
30. C. Ponnamperuma and N.W. Gabel, Current status of chemical studies on the origin of life, *Space Life Sci.* **1**, 64-96 (1968).
31. Cited in A.I. Oparin, **Genesis and Evolutionary Development of Life**, Academic Press, New York, 1968, p. 66.
32. P. Kropotkia, in **Sovetskaya Geologiya (Soviet Geology)**, Coll. 47, Gos. Nauchno-tekhn. Ind., 1955, p. 104.

20

Organic Compounds in the Universe

Meteorites are the sort of thing that invites credibility problems. It has been generally known since at least the dawn of civilization that stones and even masses of iron occasionally fall on the earth, but the Age of Reason brought a skepticism that regarded this as impossible. After a stone fell at Lucé, France, in 1768, a commission led by the eminent French chemist, Lavoisier, conducted an inquiry, but then declared the meteorite to be a terrestrial rock. Three more falls occurred in Europe in the 1790's in which specimens were preserved, but the scientific opinion persisted. Finally, it was not until a spectacular fall of thousands of stones on l'Aigle, France, on April 26, 1803, that the Royal Academy of Science of Paris conceded that stones can fall from the sky.

Meteorites fall into three major categories: irons, stones and stony irons, each of which is further subdivided by composition. Based on elemental and mineral content, there is a marked uniformity within the classes, with a great divergence between several classes. The principal

Von dem donnerſtein gefallē im xcij. iar: vor Enſiſheim

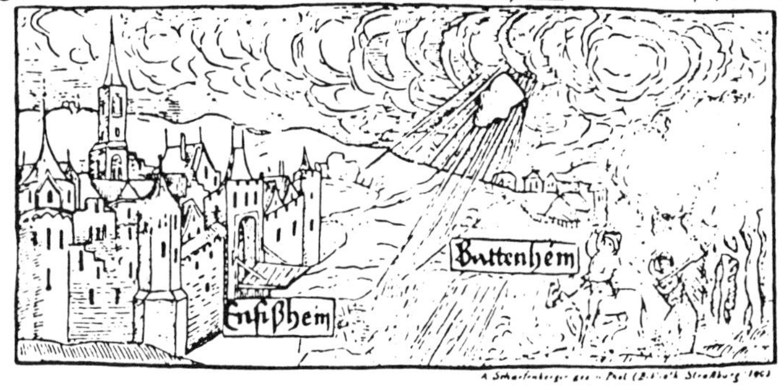

The fall of the Ensisheim meteorite, Alsace, 1492

mineral constituents all occur as terrestrial minerals and the abundance of the elements in meteorites follows the regularities known for earth.

Because stony meteorites tend to weather quickly and are hard to distinguish from ordinary rocks, it is usually the irons with their damascened exterior that are seen in museums. But of meteorites recovered soon after a fall, 94 percent have been found to be stones. Of the stones 80 percent are chondrites, characterized by rounded granules of enstatite or chrysolite embedded in the mass of meteoritic stone — and among the stony meteorites there is a small group called carbonaceous chondrites. Despite the fact that at least 2 percent of all meteorites are of this group, being friable and disintegrating rapidly by weathering, they are hard to recognize unless found soon after the fall. These meteorites received their name because some contain as much as 5 percent organic carbon.

There are 21 known carbonaceous chondrites, all of which were collected soon after the fall was observed. Berzelius[1] and Wöhler[2] both attempted to analyze the organic matter in carbonaceous meteorites, but the carbon appeared to be in the form of an insoluble polymer. Without identifying any specific compounds, they concluded the organic substance was not of biological origin.

Then on May 14, 1864, a meteorite blazed across southern France and fell near the village of Orgueil, scattering stones over a two-square-mile area. Twenty fragments, most the size of a fist but one as large as a man's head, with a combined weight of 11.523 kilograms (25.4 lbs.) were collected. It was a carbonaceous meteorite which disintegrated readily when in contact with water due to the dissolution of water-soluble salts.

The Orgueil meteorite was examined first by Cloëz,[3] and later by Berthelot.[4] Berthelot isolated certain organic materials and referred to the "coal-like" substance, but was unable to be more specific. The chemical methods of a century ago gave only limited information as to the exact nature and quantities of substances so intractable. Solving the mystery of organic material in meteorites had to wait until recent developments of analytical techniques of organic geochemistry.

The Orgueil meteorite. (Courtesy, Smithsonian Institution, Washington, D.C.)

The interest in the "bitumin" of meteorites extended from 1834 to 1885, but then followed 68 years when the subject apparently was no longer given any attention by chemists. Finally in 1953, George Mueller,[5] a geologist at the University of London, reopened the investigation. The British Museum with its collection of all 20 of the known carbonaceous meteorites supplied Mueller with a 20-gram sample of the Cold Bokkeveld, a meteorite that fell in the Union of South Africa in 1838.

Mueller attempted first to dissolve the silicates with acid to isolate the organic matter. The process took weeks and was notably more difficult than with terrestrial shale. Of the 1 percent of extractable organic material, he found it to be composed of principally carbon, hydrogen, nitrogen and oxygen, as well as sulfur and chloride. It had a low decomposition temperature. A benzene extract failed to show any optical activity, thus discounting a biological origin. Because it was soluble in alkali, Mueller concluded the material was composed of complex organic acids with some organic chloride compounds, but he was unable to identify specific chemical structures.

Mueller expressed the view that the organic material must have arisen in an atmosphere of varying illumination and temperature to permit the polymerization of complex molecules. Because it was so difficult to dissolve the silicates, he felt the organic material must have condensed on dust particles which settled and compacted on a relatively small celestial body. At no time during or after its formation did the organic material experience temperatures greater than 200-350°C. In contrast, the iron and stony iron meteorites had temperatures over 1,000°C sometime in their history.

Then in 1960, Brian Mason[6] of the American Museum of Natural History in New York proposed that the primary materials of all meteorites were hydrated silicates covered with a polymerized carbonaceous layer. Wishing to obtain a more specific determination of the organic substances found in the Orgueil meteorite, he sent a sample to chemists at the Esso Petroleum Laboratory in New Jersey for analysis.

Using mass spectroscopy, Nagy, Meinschein and Hennessy[7] analyzed the organic portion of the Orgueil and found an array of hydrocarbons, the largest being a tetracyclic hydrocarbon with a molecular weight of 428; but the most intriguing was a *n*-paraffin series up to C_{26} and peaking at C_{18}. When they compared the spectrum of their meteoritic distillate to the mass spectra from butter and recent sediments, they saw a striking similarity. From this the authors concluded the meteoritic organic material was from a biogenic source.

That same year Nagy with George Claus[8] of the New York Medical

Center examined six carbonaceous meteorites for microscopic detail. The samples were crushed in water or glycerol on glass slides and studied under a light microscope. In two meteorites they found well-defined "organized elements" whose morphology was unlike any known mineral, but bore some resemblance to certain species of algae. Since samples from the Orgueil meteorite which fell in temperate France and from the Ivuna which fell 74 years later in an arid tropical region of central Africa had "organized elements" of similar morphology, they felt the probability of the particles being due to terrestrial contamination was unlikely. Consequently, they interpreted these structures as possible microfossils indigenous to the meteorites and hence remnants of extraterrestrial life.

Needless to say, this created some controversy, and attention was brought to the substances in meteorites. Edward Anders,[9] a chemist at the Enrico Fermi Institute of the University of Chicago, pointed out that museum specimens are customarily labeled with paint, gummed labels or wax pencil markings, and since the concentrations of hydrocarbons found were around 0.1-1.0 micrograms, the possibility of the findings being due to terrestrial contamination was high. But it wasn't the results as much as the conclusion attributing the organic material to extraterrestrial life that was too conjectural.

The controversy at least reopened for investigation the question of organic matter in meteorites. Other laboratories analyzed extracts from carbonaceous chondrites and found an overwhelming preponderance of aromatic hydrocarbons over the aliphatic. Briggs and Mamikunian[10] reported that 50-90 percent of the material was aromatic polymer. Martin Studier of the Argonne National Laboratory and Ryoichi Hayatsu and Anders at the University of Chicago[11] analyzed fragments of the Orgueil, Murray and Cold Bokkeveld meteorites and identified benzene, toluene, naphthalene, anthracene, sulfonic acid esters and chlorinated hydrocarbons in the organic fraction. They also found the gases, H_2, CO, CO_2, NO, N_2, SO_2, CS_2, methane, ethane and higher homologs. These chemists found no reason to attribute the organic material to a biological origin.

Anders[12] postulated that the meteorites came from asteroids a few hundred kilometers in diameter that had broken up. For the concentration of the organic material to have been formed by the MIller type of reaction the atmospheres of the asteroids would have had to have been impossibly dense.[11] Instead, it has been shown the distribution of the aromatic and aliphatic hydrocarbons is in good agreement with the calculations of Dayhoff and her colleagues[13] on the thermodynamic equilibrium for compounds generated in a mixture of carbon, hydrogen, oxygen and nitrogen at 500^{0}K. That is to say, this organic material was formed and existed in the solar nebula even before the earth came into being.

The study of the meteorites revealed to scientists that components for generating organic substances are not oddities in the universe. It had been known since 1940 that the spectroscopic analysis of light from comets indicated CH and CN radicals. With the development of radio astronomy, when astronomers directed their antennas toward the galaxy and beyond, they discovered immense clouds of relatively complex molecules in the cosmos. In 1968, A.C. Cheung and others[14] at the radio astronomy laboratory at Berkeley using a 20-foot radio telescope detected ammonia clouds near the galactic center by their microwave emissions. The following year the Berkeley group[15] as well as Lewis Snyder and David Buhl[16]using the 140-foot radio television at Green Bank, West Virginia, detected water. Since then, carbon monoxide, [17] hydrogen cyanide,[18] formaldehyde,[19] cyanoethylene[20] and many others[21] have been reported. The densities of these molecules, like hydrogen in space, are small, but the absolute quantities are literally on an astronomical scale.

It was not difficult to accept that the intractable aromatic and aliphatic hydrocarbons of meteorites resulted from a thermodynamic equilibrium of the gases of the solar nebula. The "organized elements" of Nagy and Claus being remnants of extraterrestrial life was somewhat more difficult. The group at the University of Chicago[22] examined the Orgueil and Ivuna meteorites and failed to find the "organized elements," although they did find mineral and sulfur granules bearing a close resemblance. But then Michael Briggs and G. Barrie Kitto[23] of Victoria University in New Zealand reported complex organic microstructures in the Mokoia meteorite, though they considered the chances of the particles being biogenic as unlikely. Nagy, Claus and Hennessy[24]

MOLECULES FOUND IN THE INTERSTELLAR MEDIUM[21]

Year	Molecule	Symbol	Wavelength	Telescope	Initial discovery
1937		CH	4300 Å	Mt Wilson 100 inch	Dunham } Mt Wilson
1940	Cyanogen	CN	3875 Å	Mt Wilson 100 inch	Adams } Mt Wilson
1941		CH^+	3745-4233 Å	Mt Wilson 100 inch	Adams } Mt Wilson
1963	Hydroxyl	OH	18, 6.3, 5.0 and 2.2 cm	Lincoln Lab 84 foot	MIT/Lincoln Lab
1968	Ammonia	NH_3	1.3 cm	Hat Creek 20 foot	Berkeley
1968	Water	H_2O	1.4 cm	Hat Creek 20 foot	Berkeley
1969	Formaldehyde	H_2CO	6.2, 2.1 and 1 cm; 2.1 and 2.0 mm	NRAO 140 foot NRAO 36 foot	University of Virginia, NRAO, University of Maryland and University of Chicago
1970	Carbon monoxide	CO	2.6 mm	NRAO 36 foot	Bell Labs
1970	Cyanogen	CN	2.6 mm	NRAO 36 foot	Bell Labs
1970	Hydrogen	H_2	1100 Å	UV rocket camera	NRL
1970	Hydrogen cyanide	HCN	3.4 mm	NRAO 36 foot	University of Virginia and NRAO
1970	X-ogen	?	3.4 mm	NRAO 36 foot	NRAO and University of Virginia
1970	Cyano-acetylene	HC_3N	3.3 cm	NRAO 140 foot	NRAO
1970	Methyl alcohol	CH_3OH	36 and 1 cm; 3 mm	NRAO 140 foot	Harvard
1970	Formic acid	CHOOH	18 cm	NRAO 140 foot	University of Maryland and Harvard University
1971	Carbon monosulphide	CS	2.0 mm	NRAO 36 foot	Bell Labs and Columbia University
1971	Formamide	NH_2CHO	6.5 cm	NRAO 140 foot	University of Illinois
1971	Silicon oxide	SiO	2.3 mm	NRAO 36 foot	Bell Labs and Columbia University
1971	Carbonyl sulphide	OCS	2.7 mm	NRAO 36 foot	Bell Labs and Columbia University
1971	Acetonitrile	CH_3CN	2.7 mm	NRAO 36 foot	Bell Labs and Columbia University
1971	Isocyanic acid	HNCO	3.4 mm; 1.4 cm	NRAO 36 foot	University of Virginia and NRAO
1971	Hydrogen isocyanide	HNC	3.3 mm	NRAO 36 foot	University of Virginia and NRAO
1971	Methyl-acetylene	CH_3C_2H	3.5 mm	NRAO 36 foot	University of Virginia and NRAO
1971	Acetaldehyde	CH_3CHO	28 cm	NRAO 140 foot	Harvard University
1971	Thioformaldehyde	H_2CS	9.5 cm	Parkes 210 foot	CSIRO, Australia

followed with another article on the "organized elements" and was answered by a detailed investigation by Fitch and Anders[25] in 1963. The final consensus seems to have been that there were several types of micro-structures that fitted into either terrestrial contaminants or structured mineral or organic matter, but none indicative of extraterrestrial life.

No sooner had this been concluded than another controversy raged over the validity of still other organic compounds detected in carbonaceous chondrites. These were amino acids. In 1962, E.T. Degens and M. Bajor[26] at the California Institute of Technology found sugars and amino acids in an 80 percent ethanol extract of the Murray and Bruderheim meteorites. A detailed article the following year by Kaplan, Degens and Reuter[27] gave the results of analyzing eight carbonaceous chondrites and five non-carbonaceous meteorites. Amino acids and sugars were found in all of them. The sugars were mannose and glucose in concentrations of 5-26 micrograms per gram; and 17 amino acids were found in amounts of 30-500 micrograms per gram for the carbonaceous meteorites, 8-50 micrograms for the non-carbonaceous. Since the organic material lacked optical activity, pigments, fatty acids, and presumably nucleic acids, the authors were of the opinion the sugars and amino acids were of a chemical rather than biochemical origin.

The quantities of the amino acids found were of the order of 10^{-6} to 10^{-8} moles per gram. Biochemists who run paper chromatograms to detect amino acids with ninhydrin spray are aware the method is sensitive enough to give a positive test for amino acids from fingerprints if proper technique is not exercised. Paul Hamilton[28] at the DuPont Institute in Wilmington, Delaware, made a systematic study of the amount of amino acids that can result from handling. A single print with a dry thumb from hands washed 2 hours previously was pressed on the inside wall of a dry beaker. The print was washed into the beaker, the water evaporated, and the residue chromatographed on an ion-exchange column in the routine procedure. Seventeen amino acids of the order of 5×10^{-9} to 2×10^{-10} moles were detected. Serine was of the largest amount, followed by glycine. Oró and Skewes[29] also analyzed amino acids from fingerprints and compared the results to those found in meteorites. The amounts were of the same order of magnitude and the ratio of the amino acid pairs, Ser-Thr, Gly-Ala and Ser-Ala were in good agreement.

Since the stones had been handled and kept in museums, there was serious doubt as to the validity of amino acids in meteorites. Nonetheless, the issue was not closed. The researchers who reported the findings were aware of the difficulties involved with low levels of substances for analyses and had confidence in their procedures. Fresh evidence was needed in which there could be no question of terrestrial contamination to settle the issue one way or the other.

The opportunity came from the sky at 11:00 A.M. on September 28, 1969, when a carbonaceous chondrite fell near Murchison, Victoria, Australia. The parent object broke during the flight and scattered many fragments over a five-square-mile area. Specimens were collected soon after the fall and analyzed jointly by NASA scientists at Ames Research Center in California, Isaac Kaplan at Berkeley and Carlton Moore of Arizona State University.[30]

The Murchison meteorite contained 2 percent by weight of carbon and 0.16 percent nitrogen. When a 10-gram sample was hydrolyzed with hydrochloric acid and analyzed by chromatography, it gave peaks for glycine, alanine, valine, proline and glutamic acid. In addition to these five amino acids used in proteins, there were 2-methylalanine and sarcosine, not normally found in biological systems. In this analysis there was sufficient material to measure optical isomers, and the D and L forms were found to be in nearly equal proportions. Terrestrial organisms use almost exclusively the L isomer. The results clearly established amino acids in meteorites not to be from contamination and apparently on non-biogenic origin. A second report identified 11 amino acids in all in the meteorite.[31] The Murchison meteorite contained a total of 2×10^{-7} moles of amino acids per gram — a content higher than many desert sands.

The Murchison meteorite. (Courtesy, Field Museum of Natural History, Chicago)

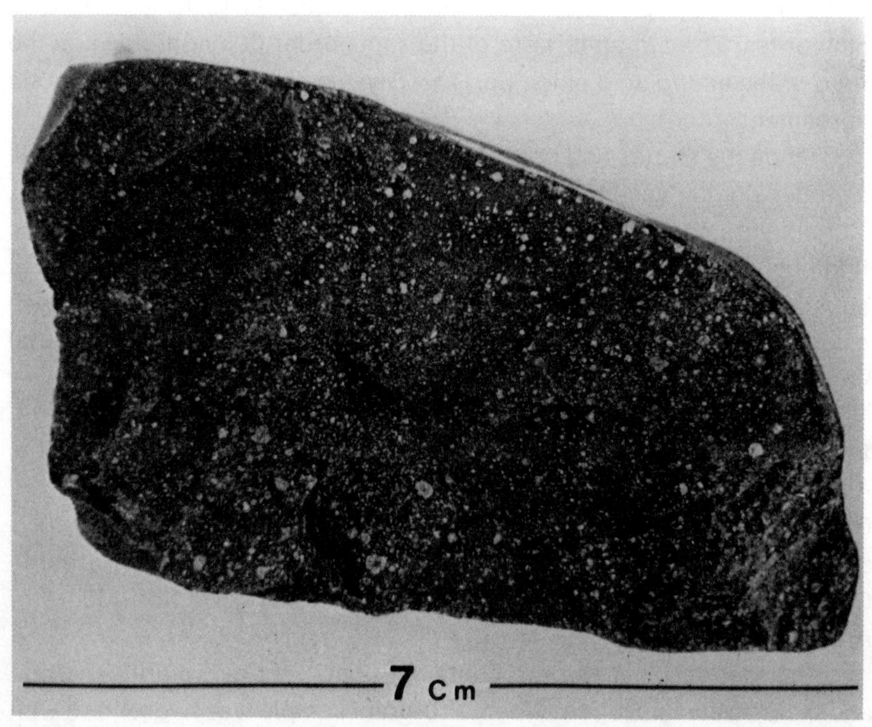

It should be pointed out that the absence of optical activity with extremely old amino acids does not rule out the fact that they may have been of only one isomeric form at one time. The stereoisomerism of amino acids is not absolutely stable. Amino acid isomers will racemize eventually at a rate dependent on the temperature—a feature that has been developed as a means of dating ancient specimens.[32] At 0°C the isomers of isoleucine and alanine have a half-life for converting to a 50-50 mixture in 4.4 and 1.1 million years; whereas, at 25°C, their half-lives are 35,000 and 11,000 years.

Meteorites are the oldest rocks known. They have been dated at 4.6 billion years and are presumed to be as old as the solar system itself. This leaves the question of the origin of the meteoritic amino acids. Were they generated by the Miller type of reaction in the solar nebula, or could they have come about in some other manner?

It is possible they may have resulted from an unforeseen source. When rocks brought back from the moon by the Apollo missions were analyzed for amino acids, to the surprise of many scientists, the initial results were negative. But these analyses were carried out on a simple water extraction of the samples. When it was found there were no free amino acids in the water extract, the extracted material was subjected to hydrolysis in the routine manner for proteins, then analyzed. Six amino acids (glycine, alanine, aspartic acid, glutamic acid, serine and threonine) were detected[33] The amounts were small — 7 to 45 nanograms per gram.

Why then should amino acids be present only after hydrolysis? Apparently on the moon in the absence of water, the amino acids do not exist, but their precursors do. The hydrolysis converted these precursors to free amino acids. Nothing is known of the chemical nature of these precursors, but it is conjectured they may be cyanides — cyanides that resulted from the ceaseless bombardment of the lunar surface by carbon and nitrogen nuclei of the solar wind.

References

1. J.J. Berzelius, Ueber Meteorstein, *Ann. Phys. und Chem,* **33**, 113 (1834).
2. F. Wöhler, Über die Bestandtheile des Meteorsteines von Kaba in Ungarn, *Sitz. Math Naturwiss. Akad. Wien* **33**, 205-209 (1859).
3. S. Cloëz, Note sur la composition chimique de la pierre métorique d'Orgueil, *Compt. rend* **58,** 900)1864); , Analyse chimique de la pierre météorique d'Orgueil, *Compt. rend.* **59,** 37 (1864).
4. P. Berthelot, La matière charbonneuse de la météorite d'Orgueil purifiée autant que possible par les dissolvants, s'est ensuite oxydée entierment, *J. prakt. Chem.* **106,** 254 (1869).
5. G. Mueller, The properties and theory of genesis of the carbonaceous complex within the cold bokevelt meteorite, *Goechim. Cosmochim. Acta* **4,** 1-10 (1953).
6. B. Mason, Origin of chondrules and chondritic meteorites, *Nature* **186**, 230-231 (1960).
7. B. Nagy, W.G. Meinschein and D.J. Hennessy, Mass spectroscopic analysis of the Orgueil meteorite: evidence for biogenic hydrocarbons, *Ann. N.Y. Acad. Sci.* **93**, 25-35 (1961).
8. G. Claus and B. Nagy, A microbiological examination of some carbonaceous chondrites, *Nature* **192**, 594-596 (1961).
9. Edward Anders, Meteoritic hydrocarbons and extraterrestrial life, *Ann. N.Y. Acad. Sci.* **93**, 649-664 (1963).
10. M.H. Brigs and G. Mamikuian, Organic constituents of carbonaceous chondrites, *Science Sci. Rev.* **1**, 647-682 (1963).
11. M.H. Studier, R. Hayatsu and E. Anders, Organic compounds in carbonaceous chondrites, *Science* **149**, 1455-1459 (1965).
12. E. Anders, Origin, age, and composition of meteorites, *Space Sci. Rev.* **3**, 583-714 (1964).
13. M.O. Dayhoff, E.R. Lippincott and R.V. Eck, Thermodynamic equilibria in prebiological atmospheres, *Science* **146**, 1461-1464 (1964).
14. A.C. Cheung, D.M. Rank, C.H. Townes, D.D. Thornton and W.J. Welch, Detection of NH_3 molecules in the interstellar medium by their microwave emmission, *Phys. Rev. Letters* **21**, 1701-1705 (1968).
15. ------, Detection of water in interstellar regions by its microwave radiation, *Nature* **221**, 626-628 (1969).
16. L.E. Snyder and D. Buh., Water-vapor clouds in the interstellar medium, *Astrophys. J.* **155**, 165-170 (1969).
17. R.W. Wilson, K.B. Jeffreys and A.A. Penzias, Carbon monoxide in the Orion Nebula, *Astrophys. J.* **161**, L43-L44 (1970).
18. L.E. Snyder and D. Buhl, Radio emission from HCN, IAU Circular No. 2251 (1970).
19. L.E. Snyder, D. Buhl, B. Zuckerman and P. Palmer, Microwave detectionof interstellar formaldehyde, *Phys. Rev. Letters* **22**, 679-681 (1969).
20. B.B. Turner, Radio emmission from interstellar cyanoethylene, IAU Circular No. 2268 (1970).

21. David Buhl, Chemical constituents of interstellar cloud, *Nature* **234**, 332-334 (1971).
22. F. Fitch, H.P. Scharcz and E. Anders, "Organized elements" in carbonaceous chondrites, *Nature* **193**, 1123-1125 (1962).
23. Micheal H. Briggs and G. Barrie Kitto, Complex organic micro-structures in the Mokoia meteorite, *Nature* **193**, 1126-1127 (1962).
24. B. Nagy, G. Claus and D. Hennessy, Organic particles embedded in the minerals in the Orgueil and Lvuna carbonaceous chondrites, *Nature* **193**, 1129-1133 (1962).
25. F.W. Fitch and E. Anders, Observations on the nature of the "organized elements" in carbonaceous chondrites, *Ann. N.Y. Acac. Sci.* **108**, 495-513 (1963).
26. E.T. Degens and M. Bajor, Amino acids and sugars in the Bruderheim and Murray meteorite, *Naturwiss.* **49**, 605-606 (1962).
27. I.R. Kaplan, E.T. Degens and J.H. Reuter, Organic compounds in stony meteorites, *Geochim. Cosmoschim. Acta* **27**, 805-834 (1963).
28. Paul B. Hamilton, Amino acids on hands, *Nature* **205**, 284-285 (1965).
29. J. Oro and H.B. Skewes, Free amino acids on human fingers: the question of contamination in microanalysis, *Nature* **207**, 1042-1045 (1965).
30. K. Kvenvolden, J. Lawless, K. Pering, E. Peterson, J. Flores, C. Ponnamperuma. I.R. Kaplan and C. Moore, Evidence for extraterrestrial amino acids and hydrocarbons in the Murchison meteorite, *Nature* **228**, 923-926 (1970).
31. K.A. Kvenvolden, J.G. Lawless and C. Ponnamperuma, Non-protein amino acids in the Murchison meteorite, *Proc. Nat. Acad. Sci.* **68**, 486 (1971).
32. G. Dungworth, Optical configuration and the racemization of amino acids in sediments and fossils, *Chem. Geol.* **17**(2), 135-153 (1976).
33. S.W. Fox and K. Harada, Accumulated analyses of amino acid precursors in returned lunar samples, in **Proceedings of the Fourth Lunar Science Conference,** *Cosmochim. Acta,* vol. 2, suppl. 4, Pergamon Press, New York, 1973, pp. 2241-2248.

21

Nucleosides, Nucleotides and ATP

When Miller reported his electric discharge experiment in 1953, protein chemistry was the main thrust of biochemistry and molecular biology was still a fledgling branch. As a result of this and the relative ease by which minute amounts of amino acids can be measured, the initial emphasis was on amino acids. But proteins are not, nor could they have been, life unto themselves. The nucleotides, the assembly units to build nucleic acids, would also have had to existed prior to the formation of a functional cell.

As pointed out in Chapter 19, HCN was the principal product generated in simulated experiments for a primitive atmosphere derived from volcanic gases. Hydrogen cyanide hydrolyzes to give ammonium hydroxide and formic acid, and additional HCN would lead to ammonium cyanide. If one considers shallow lakes or basins evaporating to or near dryness, large amounts of this chemical could have accumulated and concentrated on primordial earth.

In 1960, Juan Oró[1] of the chemistry department at the University of Houston reported that a concentrated solution of ammonium cyanide heated for one day at 90°C had produced adenine, the principal heterocyclic base in nucleic acids and many important coenzymes. The overall reaction can be depicted as five molecules of HCN in the presence of ammonia giving rise to adenine. In a following article, Oró and Kimball[2] showed that 4-aminoimidazole-5-carboxamide (AICA) and formamidine were the probable intermediates in the reaction to produce purines. Consequently, when they heated a solution of AICA to temperatures between 100 and 140°C, guanine and xanthine were also formed, each in a 1.5 percent yield.

This reaction not only gave an answer to the abiotic origin of the purines, it showed a satisfying unity to the prebiological chemistry. Since Oró and Kamat[3] revealed that HCN in 3 N ammonia at 70°C for 25 days gave glycine, alanine and aspartic acid among the products, HCN derivatives have been demonstrated to be excellent precursors of two of the principal kinds of building blocks. The synthesis of adenine and amino acids from ammonium cyanide was confirmed by C.U. Lowe and others[4] who obtained as many as 75 ninhydrin-positive products from the reaction.

But the purines may have been forming even before evaporation concentrated the ammonium cyanide. Leslie Orgel and his group[5] at the Salk Institute in San Diego have shown that ultraviolet light transforms the HCN to yield adenine, or it can hydrolyze to AICA which can condense with cyanide, formamidine or cyanogen to produce guanine and xanthine.

These experiments demonstrated that purines were as easily synthesized on primordial earth as amino acids. On the other hand, the pyrimidines, cytosine, uracil and thymidine are the other heterocyclic bases of nucleic acids, and simulation experiments to form pyrimidines are not as confirmative as for the purines. Fox and Harada[6] showed uracil could be formed by heating urea and malic acid in polyphosphoric acid, but whether malic acid could have been present on prebiotic earth is doubtful, as is polyphosphoric acid.

The most plausible synthesis of pyrimidines is by the group at the Salk Institute[5,7] using cyanoacetylene, the second most prevalent

CONDENSATION REACTIONS OF HCN IN PREBIOTIC SYNTHESIS

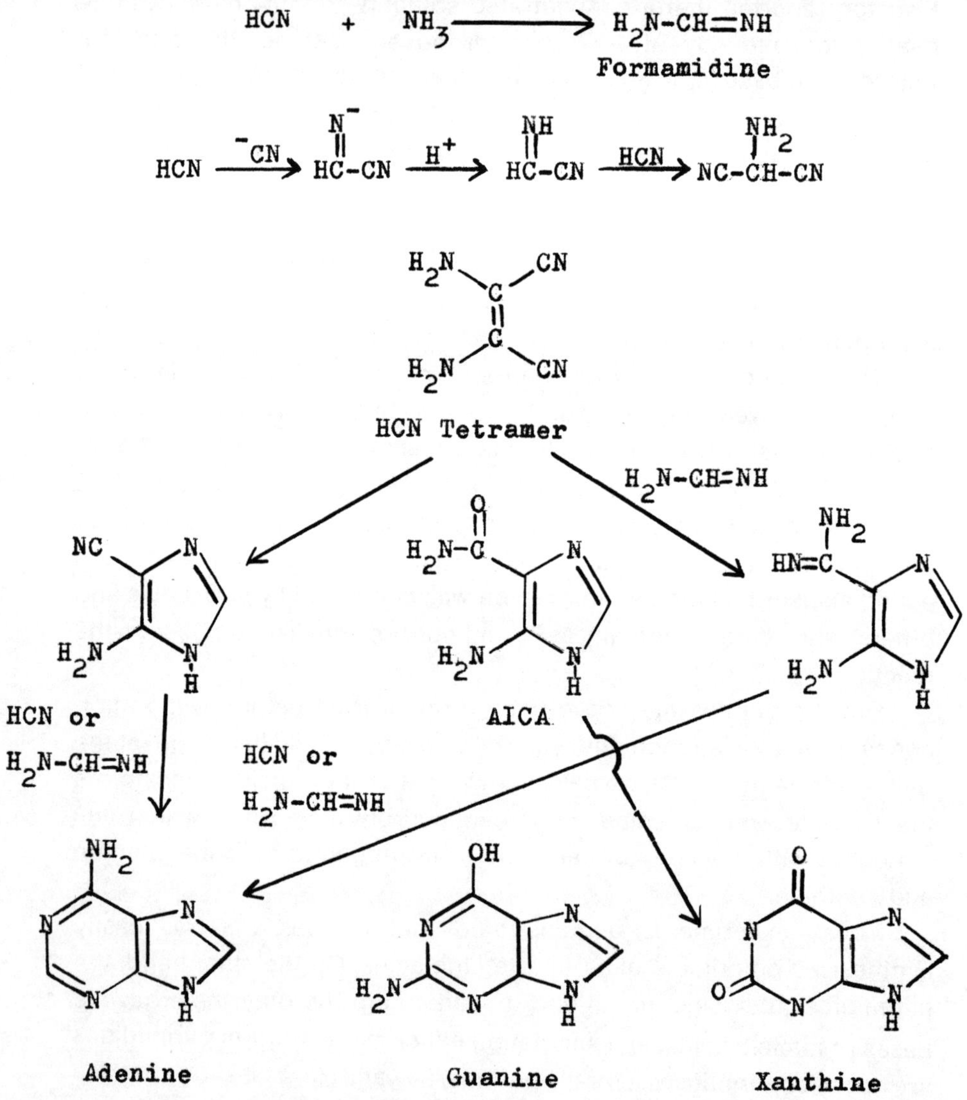

$$HCN + NH_3 \longrightarrow H_2N\text{-}CH{=}NH$$

Formamidine

$$HCN \xrightarrow{^{-}CN} HC(=N^{-})\text{-}CN \xrightarrow{H^{+}} HC(=NH)\text{-}CN \xrightarrow{HCN} NC\text{-}CH(NH_2)\text{-}CN$$

$(H_2N)(NC)C{=}C(CN)(NH_2)$

HCN Tetramer

$H_2N\text{-}CH{=}NH$

AICA

HCN or $H_2N\text{-}CH{=}NH$

HCN or $H_2N\text{-}CH{=}NH$

Adenine

Guanine

Xanthine

intermediate produced by electric discharge experiments. Sanchez and the others reported a 0.1 M concentration of cyanoacetylene in an aqueous solution of 1 M KCN heated at 100°C for one day gave a 5 percent yield of cytosine; the reaction at room temperature for 7 days yielded 1 percent. Once cytosine was formed, uracil followed by an easy hydrolysis.

$$HC \equiv C{-}C \equiv N \xrightarrow{NH_3} NC{-}CH{=}CH{-}NH_2 \xrightarrow{KCN} \text{Cytosine} \xrightarrow{H_2O} \text{Uracil}$$

Cyanoacetylene Monoaminomalonitrile Cytosine Uracil

The formation of hydrogen cyanide and cyanoacetylene from the gases of primitive earth could demonstrably have given the ammonium cyanide, the HCN tetramer and ultimately the amino acids, purines and pyrimidines necessary for the biologically important building blocks to proteins and nucleic acids. The heterocyclic bases, nevertheless, have to be condensed with a sugar moiety and phosphoric acid to make the nucleotides for the polymerization to nucleic acids.

At first glance, the prebiotic synthesis of sugars would appear to be the easiest of all simulation experiments to devise. Formaldehyde is one of the common compounds formed in the prebiotic experiments, and as early as 1861, Buterlow showed that formaldehyde undergoes condensation to form sugars in alkaline solutions. After the formation of glycoaldehyde the synthesis proceeds to the higher sugars, the tetroses, pentoses and hexoses, including ribose and glucose.

As attractive as the condensation of formaldehyde appears for the prebiotic synthesis of sugars, there are serious chemical objections. The reaction occurs only in formaldehyde condensations greater than 0.01 M; and the sugars are unstable in water, especially if the pH is much above 7, decomposing to lactic acid as the major product. Moreover, sugars react with amino acids by the browning (Maillard) reaction to form non-biological products. Since it has to be assumed the simplest arrangement for the origin of life required all the starting components to be formed and present together simultaneously, interactions that would generate inactive products have to be considered.

$$2\ \mathrm{HCHO} \longrightarrow \underset{\mathrm{OH}}{\underset{|}{\mathrm{CH_2}}}\mathrm{-CHO} \xrightarrow{\mathrm{HCHO}} \underset{\mathrm{OH}}{\underset{|}{\mathrm{CH_2}}}\mathrm{-}\underset{\mathrm{OH}}{\underset{|}{\mathrm{CH}}}\mathrm{-CHO} \rightleftharpoons \underset{\mathrm{OH}}{\underset{|}{\mathrm{CH_2}}}\mathrm{-}\overset{\mathrm{O}}{\overset{\|}{\mathrm{C}}}\mathrm{-}\underset{\mathrm{OH}}{\underset{|}{\mathrm{CH_2}}}$$

Formaldehyde Glycoaldehyde

$$\xrightarrow{\mathrm{HCHO}} \underset{\mathrm{OH}}{\underset{|}{\mathrm{CH_2}}}\mathrm{-}\underset{\mathrm{OH}}{\underset{|}{\mathrm{CH}}}\mathrm{-}\overset{\mathrm{O}}{\overset{\|}{\mathrm{C}}}\mathrm{-}\underset{\mathrm{OH}}{\underset{|}{\mathrm{CH_2}}} \rightleftharpoons \underset{\mathrm{OH}}{\underset{|}{\mathrm{CH_2}}}\mathrm{-}\underset{\mathrm{OH}}{\underset{|}{\mathrm{CH}}}\mathrm{-}\underset{\mathrm{OH}}{\underset{|}{\mathrm{CH}}}\mathrm{-CHO}$$

This would appear to be enough to exclude sugars, but actually only two sugars are vital for the initial assembling of a functional cell. They are ribose and deoxyribose, the essential components of the nucleotides. In this capacity, the chemical problems with sugars disappears; ribose combined in the form of nucleotides no longer has the intrinsic instability of sugars. Oro´and Cox[8] investigated relevant conditions under which ribose and deoxyribose could have been formed on primitive earth. They learned that aqueous solutions of acetaldehyde (CH_3CHO) with formaldehyde (HCHO) or with glyceraldehyde (CH_2OH-CHOH-CHO), maintained at 50°C and catalyzed with calcium oxide gave a 3 percent yield of deoxyribose. Moreover, ammonium hydroxide proved to be an even more satisfactory catalyst.

The generation of formaldehyde and acetaldehyde would have required hydrocarbon gases. Since the occurrence of hydrocarbons in some igneous rocks and meteorites suggests a prebiological presence of methane and its homologs, this would have been the source for the precursors to the aldehydes and fatty acids.

The coupling of adenine and deoxyribose to form deoxyadenosine occurs readily. When the two reactants were allowed to stand together at room temperature in the presence of cyanide, a 1 percent yield of deoxyadenosine was formed;[9] with phosphate present the yield increased to 5 percent; when ultraviolet light was used with cyanide, 7 percent was obtained. Unfortunately, the other bases do not produce their nucleotides by this reaction, but these could have formed by other means. A mixture of sea salts, for instance, is an effective catalyst for forming nucleosides when purines are heated with ribose,[10] giving yields in the order of 1.5 to 4.5 percent.

This procedure does not work for pyrimidines. Although pyrimidine nucleosides do not form from direct combination of the base and ribose, they conceivably could have arisen less directly. When ribose-5-phosphate was equilibrated with ammonia to form ribosylamine, which was then treated successively with cyanogen and cyanoethylene, the main product was α -cytidylic acid. The biological form, however, is the β isomer. Sunlight, which has been implicated in most of the

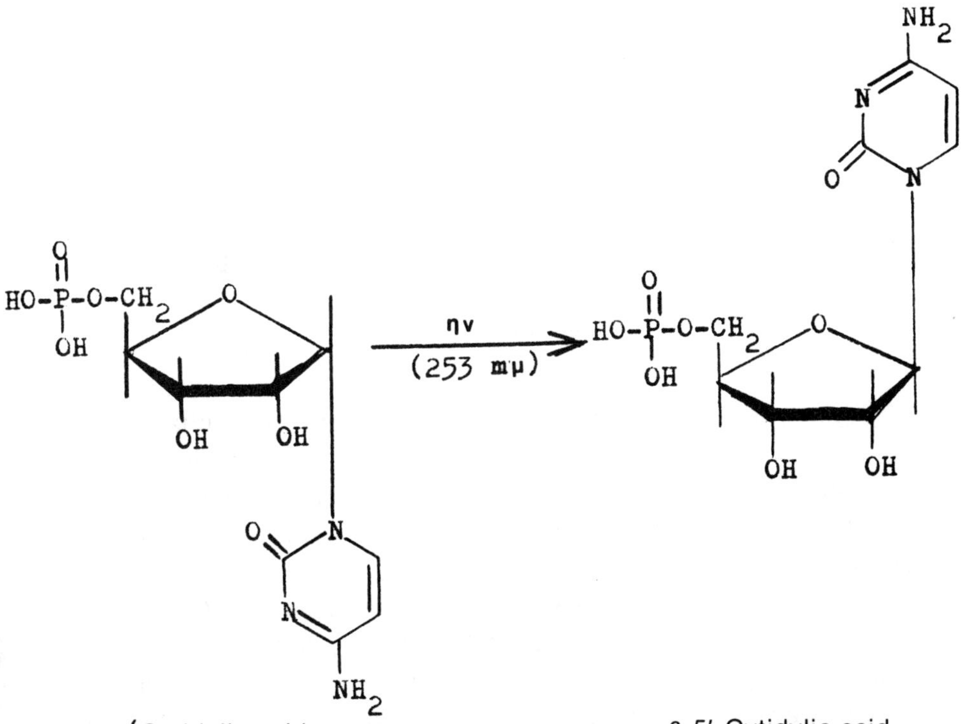

α -5'-Cytidylic acid

β-5'-Cytidylic acid

simulation experiments, plays a decisive role here. When α -cytidylic acid was radiated with ultraviolet light, as much as 10 percent was converted to the β-cytidylic acid, the isomer used by biological systems.[11]

To proceed from nucleoside to nucleotide involves phosphorylation, or attachment of a phosphoric acid group to the sugar moiety. This step is closely connected with the general problem of the prebiological formation of phosphate derivatives. The compound that transfers chemical energy in biological systems is usually ATP.

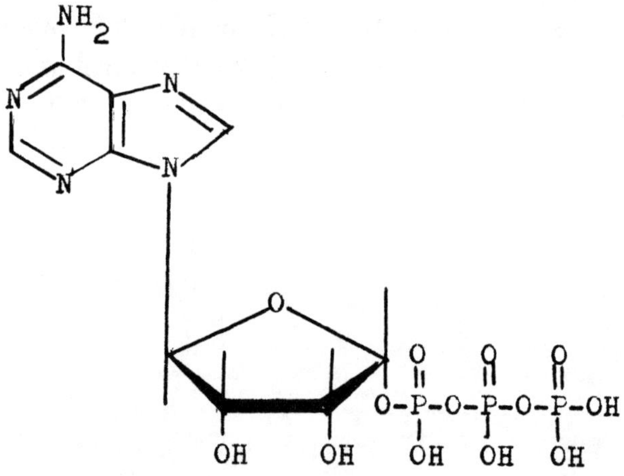

Adenosine triphosphate (ATP)

It is the energy from the hydrolysis of the pyrophosphate bond degrading ATP to ADP that fuels the reaction of most biochemical syntheses. Pyrophosphates were essential from the beginning and ATP has the chemical stability and reactivity to make it most appropriate for the task.

Since nucleic acids are polymers of nucleotides joined through the phosphate group in a 3′-5′-linkage of their sugar groups, a prebiological means of phosphorylating nucleosides must have existed on primordial earth. If one can justify the geologic occurrence of phosphoric acid and its derivatives on primitive earth, the simulation experiment is not difficult. Dissolving nucleosides in polyphosphoric acid at 0-22°C gives 25 to 45 percent yields of the monophosphates.[12] But the possible occurrence of polyphosphoric acid under geologic conditions is too remote to be considered as a plausible procedure.

The difficulty with phosphorus is the extreme insolubility of its calcium salt, apatite. Since calcium exceeds the abundance of phosphorus in basalt by approximately 20-fold (10-fold in granite), phosphorus is effectively removed from seawater by precipitation of the calcium salt. On the other hand, phosphorus makes up to 0.6 percent of the mineral content of igneous rocks.[13] And although hydroxyapatite may form in the precipitation of phosphorus from pure aqueous solutions, in a marine environment phosphorus is deposited as a carbonate fluorapatite. As a result, the concentration of phosphorus in seawater remains extremely low at 2.2 micromolar.

The difficulty then, is to find the circumstances compatible with primitive earth by which phosphorus could have been available to be incorporated into organic compounds; in other words, to demonstrate a chemical form of the element which could have been capable of phosphorylation reactions. Miller and Parris[14] succeeded in producing pyrophosphate on the surface of hydroxyapatite with cyanate salts. Since calcium pyrophosphate is as insoluble as apatite, any synthesis would have had to have been on the crystal surface. This is conceivable, but not really convincing; a more soluble form of phosphate with the emergence of the functioning cell in mind would appear more favorable.

Alan Schwartz[15] of the University of Nijmegen, The Netherlands, proposed a procedure in which the phosphate could have been solubilized and concentrated within a functional level. Oxalic acid is a strong complexing agent for calcium. If oxalic acid, which could have been formed by the decomposition of glycine or formic acid or by the hydrolysis of cyanogen, reaches a concentration of 0.01 M at pH 5 in contact with apatite, then it frees phosphate to the extent of 0.003 M, a relatively large amount of phosphate in solution. Schwartz feels that cyanogen, being a prebiological water-soluble gas, could have provided a constant supply of oxalate at every rock surface exposed to weathering and phosphoric acid derivatives would have been available by this means.

Once the hurdle is overcome to account for the geologic presence of phosphoric acid salts, phosphorylation reactions are known that could have occurred. When a nucleoside is heated from 50° to 160° C with a number of hydrogen phosphate compounds, the mononucleotide results.[16] But a more effective phosphorylation occurs in the presence of urea. Nucleosides heated to 100° C in a dry mixture of urea, sodium hydrogen phosphate, ammonium chloride and ammonium bicarbonate are converted to phosphorylated derivatives in yields in excess of 90 percent.[17]

Urea has been a product of most simulation experiments of prebiotic conditions and must have been common on primitive earth. It would have been present in any exposed solutions of ammonium cyanide since ultra-violet radiation promotes the conversion of ammonium cyanide to urea. And on further studies of urea-catalyzed phosphorylation reaction, Österberg, Orgel and Lohrmann.[18] discovered that when phosphate exceeds nucleosides in the mixture, pyrophosphate bonds are formed. Four days of heating at 100° C gave a 15 percent yield of a thymidine triphosphate.

It appears then that the nucleoside triphosphates arose prebiologically under plausible geologic conditions. The essential requisite was the occurrence of the phosphate as its acid salt. To visualize how this could have come about we need to return to the setting of the earliest micro-organisms on earth.

The Onverwacht Group rocks in which the microfossils occur are cherts that lie on top of extrusive sub-aqueous volcanic rocks. Although the cherts are found in extensions, more often they occur as pockets in the surface of the ancient lava. What occurred then is probably the same as today with many such extrusives. The juvenile water brought to the surface either at the time of eruption or in fumaroles is extremely rich in nutrients — charged with carbon dioxide and the essential minerals of phosphorus, sulfur and nitrogen. Presumably the high temperatures of volcanism liberates the phosphorus from the minerals in the igneous rocks and brings it to the surface as soluble acid salts where it enriches the waters of volcanic lakes.

The same phenomenon is evident today where the microflora of volcanic pools often grow so profusely they form crusts which eventually cover the entire surface of these pools. When the lakes are large like Waimungu in New Zealand, the growth creates crusts at the edges and extends for great distances toward the center of the lake.[19] It is quite possible life began on earth over three and a half billion years ago, not in an ocean with the consistency of a "primordial soup," but in the phosphorus and sulfur-rich volcanic pools that pock-marked the earth's surface during the early Archean Era.

References

1. J. Oró, Synthesis of adenine from ammonium cyanide, *Biochem. Biophys. Res. Comm.* **2**, 407-412 (1960).
2. J. Oró and A.P. Kimball, Synthesis of purines under possible earth conditions I. Adenine from hydrogen cyanide, *Arch. Biochem. Biophys.* **94**, 217-227 (1961).
3. J. Oró and J.S. Kamat, Amino acid synthesis from hydrogen cyanide under possible primitive earth conditions, *Nature* **190**, 442-443 (1961).
4. C.U. Lowe, R.W. Rees and R. Markham, Synthesis of complex organic compounds from simple precursors: formation of amino acids, amino-acid polymers, fatty acids and purines from ammonium cyanide, *Nature* **199**, 219-222 (1963) .
5. R.A. Sanchez, J.P. Ferris and L.E. Orgel, Cyanoacetylene in prebiotic synthesis, Science **154**, 784-785 (1966).
6. S.W. Fox and K. Harada, Synthesis of uracil under conditions of a thermal model of prebiological chemistry, *Science* **133**, 1923-1924 (1961).
7. J.P. Ferris, R.A. Sanchez and L.E. Orgel, Studies in prebiotic synthesis III. Synthesis of pyrimidines from cyanoacetylene and cyanate, *J. Mol. Biol.* **33**, 693-704 (1968).
8. J. Oró and A.C. Cox, Non-enzymic synthesis of 2-deoxyribose, *Fed. Proc.* **21**, 80 1962).
9. C. Ponnamperuma and P. Kirk, Synthesis of deoxyadenosine under simulated primitive earth conditions, *Nature* **203**, 400-401 (1964).
10. S.L. Miller and L.E. Orgel, **The Origins of Life on Earth**, Prentice-Hall, Inc., Englewood Cliffs, N.J., 1974. p. 113.

11. R.A. Sanchez and L.E. Orgel, Studies in prebiotic synthesis V. Synthesis and photoanomerization of pyrimidine nucleoside, *J. Mol. Biol.* **47**, 531-543 (1970).
12. T.V. Waenheldt and S.W. Fox, Phosphorylation of nucleosides with polyphosphoric acid, *Biochim. Biophys. Acta* **134**, 1-8 (1967).
13. B. Mason, **Principles of Geochemistry**, John Wiley, New York, 1966, p. 100.
14. S.L. Miller and M. Parris, Synthesis of pyrophosphates under primitive earth conditions, *Nature* **204**, 1248-1250 (1964).
15. A.W. Schwartz, Phosphate: solubilization and activation on the primitive earth, in Molecular Evolution, Buvet and Ponnamperuma, eds. North-Holland Publ. Co., Amsterdam, 1971, pp. 207-223.
16. C. Ponnamperuma and R. Mack, Nucleotide synthesis under possible primitive earth conditions, *Science* **148**, 1221-1223 (1965).
17. R. Lohrmann and L.E. Orgel, Urea-inorganic phosphate mixtures as prebiotic phosphorylating agents, *Science* **171**, 490-494 (1971).
18. R. Österberg, L.E. Orgel and R. Lohrmann, Further studies of urea-catalyzed phosphorylation reactions, *J. Mol. Evol.* **2**, 231-234 (1973).
19. J. Brooks and G. Shaw, **Origin and Development of Living Systems**, Academic Press, New York, 1973.

22 Polypeptides

The chemistry of biological systems is based on the hierarchical construction of ever more complex arrangements. The first step was the action of intense radiation energy on the gaseous components of the primitive atmosphere to generate the highly reactive chemical radicals and precursors which reacted to give low-energy combinations as amino acids, aldehydes and acids. From then on, condensation reactions enlarged upon the chemical architecture; the heterocyclic bases were condensed from cyanides, ribose from formaldehyde and deoxyribose from triose and acetaldehyde. In turn, nucleotides resulted from the successive condensation of the bases with ribose or deoxyribose, and then phosphoric acid. The amino acids and nucleotides are the building blocks, but the condensation of these units into long linear chains makes the genes and enzymes that are the very essence of life. Only by condensing the monomers into non-repetitive macromolecules is it possible to attain the large variablility necessary for the information storage and enzyme specificities of the functional cell.

Just as the attitude of the 1950's placed emphasis on amino acids as the most significant building blocks, so too, it seems there was an emphasis to find an abiotic origin of proteins, and consequently, enzymes, on the belief that once the enzymes were formed, the synthesis of all the other components was possible. Perhaps it was more conceivable to think of the abiotic appearance of a polypeptide with enzymic properties than to imagine a gene, which can occur in contemporary organisms with a molecular weight in the millions, to have formed outside a biological system. But it seems likely the attention to proteins was because biochemists were more familiar with amino acids and the established history of the chemistry of polymerizing them to polypeptides in the laboratory.

Even before 1902 when Hofmeister[1] and Fischer[2] confirmed that proteins were biopolymers that resulted from the polyamide linkage of amino acids, chemists were attempting to polymerize amino acids by heating them together. In 1897, Hugo Schiff[3] condensed aspartic acid at temperatures of 190-200°C; and three years later, Balbiano and Trasciatti[4] prepared polyglycine by heating the amino acid glycerol. The other neutral amino acids could not be polymerized by this procedure, but the ester of alanine could, albeit very slowly.[5] Heated without a solvent, glycine gave a mixture of peptides and glycine anhydrides.[6] Certainly the most successful application of polymerizing amino acids by heating was by Wallace Carothers.[7] In 1936, while working for the Du Pont Company, Carothers used the omega (Ω) amino acids, where the amino group is on the carbon farthest from the carboxyl end, to prepare polyamide polymers which became known as Nylon.

The polymerization is a dehydration step and the reverse of hydrolysis. That is to say, a molecule of water has to be removed for each peptide linkage formed when condensing the amino acids. So to achieve the polymerization, a logical approach would be to find applicable dehydrating conditions. The image of macromolecules being formed from the condensation of the monomers prebiologically in a primitive ocean as is so often written is thermodynamically untenable: the free energy requirement is too high for the reaction to occur in an aqueous environment by the monomers merely condensing by themselves. The fact that organisms grew and evolved in the oceans does not necessitate the essentials of the first functional cell to be formed there.

One of the earliest attempts to find a prebiological origin of enzymes or enzyme-like amino acid polymers was by Sidney Fox, presently at the University of Miami. In a paper with M. Middlebrook to the American Society of Biological Chemists in 1954,[8] he reported that heating certain amino acids at 200°C for one-half to three hours gave anhydropolymers. Fox compared the results of these condensations to an earlier paper of his describing a selectivity of amino acids to couple with each other in an enzyme-promoted condensation.[9]

Then in 1959, Fox, Harada and Vegotsky[10] reported on the thermal polymerization of amino acids in a paper espousing a theory that the thermal synthesis of biochemicals preceded the origin of life in a prebiological evolution resembling the pathways of biosynthesis. For instance, when malic acid was heated with urea or ammonia, aspartic acid resulted.[11] The aspartic acid could be degraded in turn to α- or β-alanine. Furthermore, aspartic acid reacted with urea in the presence of $Ca(OH)_2$ or $Mg(OH)_2$ to give ureidosuccinic acid, an intermediate in the biosynthesis of pyrimidines. By heating the salt of an acid from the Krebs cycle, they were generating some products that formed biogenetically by a similar pathway. It was an attractive hypothesis, but the correlation applied only to a few simple structures and did not extend farther along biosynthesis pathways.

Biochemists knew that when a mixture of amino acids in the ratios found in proteins was heated, the result was pyrolysis to a dark brown tar with a disagreeable odor. Since aspartic acid polymerizes readily by heating but glutamic acid does only reluctantly, Fox and Harada discovered glutamic acid mixed and heated with aspartic acid, copolymerized with it. Except for glycine, the neutral amino acids do not form homopolymers by heating. By using a mixture that was predominantly aspartic and glutamic acid with an equimolar mixture of the remaining 16 amino acids in a 2:2:1 ratio, Fox and Harada were able to heat an amino acid mixture and obtain a non-dialyzable product that analyzed for all the amino acids to some extent.

The procedure was reported in 1958[12] as the thermal polymerization of amino acids to a product resembling protein. An amino acid mixture containing 80 percent aspartic and glutamic acid heated in an oil bath at 170°C for three hours gave a glass-like product. After this material was dissolved in water, dialyzed and dried by lyophilization, the resulting brown powder showed a mean chain weight (molecular weight) of 4,900, contained 71 percent aspartic acid, 15 percent glutamic acid and 14 percent of all the other amino acids. From the N-terminal amino acid analysis, the conclusion drawn was that there was a non-random arrangement of the monomers in the polymer.

This concept that a polymer resembling protein could be attained by heating a proper proportion of amino acids received considerable attention in the 1960's, and a large number of papers attempting to correlate many of the physical and chemical properties of proteins to these thermal polymers were published.[13] Most of the comparisons were of uncritical properties such as elemental analysis or color tests due to amino acids or short peptide linkages. On the other hand, these thermal polymers failed to elicit any immune response when tested for antigenicity,[14] an extremely sensitive test for protein structure.

Fox coined the name "proteinoid" for these thermal polymers he contended contained all the 18 amino acids found in proteins (glutamine and asparagine are excluded). The types of "proteinoids" was extended to basic ones which were predominantly lysine, an amino acid that can also form a homopolymer. A series of extremely weak catalytic properties were associated with various thermal polymers and were suggested to be "enzyme-like" activities.[15]

Because of their heterogeneity, it was impossible to determine the amino acid arrangement in these thermal polymers by sequencing as performed routinely with natural peptides. As a result, much of Fox's interpretation regarding the structure was directed to show that there was "limited heterogeneity" and non-randomness, the implication being that amino acids heated together condensed with a degree of selectivity to their order to form sequencing resembling that found in proteins.

Unequal proportions of amino acids in a thermal polymer, of course, is no indication whatever of a correlation to the arrangement of amino acid residues in proteins. Except for glycine, only the α -amino acids with an additional acid or base group in the side-chain, making them like Carothers' Ω -amino acids, form thermal polymers. The neutral α-amino acids, excluding glycine, simply cannot form polyamide condensation by heating because of steric interference from the bulky side chains. This, however, does not mean they cannot react on the ends of polymers.

Aspartic acid polymerizes readily upon heating because it can form an anhydride which then reacts with any available amino group. Chemically, aspartic acid is the amino derivative of succinic acid that can condense with itself.[16]

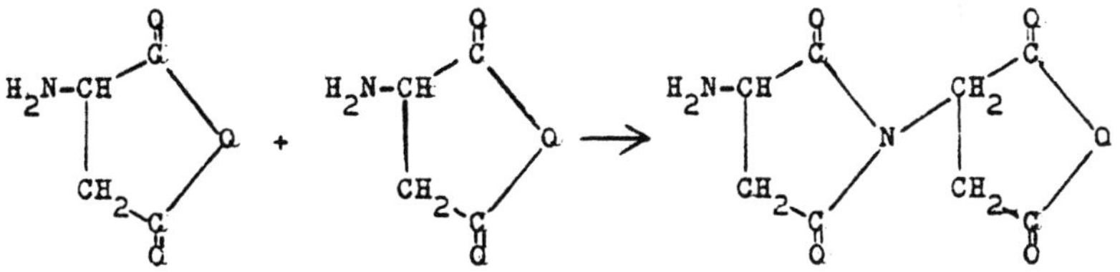

H$_2$N-CH, C=O, O, CH$_2$, C=O + H$_2$N-CH, C=O, O, CH$_2$, C=O → H$_2$N-CH, C=O, N, CH$_2$, C=O, CH$_2$, C=O, O, CH$_2$, C=O

Once the polymerization is initiated, it can proceed until it exhausts the available aspartic acid or is terminated by a neutral amino acid that cannot extend the process.

By using amino acid mixtures consisting of predominantly either aspartic acid or lysine — amino acids that polymerize to large homopolymers easily — Fox obtained polymerization of these amino acids with small amounts of the others incorporated. The high molecular weights reported for "proteinoids" alleged to be analogous to proteins were attainable only if the polymer was essentially polyaspartic acid or polylysine. A feature of the reaction was that the larger the proportion of neutral amino acids, the lower the average molecular weight of the product — an indication these amino acids, unable to continue the polymerization, were terminating it when they reacted.

At first glance the amino acid analysis of these thermal polymers looks like the analysis of a standard protein with the mole-percent for all 18 of the amino acids listed. The fallacy in the interpretation of the analysis was the fact that the molecular weights of these thermal polymers were only 4,000-5,000. With a molecular weight of 4,500, the analysis indicated the polymer contained 22 aspartic acids, 3 glutamic acids and 8 of the others,[14] when the molecular weight was 4,900, the calculated composition was 26 aspartic acids, 8 glutamic acids and 7 others.[7] In other words, despite giving an analysis for all 18 amino acids, neither polymer was large enough to contain more than 7 or 8 of the other 16 amino acids in addition to the aspartic and glutamic acids in one molecule. For many of the amino acids, such as tyrosine or phenylalanine, they analyzed in a percentage so low the molecular weight of the thermal polymer would have had to have been 3 or 4 times larger to contain even one residue. It was clear the results did not indicate copolymerization of 18 amino acids in the same polymer, and by definition the thermal polymers were not even "proteinoids."

It is now recognized the thermal polymerization of amino acids does not result in a copolymerization in sequencing resembling natural proteins. Because of the steric hindrance the amino acids with hydrophobic side chains can react only at terminal positions in the thermal reactions. As a result, the "proteinoids" were in effect mixtures of polyaspartic acid and polylysine molecules interspersed with glutamic acid or glycine and with the neutral amino acids terminal. Since extended heating or higher temperatures increased the number of neutral amino acids incorporated, this was consistent with the imide bond of aspartic acid reacting with the addition of amino acids to its side chain. Afterall, the "copolymerization" of all 18 amino acids was based on the amino acid analysis of the product showing all present to some extent, but when polyaspartic acid is heated with a similar mixture of amino acids, the resulting polymer also gives an analysis for all the amino acids in the same manner as the so-called proteinoids.[17]

There have been several schemes proposed on ways in which polypeptides could have formed prebiologically. One method, based on a reaction first reported by Krewson and Couch[18] in 1943, does not begin with amino acids. In August of 1957, two months before the launch of Sputnik, the First International Symposium on the Origin of

Life was convened at Moscow under the aegis of Oparin and his fellow scientists. At this meeting, Shiro Akabori from the Institute for Protein Research at Osaka University presented a paper on one way in which polypeptides with molecular weights as large as 15,000 could have formed under primordial conditions.[19] He circumvented the free energy dehydration problem by synthesizing polyglycine on clay from formaldehyde, ammonia and hydrogen cynanide through amino acetonitrile as the intermediate.

$$CH_2O + NH_3 + HCN \longrightarrow \underset{\text{Aminoacetonitrile}}{H_2N\text{-}CH_2\text{-}CN}$$

$$H_2N\text{-}CH_2\text{-}CN \rightarrow (\text{-}NH\text{-}CH_2\text{-}\underset{\underset{NH_2}{|}}{C}\text{-})_x \xrightarrow{x\ H_2O} (\text{-}NH\text{-}CH_2\text{-}\overset{\overset{O}{\|}}{C}\text{-})_x + x\ NH_3$$

After polyglycine was formed, side chains could be introduced by reaction with aldehydes or with unsaturated hydrocarbons. In this way, when Akabori treated polyglycine on kaolinite with formaldehyde, he converted 2 to 3 percent of the glycine to serine; acetaldehyde gave 1.5 percent threonyl groups. By this procedure he considered valine, leucine, and isoleucine would be formed from propylene, isobutene and but-2-ene; and reaction with acrylonitrile could lead to glutamine, arginine, and lysine.

$$\begin{matrix} | \\ NH \\ | \\ CH_2 \\ | \\ C{=}O \\ | \end{matrix} \xrightarrow{CH_2O} \begin{matrix} | \\ NH \\ | \\ CH\text{-}CH_2\text{-}OH \\ | \\ C{=}O \\ | \end{matrix} \rightarrow \begin{matrix} | \\ NH \\ | \\ C{=}CH_2 \\ | \\ C{=}O \\ | \end{matrix} \xrightarrow{H_2S} \begin{matrix} | \\ NH \\ | \\ CH\text{-}CH_2\text{-}SH \\ | \\ C{=}O \\ | \end{matrix}$$

It was an ingenious scheme. Whether it is plausible for the prebiotic protein is hard to judge. Bernal[20] in 1951 had suggested life may have originated on the surface of clay which could have accumulated large amounts of organic substances. One difficulty is removing the product from clay after it is adsorbed. Akabori extracted his with dilute sodium hydroxide.

Clay is a common natural substance with structural and catalytic properties that have made it a useful material as a clarifying agent and adsorbent. The weathering of soils and different rock types leads to the formation of clay minerals as small particles that are essentially crystalline hydrous aluminum silicates. The minerals consist of combinations of two basic structural units: one unit is made up of silica tetrahedra with four oxygens or hydroxyls equidistant from a central silicon atom arranged as a repeating hexagonal network to form a sheet; in the other structural unit, two sheets are formed from minerals in which oxygen and hydroxyls are octahedrally coordinated around aluminum, iron or magnesium atoms. Clays are grouped into ilites, chlorites, kaolinites, montmorillonites and others by their amorphous or crystalline features, as well as their swelling attributes. The ability of clay minerals to hold certain cations and anions which are readily exchangeable for other cations and anions is one of their most valued chemical properties.

Since there was ample evidence to indicate amino acids could

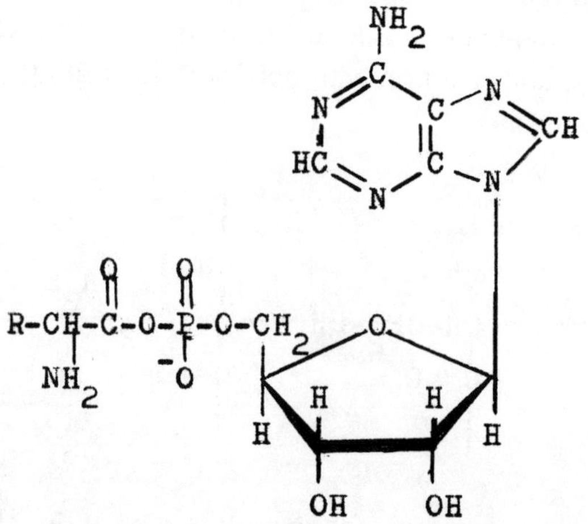

The structure of amino acid adenylates

have been formed readily under prebiological conditions, an abiotic condensation of the amino acids themselves appeared as a more direct means of synthesizing polypeptides. But there remained the high free energy requirement to polymerize the monomers. Amino acids have to be activated to polymerize them under normal circumstances, and in order to do this, the activation is usually achieved by the formation of a mixed anhydride between the amino acid and another acid. In biosynthesis the other acid is the phosphoric acid group of ATP and the resulting anhydride is the amino acid adenylate.

Once the adenylate is formed, the amino acid is elevated to an energy level high enough for the polymerization to occur spontaneously. But for the amino acid adenylate to react with another amino acid, the amino group of that monomer must be without an electrical charge. Amino acids in near neutral solutions exist as zwitterions in which the amino and carboxyl groups are ionized. In order for either group to be reactive it must be without its charge, a condition that exists for the carboxyl below pH 5.4, for the amino group, above about pH 8.

$$\underset{^{+}NH_3}{R\text{-}\overset{|}{C}H}\text{-}C{\begin{matrix}\nearrow O \\ \searrow OH\end{matrix}} \xrightarrow[H^+]{< pH\ 5.4} \underset{^{+}NH_3}{R\text{-}\overset{|}{C}H}\text{-}C{\begin{matrix}\nearrow O \\ \searrow O^-\end{matrix}} \xrightarrow[OH^-]{> pH\ 8} \underset{NH_2}{R\text{-}\overset{|}{C}H}\text{-}C{\begin{matrix}\nearrow O \\ \searrow O^-\end{matrix}}$$

If an amino acid and ATP are allowed to stand together at pH 7, no formation of the adenylate will occur. It will form in an acid solution where the un-ionized carboxyl group exists, but the amino adenylate hydrolyzes quickly at this side of neutrality. And too, the amino group cannot react unless the pH is up around 8. What was needed for polymerization under natural conditions was a situation in which both the carboxyl and amino groups of amino acids would be reactive at the same pH.

This condition was found by Mella Paecht-Horowitz and Aharon Katchalsky[22] at the Weizmann Institute in Israel. They investigated clays, looking for the right silica clay that would have enough groups to combine with the amino acids to give a silicate salt of the amino group and free the carboxyl group from the zwitterion at neutral pH.

Once free, the carboxyl could react with ATP to form the reactive mixed anhydride. They found zeolites performed this function, and when used with a mixture of an amino acid and ATP, the adenylate was generated, but polymerization did not take place. Then recalling earlier success with montmorillonite, they attempted the experiment with this clay and polymerization of the amino acid proceeded.

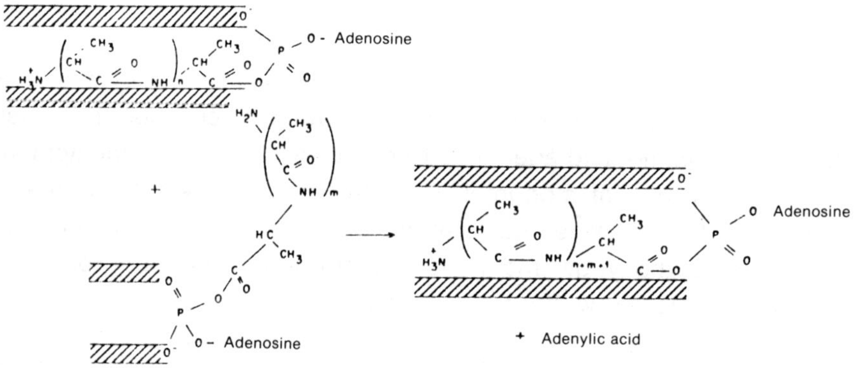

Amino acid adenylate polymerization on montmorillonite. (Paecht-Horowitz, Biosystems **9**, *93 1977)*

Under the experimental conditions, amino acids polymerized by being mixed with ATP and montmorillonite at pH 7.5-8.5. Because adenylic acid was liberated in the reaction, the pH had to be maintained by the continual addition of alkali, otherwise the polymerization would stop as the pH became acidic. The extent of polymerization achievable was impressive. Within a few hours, chains of 50 monomers and larger were attained. But there were drawbacks. Some amino acids like alanine and serine, or alanine and proline copolymerized strongly, but a mixture of alanine and aspartic acid tends to give only homopolymers of each. And too, the basic amino acids do not polymerize because they are too strongly adsorbed to the clay.

An attractive feature of the reaction is that theoretically it could form the polyadenylic acid from the same starting material as a byproduct of the reaction.[23] This has not yet been demonstrated experimentally, but if polyamino acids and polynucleic acids could be formed simultaneously as postulated by Eigen,[24] a principal hurdle in the solution to the origin of life would have been cleared.

In order for amino acids to condense on clay their concentrations have to be above 10^{-3} moles per liter. Most laboratory experiments have been carried out at relatively high concentrations in order to achieve optimal results, but the concentration of amino acids in the oceans may never have been very high. Dose,[25] by taking into account the production and destruction processes, calculated the concentration of amino acids in the primitive ocean to be about 10^{-7}M. And Lahov and Chang[26] found the adsorption of amino acids at pH 8 too weak for these monomers to have accumulated on the surface of clays as suggested by Bernal.[20] For this reason, they feel any reaction on clay would have been preceded by a concentration step, such as evaporation in a lake or lagoon.

It has been reported that clays have been found to be rare in Precambrium sediments.[27] But though they may not have been as abundant as the accumulation from sedimentary rocks, clays nonetheless can result from the transformation of volcanic glass into argillaceous rocks. The hydrothermal action of volcanic fumaroles or weathering on volcanic ash and tuff produces mostly montmorillonite.[28] There would, therefore, probably have been clays present during the Archean Era to promote the polymerization of amino acids as postulated by Paecht-Horowitz and her colleagues.

The clay-catalyzed reaction is with merit and at the same time objectionable for another reason. The greatest feature of the condensation reaction on clay is that it is an interfacial polymerization, a mechanism that is closely analogous to biological systems in which physical structure such as surface-activated reactions between water-lipid interfaces is so important.

The most serious objection to the reaction is not the mechanism, but whether it is applicable. The preceding experiments by Paecht-Horowitz, Akabori and Fox have been efforts to demonstrate geological conditions whereby large polypeptides could have been produced, apparently with the supposition that this could ultimately result in a prebiological synthesis of enzymes or enzyme-like substances. And once polypeptides were present to catalyze the fundamental biochemical reactions, a functional living cell could assemble. But not only is it doubtful whether anything resembling an enzyme could ever result from these reactions, they are dead-end issues. The sequence of any utilizable polypeptide would not be retained to pass on to succeding generations because it would not be from a replicating system.

References

1. F. Hofmeister, Über Bau und Gruppierung der Eiweisskörper, *Ergeb. Physiol.* **1**, 759-802 (1902).
2. E. Fischer, Ueber einige Derivate des Glykocolls, Alanins und Leucins, *Ber.* **35**, 1095-1106 (1902).
3. H. Schiff, Ueber polyaspartsäuren, *Ber.* **30**, 2449-2459 (1897).
4. L. Balbiano, Ueber ein neues Glykocollanhydrid, *Ber.* **34**, 1501-1504 (1901); L. Balbiano and D. Trasciatti, Ueber ein neues Derivat des Glykocolls, *Ber.* **33**, 2323-2326 (1900).
5. M. Frankel and A. Katchalski, Poly-condensation of α-amino acid esters. II. Poly-condensation of alanine ethyl ester, *J. Am. Chem. Soc.* **64**, 2268-2271 (1942).
6. T. Curtius and A. Benrath, Ueber Benzoyl-pentaglycerlamide essigsäure (γ-Säure), *Ber.* **37**, 1279-1310 (1904).
7. W.H. Carothers, Polymers and polyfunctionality, *Trans. Faraday Soc.* **32**, 39-53 (1936).
8. S.W. Fox and M. Middlebrook, Anhydrocopolymerization of amino acids under the influence of hypothetically primitive terrestrial conditions, *Fed. Proc.* **13**, 211 (1954).
9. Sidney W. Fox and Milton Winitz, Enzymic synthesis of peptide bonds. IV. Effects of varitation in substrate structure on relative extents of synthesis of benzoylamine acid anilides as catalyzed by papain and ficin, *Arch. Biochem.* **35**, 419-427 (1952).
10. S.W. Fox, K. Harada and A. Vegotsky, Thermal polymerization of amino acids and a theory of biochemical origins, *Experientia* **15**, 81-84 (1959).
11. S.W. Fox, Evolution of protein molecules and thermal synthesis of biochemical substances, *Am. Scientist* **44**, No. 4, 347-359 (1956).

12. S.W. Fox and K. Harada, Thermal polymerization of amino acids to a product resembling protein, *Science* **128**, 1214 (1958).
13. S.W. Fox and K. Dose, **Molecular Evolution and the Origin of Life**, Freeman and Co., San Francisco, 1972.
14. S.W. Fox and K. Harada, The thermal copolymerization of amino acids common to protein, *J. Am. Chem. Soc.* **82**, 3745-3751 (1960).
15. D.L. Rohlfing and S.W. Fox, Catalytic activities of thermal polyanhydro-α-amino acids, in *Advances in Catalysis* **20**, 373-418 (1969).
16. J. Kovacs, I. Koenyves and A. Pusztai, Darstellung von Polyasparagin-sauren (Polyaspartsäuren aus dem thermischen Autocondensations produkt der Asparaginsaure, *Experientia* **9**, 459-460 (1953).
17. J. Kovacs, in **Polyamino acid, Polypeptides and Proteins,** M. Stahman, ed., University of Wisconsin Press, Madison, 1962, p. 53-54.
18. C. Krewson and J. Couch, The hydrolysis of nicotinonitrile by ammonia, *J. Am. Chem. Soc.* **65**, 2256-2257 (1943).
19. S. Akabori, in **Origin of Life on Earth**, A.I. Oparin, ed., pp. 189-196, Pergamon Press, Oxford, 1959; ———, *Kagaku (Science, in Japan)* **25**, 54 (1955).
20. J.D. Bernal, **The Physical Basis of Life**, Routledge and Kegan Paul, London, 1951.
21. M. Paecht-Horowitz and A. Katchalsky, Polycondensation of amino acid phosphoanhydrides. II. Polymerization of proline adenylate at constant phosphoanhydride concentration, *Biochem. Biophys. Acta* **140**, 14-23 (1967).
22. M. Paecht-Harowitz, J. Berger and A. Katchalsky, Prebiotic synthesis of polypeptides by heterogeneous polycondensation of amino acid adenylates, *Nature* **228**, 636-639 (1970).
23. A. Katchalsky, Prebiotic synthesis of biopolymers on inorganic templates, Naturwiss. **60**, 215-220 (1973).
24. M. Eigen, Self-organization of matter and the evolution of biological macromolecules, *Naturwiss.* **58**, 465-523 (1971).
25. K. Dose, Peptides and amino acids in the primordial hydrosphere, *Biosystems* **6**, 224-228 (1975).
26. N. Lahav and S. Chang, The possible role of solid surface area in condensation reactions during chemical evolution: reevaluation, *J. Mol. Evol.* **8**, 357-380 (1976).
27. H.A. Ireland, in **Silica in Sediments**, H.A. Ireland, ed., Spec. Publs. Soc. Econ. Paleont. Miner., No. 7, Tulsa, 1959.
28. G. Millot, **Géologie des Argiles altérations, sédimentologie géochemie**, Masson et Cie, Paris, 1970; (trans. W.R. Parrand and Hélène Paquet), **Geology of Clays**, Chapman and Hall, London, 1970; pp. 45-48.

23
Biochemical Syntax

The attempts of some investigators to polymerize amino acids into enzymes or enzyme-like substances have been in response to a perplexing problem. A living cell consists, not of the building blocks, but of the assembly of biopolymers condensed from them; and it is the relationship between nucleic acids and enzymes that constitutes the foundation of a biological system.

Therein lies the problem. In organisms as we know them, all biochemical reactions are catalyzed by enzymes, including those reactions that lead to the synthesis of the nucleic acids and enzymes themselves. If then, enzymes are needed to create the nucleic acids and enzymes, both of which are needed to make enzymes, where did the initial enzymes come from? The work of Fox, Akabori and Paecht-Horowitz discussed in the previous chapter is directed to solve this riddle by attempting to show how prebiological counterparts of biotic enzymes would have existed prior to life's origin.

Because these prebiotic substances would not have been genetically programmed, however, their involvement is not consistent with the principle upon which life is founded. A biological system is based on two key features: it conserves its construction, thus protecting its survival, while it explores modifications for improving its efficiency and chances of survival. Nothing is discarded. It is tantamount to living in a house while adding to it, continually making improvements — improvements that are used to construct the additions. By reproducing the whole organism each generation and testing the modifications for survival value, improvements are introduced into the evolutionary chain.

A cell can conserve its composition only by having its information retained; and it improves its efficiency by enhancing the catalysis of its chemical reactions. DNA's own reproduction is intrinsic in the chemical structure of the molecule; but for the entire cell, reproduction of its components has to be tied to the structure of the DNA. When, therefore, DNA is altered, the change is reflected as a modification in the cellular components. By having catalysts genetically programmed, it was possible for the information to reconstruct all efficient enzymes to be retained in a gene and repeated each generation, yielding only to modifications that proved to be superior.

We observe contemporary organisms and are astounded by the complexity and the highly specific nature of enzymes. It creates the impression that these proteins were essential for the existence of any primeval biological system. Enzymes, however, are the product of nearly 4 billion years of refinement. Life did not begin with enzymes, but grew into them through selective advantages they offered at each stage of their development.

The question of origin then centers on how a biological system began in the absence of enzymes and how enzymes entered the scheme of things. There are many substances — various multivalent metal ions, imidazole derivatives, certain heterocyclic compounds — that catalyze chemical reactions. Large groups of enzymes contain these auxillary components as essential for enzymatic activity. The catalysts themselves, however, lack the narrow specificity of enzymes, and the wedding together their catalytic function with a protein must have introduced this and other properties the catalysts alone were lacking.

We find that proteins, once they became a part of the biological system, added a variability that permitted them to create the individual character of each living thing. There are tens of thousands, perhaps as many as 100,000, different kinds of proteins in every human body, representing more than half of the body's dry weight. They range in molecular size from 6,000 to as large as 10 million. Most, however, are in the range between 12,000 and 36,000 (100 to 300 amino acids), the size of polypeptide chains usually synthesized by the ribosomes.

Proteins serve in many capacities. As myosin and collagen, they are the structural component of muscle and connective tissue; hair and nails are keratin; as enzymes, they control essentially every biochemical reaction; as some hormones, they are regulatory agents of cellular processes. They are antibodies that act in the immune response against alien proteins; and as histones and protamines, they suppress the expression of unneeded genes. Why is it the proteins have been given such a wide range of chores in the cell's operation? The answer is because proteins can do what few other substances are capable of doing. They are endowed with the ability to recognize and distinguish between different molecules.

The ability of proteins to recognize other molecules gives enzymes their highly precise specificity. As life evolved in complexity, the number of biochemical reactions increased immensely. This evolution depended upon the cell's ability to coordinate and exercise control over many processes. It was achievable by evolving a particular enzyme to monitor each reaction. For this reason, not only are enzymes amazingly specific catalysts, but their number is extremely large.

This then, appears to be the manner in which enzymes arose — peptides synthesized by primitive cells became attached to catalysts and improved their effectiveness through enhanced specificity and other properties. The experiments by Paecht-Horowitz demonstrate the relative ease in which amino acid adenylates can form and polymerize without the assistance of enzymes. But to form the adenylates, the early cells would have needed to generate ATP; and for this a rudimentary photosynthesis probably occurred as one of the earliest biochemical processes.

This returns us to ferredoxin, the iron-containing protein that is essential for the retention of energy trapped from sunlight and electron transfer. According to Dayhoff, the ancestral ferredoxin may have been a complex of ferrous sulfide with a peptide of four amino acids consisting of alanine, glycine, aspartic acid and serine. These are four of the most common amino acids formed in simulation experiments and are produced readily by heating ammonium cyanide.

Ferredoxin, like the other primal enzymes, began as a catalyst attached to a peptide. The path toward the evolved protein would have begun when the primitive cell synthesized its own peptide for ferredoxin. The initial ferredoxin, however, could have contained peptides found in the environment, because the condensation reactions of HCN and its ammonium salt produce not only amino acids and purines, but also peptides.[1–3] Once the synthesis of peptides was genetically derived, the elementary enzymes grew in size and number until they evolved into elaborate protein structures of today's organisms. They are the most complex biological compounds known.

But how complicated is the chemical structure of an enzyme, and how could so many complex molecules of such precision have developed within the time of life on earth? We know that all proteins, heated in 6 N hydrochloric acid at 115°C for several hours, are hydrolyzed to their subunits, the amino acids. These form the alphabet of protein structure. It is the linking together of amino acids in long chain-like molecules that make the proteins. There are twenty amino acids commonly found in proteins, and it is the order of arrangement of these various amino acids that gives proteins individuality. Protein structure is like a written language: the amino acids are the letters that form words; the words are arranged in sentences which in turn become a fully expressed message. The message — the biological role of the protein — is spelled out in the total structure of the molecule.

The amino acids make up a series of biochemical compounds with fundamentally the same structure, but each is distinguished by its side-chain group. All amino acids contain both an acidic carboxyl group and a basic amino group in the same molecule. In the case of amino acids found in proteins, the carboxyl and amino groups are attached to the same carbon atom. Since this carbon is designated alpha to the carboxyl group in chemical nomenclature, the compounds are referred to as α-amino acids.

Amino acids contain two different mutually reactive chemical functions on the same molecule that allows them to react with each

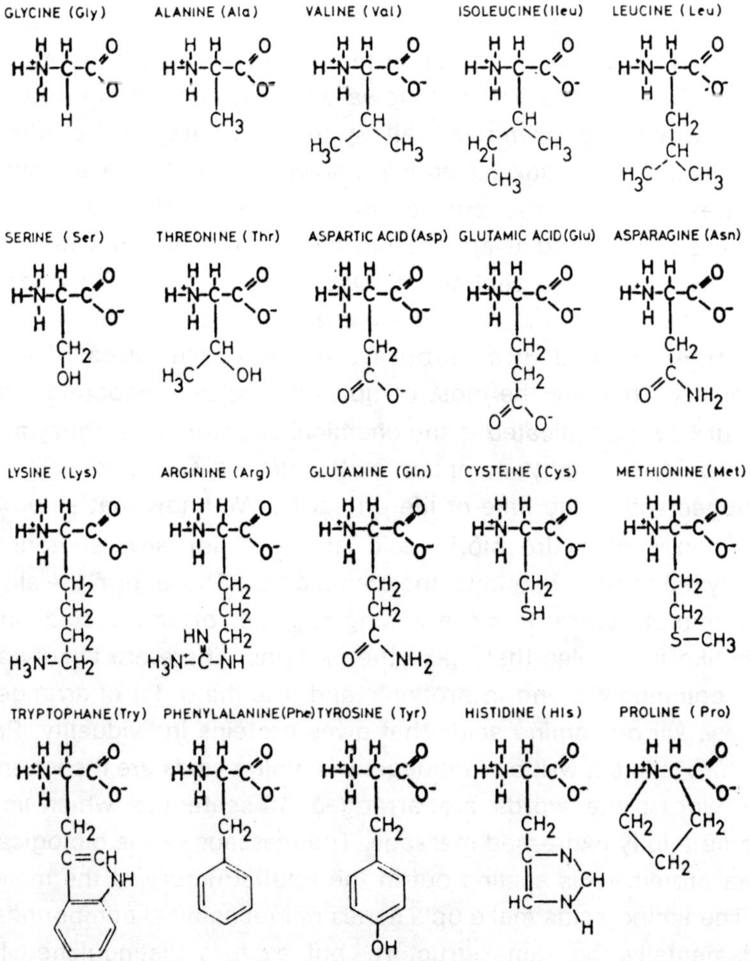

GLYCINE (Gly) ALANINE (Ala) VALINE (Val) ISOLEUCINE (Ileu) LEUCINE (Leu)

SERINE (Ser) THREONINE (Thr) ASPARTIC ACID (Asp) GLUTAMIC ACID (Glu) ASPARAGINE (Asn)

LYSINE (Lys) ARGININE (Arg) GLUTAMINE (Gln) CYSTEINE (Cys) METHIONINE (Met)

TRYPTOPHANE (Try) PHENYLALANINE (Phe) TYROSINE (Tyr) HISTIDINE (His) PROLINE (Pro)

The twenty common amino acids found in protein.

other under the proper conditions. They polymerize to large combinations by linking together, the polymerization being a condensation reaction common to the formation of all biological polymers in which water is removed from between two reactants, joining them through a covalent bond.

$$H_2N-\underset{\displaystyle R}{\underset{|}{CH}}-\overset{\displaystyle O}{\overset{\|}{C}}-OH \quad + \quad H-\overset{\displaystyle H}{\overset{|}{N}}-\underset{\displaystyle R'}{\underset{|}{CH}}-\overset{\displaystyle O}{\overset{\|}{C}}-OH \xrightarrow{-H_2O}$$

$$H_2N-\underset{\displaystyle R}{\underset{|}{CH}}-\overset{\displaystyle O}{\overset{\|}{C}}-NH-\underset{\displaystyle R'}{\underset{|}{CH}}-\overset{\displaystyle O}{\overset{\|}{C}}-OH$$

A dipeptide

R, R' = Side-chain groups

Two amino acids connected by the carboxyl function of one to the amino group of the other form a dipeptide. Longer peptides are given names specifying the number of amino acids they contain until the number becomes too large to be convenient. They are then called polypeptides. Proteins are naturally occurring polypeptides of high molecular weights.

The ability of proteins to distinguish between different molecules depends upon their three-dimensional shape. As life evolved and became more complex, so too did the complexity of its proteins increase. If biochemists were ever to understand how proteins function in a cell, they realized they needed to learn the precise spatial conformation of the molecules. This became one of the most formidable tasks encountered in unraveling the chemistry of life.

A polypeptide is a string of amino acids connected in sequence; nevertheless, the molecule is not linear, but is contorted by a number of factors into a spatial configuration. The variety of functional groups on the side-chains of the amino acids allows for interactions that stabilize some conformations and destabilize others. The sulfhydryl groups of two cystines can oxidize to form the strong disulfide bond; and the hydrogen donor groups such as >NH can form hydrogen bonds with the carbonyl carbons (− C=O); the steric repulsion of bulky side-chains can prevent certain conformations; and water as a solvating structure around charged and polar groups exerts a strong influence.

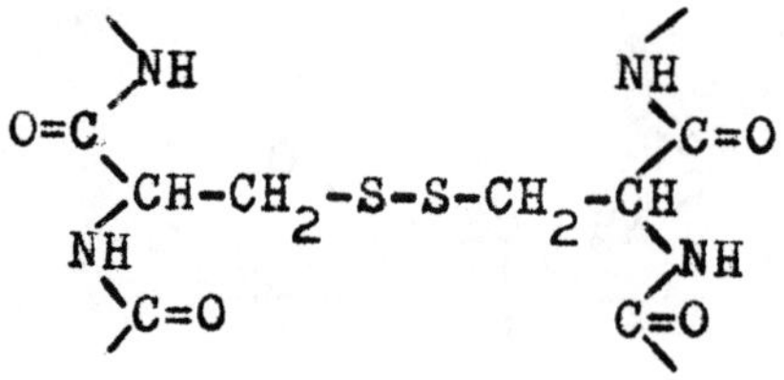

```
      \NH               NH
 O=C/                     \C=O
     \CH-CH2-S-S-CH2-CH/
     /NH                  \NH
     \C=O                 C=O
```

Peptides united by
a disulfide bond

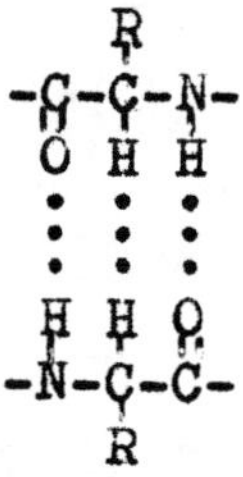

```
      R
 -C-C-N-
  O H H
  : : :
  : : :
  H H O
 -N-C-C-
    R
```

Hydrogen bonds

In order to define the full three-dimensional shape and size of proteins, their structures are classed in four stages. The primary structure of proteins is the amino acid sequence in the polypeptide chain. The other three stages are different spatial arrangements the polypeptide chain assumes either alone or with other polypeptides.

It was Linus Pauling, Robert Corey and their associates[4] at the California Institute of Technology who established that the only way to mesh together asymmetrical building blocks of a polymer so each has the same relation to its neighbor is for them to form a helix, like a spiral staircase. It is then the spiraling of the amino acid chain that becomes the secondary structure of protein conformation.

The third stage of the three-dimensional arrangement is the manner in which the polypeptide chain turns, coils and wraps around to make a definite shape to bring the side-chain groups of particular amino acid residues into precise orientation. When the polypeptide chain is folded, it tends to bring the polar groups to the outside where they associate with water molecules, and the non-polar groups to the inside to form hydrophobic interactions. This leads to a spherical shape with a polar and charged surface and a lipid-like interior.

There is a fourth level of organization to protein structure: the quaterary. Instead of a single polypeptide chain, several polypeptides, either similar or dissimilar, each with its own primary, secondary and tertiary structures, can associate into an organized structure that has properties and specifications not exhibited by any of the monomeric units.

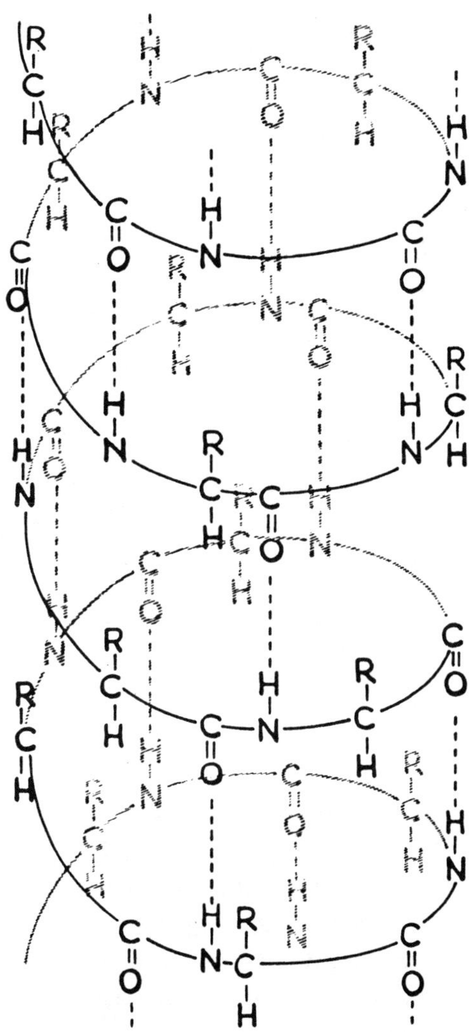

Alpha helix structure of a protein.

The awe-inspiring feature of enzymes that had been difficult to understand is how they can promote reactions so rapidly and for only one specific reaction. Emil Fischer, the German chemist who elucidated the nature of the peptide bond, pondered the question. When, in 1890, he discovered yeast would grow on the D-isomer of sugar but not on the L-isomer, Fischer reasoned that there must be some way in which only one isomer of the sugar molecule is able to fit into the enzyme, much like the way a key fits a lock. This became the lock-and-key hypothesis to explain the specific interaction between an enzyme and its substrate (molecules acted upon by enzymes).

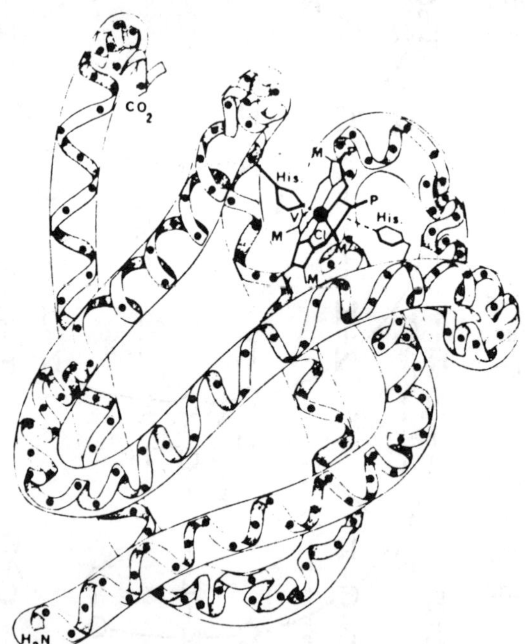

Representation of primary, secondary and tertiary structure of a protein (myoglobin)[5]. Dots represent the α-carbon of amino acids.

Fischer's lock-and-key concept was elaborated upon by Leonor Michaelis and Maude Menton in 1913 when they hypothesized that the high specificity of enzymes results from the enzyme providing a site in its surface which a substrate molecule can bind to in a precise manner, forming an intermediary enzyme-substrate complex. Once the complex is formed, reactive groups in the enzyme promote the required chemical reaction on the substrate.

When protein chemistry advanced to the point that the amino acids in the active site could be identified in the primary sequence, it was discovered the participating amino acids were generally quite distant from each other in position in the long polypeptide chain. It became apparent why enzymes had evolved to large sizes. It was out of necessity. Polypeptide chains are synthesized as a linear sequence of amino acid residues, but since the function of enzymes depends upon its three-dimensional shape to recognize a substrate and to have groups oriented precisely for an active site, the chain of amino acids can accomplish these only by having a polymer long enough to be contorted into a globular shape.

Not until 1966 was the full three-dimensional structure of any enzyme determined. It was an enzyme first observed in 1922 by Alexander Fleming, the discoverer of penicillin. While working in London, Fleming came down with a cold. In his inquisitive manner, he used the occasion to add a drop of his nasal mucus to a culture of bacteria. To his astonishment, a few days later the bacteria nearest the drop of mucus were eaten away. Fleming recognized that the bacterial consumption was due to an enzyme, and since it could lyse, or dissolve, the bacterial cells, he named it lysozyme.

Lysozymes are widespread and have been found in several organs, in blood cells and plasma, in saliva, milk, tears and egg white. The egg white lysozyme, whose primary structure was determined independently by Pierre Jollès and his colleagues[6] at the University of Paris and Robert S. Canfield[7] of Columbia University College of Physicians and Surgeons, is a single polypeptide of 129 amino acid subunits. Since the lysozyme molecule may be readily unfolded and refolded, not only its catalysis and specificity, but also its three-dimensional structure, are determined solely by these residues.

The function of lysozyme is to split a particular bond on a mucopolysaccharide, a long-chain complex sugar that is a component of bacterial cells walls. The cleavage is brought about by catalyzing the hydrolysis of a C-O bond. How lysozyme is able to achieve this cleavage of that specific bond became the research goal of an investigation by David Phillips and others[7] at the Royal Institution of London in 1960. The objective was to work out the three-dimensional structure of lysozyme in atomic detail using the X-ray crystallography method.

In science's pursuit of methods to bring within visual observation ever smaller objects, it has succeeding in exposing the atoms themselves. The electron microscope with magnetic lenses was invented to see cellular detail and molecules too small to be resolved by the optical microscope. To obtain images of atomic dimensions, the shorter wavelengths of X-rays have to be employed, and the procedure is different from that of a conventional microscope. When light or

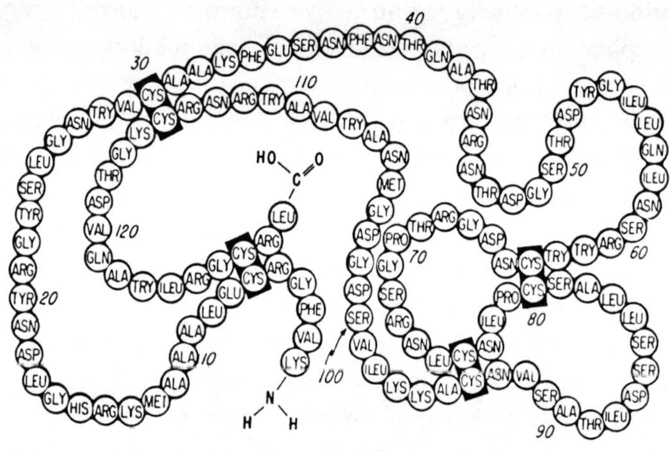

Amino acid sequence of egg white lysozyme. (Canfield and Liu, J. Biol. Chem. **240**, *1997-2002, 1965)*

other radiation strikes an object, the rays are scattered in all directions forming a diffraction pattern. With microscopes, lenses collect the diffracted rays and reassemble them into an image. But unlike light waves and the electron beam, no means of focusing X-rays into an image has ever been devised. Consequently, the X-ray diffraction pattern has to be recorded and the image obtained from it by calculation.

The lysozyme molecule contains some 1,950 atoms. The task to determine the three-dimensional structure of the enzyme demanded that all or nearly all of the positions of these atoms be established. In 1962, Phillips obtained a low-resolution image of the structure from 400 diffraction maxima and saw the general shape of the molecule. He had realized his goal was not to be an easy one, but the arrangement of the polypeptide chain was even more complex than Phillips had anticipated.

Three years later, after development of more efficient methods of measuring and calculating the data and the use of nearly 10,000 diffraction patterns, an image was obtained. This time the resolution was high enough for many of the groups of atoms to be clearly recognizable. Phillips and his colleagues found the giant molecule consisted of three sections of α-helix, two lengths of polypeptide chain running parallel to each other in the opposite direction, a hairpin bend in the chain, and other folding too irregular to describe briefly. The result of this coiling and turning of the polypeptide chain was the structure shown, forming two wings lying at an angle to each other.

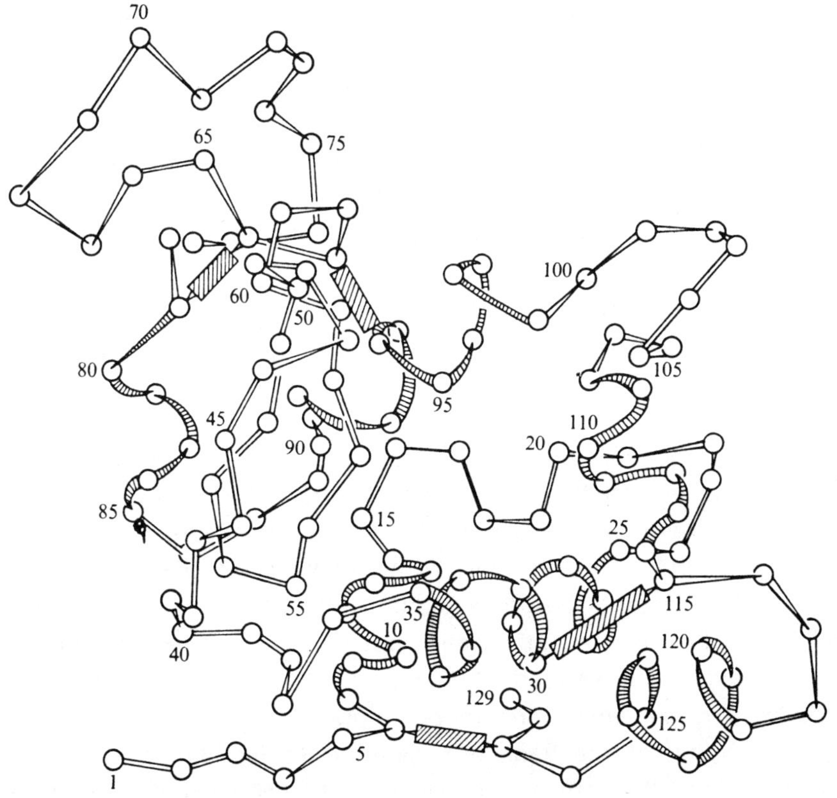

The lysozyme molecule. Disulfide bridges linking parts of the polypeptide chain are shown by diagonally hashed bars. The other hashed sections indicate the alpha helix. (Sketched by Sir Lawence Bragg)

The gap between the wings transformed into a deep cleft running up one side of the molecule. It was this cleft that formed the active site of the enzyme that the substrate fitted into.

The lysozyme molecule attaches to a bacterial cell wall so the substrate fits closely into the irregular cleft in the surface of the enzyme. By studying the interaction between lysozyme and eight different amino sugars, Phillips was able to show the active site was bound by hydrogen bonding to six exposed amino sugar residues on the substrate. The many amino acids lining the cleft that are responsible for the bonding of the substrate and the enzyme are widely scattered along the chain. The most favored arrangement in which a model of the enzyme's substrate can be fitted into the cleft places the bond that is hydrolyzed directly between the carbonyl group of the aspartic acid in position 52 and the carboxyl group of the glutamic acid in position 35. Structural observations indicate these two amino acids are the participants in the mechanism of action of lysozyme.

Lysozyme illustrates how a single polypeptide chain, by being long enough and with a variety of amino acids, can create a three-dimensional shape with a surface and orientation of amino acids to be a catalyst of extreme specificity. The ancestral genes that translated to peptides in the development of enzymes, mutated by doubling and substitution repeatedly, thus improving the old enzymes, but also introducing potentially new ones. Each type of enzyme of the 100,000 or so found in the human body did not develop independently, but all are evolved from the few primeval genes that assisted in the formation of life. In this way the information for evolving entire sequences of amino acids was retained and used for making new enzymes as proteins became larger and more complex.

The mutation mechanism expanded the number and roles of enzymes, as well as other proteins throughout the evolution of life. As the detailed chemistry of more proteins is determined by modern techniques, the process of evolution becomes more apparent. It has been discovered that the amino acid sequence of lysozyme and lactalbumin, one of the principal proteins of milk, are similar, but the functions are not. While lysozyme cleaves a β-1,4-glycosidic bond between amino sugars in bacterial cell walls, α -lactalbumin facilitates the synthesis of a β -1,4-glycosidic bond between glucose and galactose to form lactose, commonly called milk sugar. Lactalbumin has the general shape of the molecule with the active site groove conserved, but at the position of the catalytically active glutamic acid in lysozyme, lactalbumin has threonine. Apparently, the genes for lysozyme and lactalbumin resulted from gene duplication around 350 million years ago at the time of divergence of the amphibian line from that leading to the reptiles, birds and mammals. The ancestral protein probably functioned like lysozyme today, but lactalbumin became more specialized and is found only in lactating mammary tissue.[8]

References

1. C Ponnamperuma and N.W. Gabel, Current status of chemical studies on the origin of life, *Space Life Sciences* **1**, 64-96 (1968).
2. C.N. Mattews and R.E. Moser, Peptide synthesis from hydrogen cyanide and water, *Nature* **215**, 1230-1234 (1967).
3. C.U. Lowe, R.W. Rees and R. Markham, Synthesis of complex organic compounds from simple precursors: formation of amino acids, amino acid polymers, fatty acids and purines from ammonium cyanide, *Nature* **199**, 219-222 (1963).
4. L. Pauling, R.B. Corey and H.R. Branson, The structure of proteins: two hydrogen-bonded helical configurations of the polypeptide chain, *Proc. Nat. Acad. Sci.* **37**, 205-211 (1951).
5. R.E. Dickerson, X-ray analysis and protein structure, in **The Proteins**, H. Neurath, ed., 2nd edn., vol. II, Academic Press, New York, 1964, p. 634.
6. J. Jollès, J. Jauregui-Adell, I. Bernier and P. Jollès, La structure chemique du lysozyme de blanc d'oeuf de poule: Étude detaillee, *Biochim. Biophys. Acta* **78**, 668-689 (1963).
7. D.C. Phillips, The hen egg-white lysozyme molecule, *Proc. Nat. Acad. Sci.* **57**, 484-495 (1967).
8. **Atlas of Protein Sequence and Structure,** M.O. Dayhoff, ed., vol. 5, National Biomedical Research Foundation, Silver Spring, Md., 1972, pp. D-133, D-134.

24

To Splint A Gene

A prebiological presence of large polypeptides may not have been necessary for the origin of a living cell, but the polynucleotides were definitely essential. A basic feature of biological systems that makes life possible is the replication of the nucleic acids and the translation of their structures to proteins. All attempts to devise reproductive systems not based on nucleic acids that could have preceded the biological systems remain unconvincing. It appears that only when we have a matter demonstrating how the polymerization of nucleotides could have taken place under prebiological conditions on primordial earth has the riddle to life's beginning been solved.

There are four major nucleotide types: adenylic (AMP), guanylic (GMP), cytidylic (CMP) and uridylic (UMP) acids. Each nucleotide is a unit constructed of a purine or pyrimidine base, a 5-carbon sugar and phosphoric acid. Without the phosphate group the nucleotide is called a nucleoside. In describing nucleotides, the hydroxyl groups of ribose are numbered to designate the position of attachment of the phosphate. In nucleic acids, the nucleotides are linked together in chain-like polymeric molecules by a phosphate bridge between the 3′ position of the sugar of one nucleotide and the 5′ position of the adjacent monomer. The nucleotides that form DNA differ from those that make up RNA by the absence of the hydroxyl in the 2′ position of ribose, hence the sugar moiety is called 2-deoxy-ribose. Deoxyadenylic acid (d-AMP) and the other DNA nucleotides are designated with the prefix d.

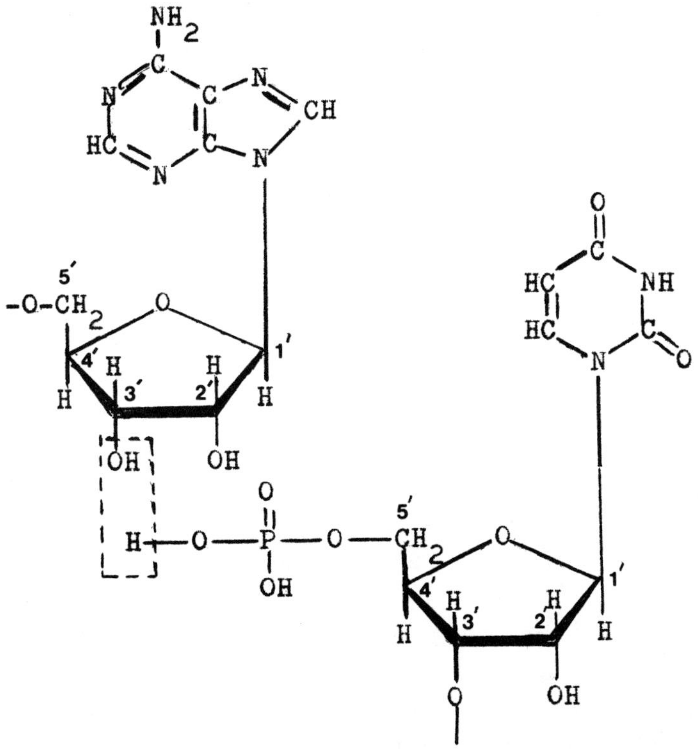

The task for researchers in the origin of life studies has been to find some natural geologic condition in which the nucleotides could joined end-to-end, creating prebiological nucleic acids. Leslie Orgel of the Salk Institute at La Jolla, California, and Juan Oró's group at the University of Houston are among those who have been attempting to find an abiotic synthesis of polynucleotides under conditions simulating those of primordial earth.

As with amino acids, the polymerization of nucleotides is a dehydration reaction in which a molecule of water must be removed from each bond formed between two monomers. Unfortunately, the problem is rendered difficult by the relatively unreactivity of the phosphoric acid to form the ester bond with the sugar hydroxyl. One cannot condense nucleotides merely by heating; pyrolytic destruction occurs before ester formation. Some nucleotides have been condensed using laboratory reagents,[1,2] but the problem remained to discover the natural circumstances on primordial earth under which abiotic polynucleotides could have formed. The solution to the riddle called for unraveling how the nucleotides could have become linked together to form genes of the first cells.

Nucleotides are not just ordinary chemicals. Formed by the joining of a purine or pyrimidine to a ribose and phosphoric acid group, these chemical units have singular properties that give them specific chemical behavior the living cell has been built upon. One such property is that the mononucleotides can be activated to polyphosphate derivatives by further phosphorylation, in this way creating the high-energy phosphate carriers of chemical energy. But the uniqueness of nucleotides is that hydrogen bonding between complementary base pairs offers a built-in orientation mechanism for aligning nucleotides that has been the basis of their ability to replicate and to translate their structure through the genetic code.

It is this interaction of purines with pyrimidines through hydrogen bonding that is the molecular basis for much of the biological activity of nucleic acids. The hydrogen bond is of low energy — about one-fifth the energy of ordinary chemical bonds — but with chains of polynucleotides coupled in double strands the binding force can be large just from the accumulated bonding. And too, the base pairing is highly specific — guanine combines with cytosine and adenine with uracil. It is an intrinsic self-ordering associated with the chemical nature of the molecules.

The orienting of nucleotides in position before being condensed is an important step in biological and non-biological polymerization alike. When Kornberg and others[3] demonstrated nucleic acids could be synthesized outside the living cell by using the enzyme polymerase and magnesium ions acting on the nucleoside triphosphates, they reported the polymerization was very slow unless a primer nucleic acid was added to act as a template.

It was this self-aligning of nucleotides that Leslie Orgel and his group[4] at the Salk Institute tried to use to assist them to polymerize nucleotides in aqueous solutions in their search for the prebiological formation of polynucleotides. For nucleotides, they chose the monophosphates since they are more stable than the di- and triphosphates and would have been more prevalent on prebiological earth. To condense AMP, they added polyuridylic acid (poly U) to act as a template for the AMP to orient on. But since the phosphate group is not very reactive toward the sugar hydroxyl to form the diester linkage, they tried to handle this problem by using a water-soluble carbodiimide as a condensing agent.

Carbodiimides (described below) are laboratory reagents that complex with anionic groups (e.g., $-COO^-$, $-O-PO_3H^-$) form activated derivatives which react readily with hydroxyls or amines to give the respective esters and amines.

The results of the experiment with AMP on poly U with the carbodiimide indicated coupling of AMP molecules occurred and was template directed, but the reaction was extremely inefficient. Furthermore, the dimers that formed were not of the 3′, 5′-linkage found in nucleic acids, but a mixture of 2′,5′- and 5′,5′-bonded dinucleotides.

Orgel and his group tried another approach. Instead of using the relatively unreactive monophosphates, they decided to use activated derivatives of the nucleotides as the starting material. After all, when biological systems make nucleic acids, they use the triphosphate derivatives as the reactants. But organisms have an enzyme to promote the polymerization reaction. When ATP was mixed with the template in water containing magnesium ions, the ATP formed a stable helical complex with poly U, but then hydrolyzed to ADP and AMP before any appreciable amounts of oligonucleotides (up to seven units) were formed. The nucleoside polyphosphates seemed too unstable in water to have been the answer, so the researchers began to look for some other type of activated nucleotide that could have existed on prebiotic earth that was more stable under the conditions than the triphosphates.

In examining the behavior of amines, including amino acids, when warmed with ATP and Mg^{++}, both in solution and in the dry state, one of the group, R. Lohrmann, discovered a novel series of reactions. Amino acids react with ATP when sufficient Mg^{++} is present to form phosphoramidates.

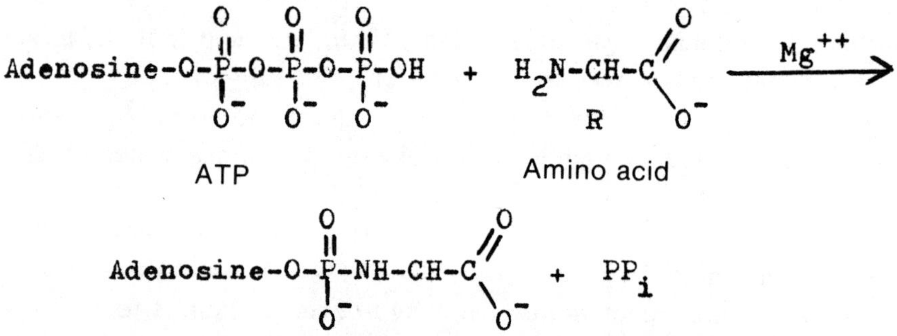

$$\text{Adenosine-O-}\underset{O^-}{\overset{O}{\overset{\|}{\underset{|}{P}}}}\text{-O-}\underset{O^-}{\overset{O}{\overset{\|}{\underset{|}{P}}}}\text{-O-}\underset{O^-}{\overset{O}{\overset{\|}{\underset{|}{P}}}}\text{-OH} + H_2N\text{-}\underset{R}{\underset{|}{CH}}\text{-}C\begin{smallmatrix}\nearrow O \\ \searrow O^-\end{smallmatrix} \xrightarrow{Mg^{++}}$$

ATP Amino acid

$$\text{Adenosine-O-}\underset{O^-}{\overset{O}{\overset{\|}{\underset{|}{P}}}}\text{-NH-CH-}C\begin{smallmatrix}\nearrow O \\ \searrow O^-\end{smallmatrix} + PP_i$$

A Phosphoramidate

Other amines, including ammonia, imidazole and ethylenediamine, also gave phosphoramidates with ATP and other polyphosphates. The importance of phosphoramidates is that they are exceedingly resistant to hydrolysis in alkaline solution while still being activated at the phosphate group. Lohrmann[5] discovered that the imidazole derivative of adenylic acid, adenosine-5′-phosphorimidazole, condensed very efficiently on a poly U template to give dimers and higher oligonucleotides.

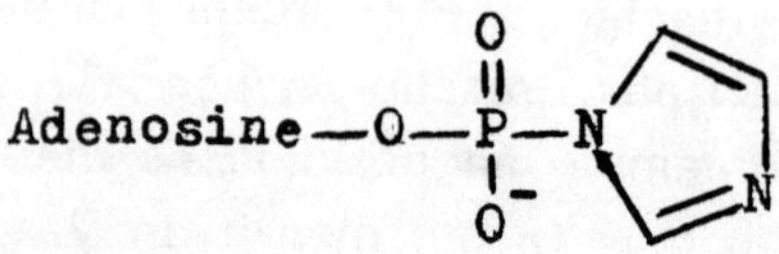

$$\text{Adenosine—O—}\underset{O^-}{\overset{O}{\overset{\|}{\underset{|}{P}}}}\text{—N}\langle\text{imidazole ring}\rangle$$

Adenosine-5′-phosphoramidazole

Thus, the Mg^{++} catalyzed reactions of amino acids, imidazole, or other amines could have provided nucleotide derivatives that could have taken part directly in prebiotic polynucleotide syntheses. The activated intermediates, which formed best under dry conditions, would have formed in the solid state, and subsequently reacted in the presence of a small amount of water to form condensed nucleotides.

Renz, Lohrmann and Orgel[6] explored the reaction further by using adenosine 2′, 3′-phosphate, the cyclic internal ester of adenylic acid.

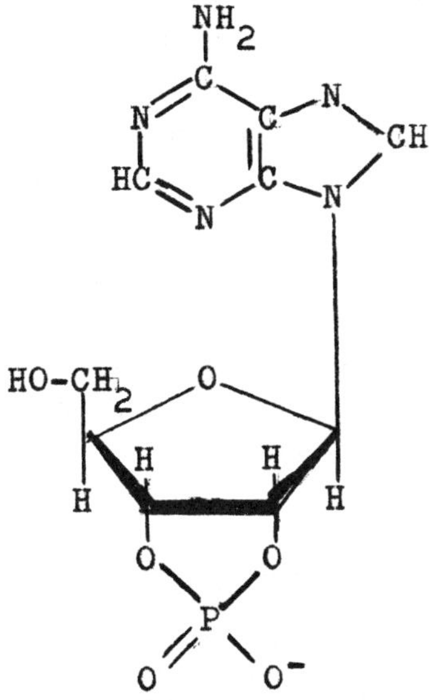

Adenosine 2′,3′-phosphate

The cyclic 2′,3′-phosphates are the major product of the urea-catalyzed phosphorylation of nucleosides in the dry state and would have been a plausible chemical form of the nucleotides on primordial earth. Adenosine 2′, 3′-phosphate did not condense on a poly U template with magnesium ions, but when the ions were replaced with simple catalysts such as glycinamide, ethylenediamine or poly-ethylenediamine, good yields of the di- and tri-nucleotides were obtained. Presumably, the active intermediate in the reaction was the phosphoramidate formed by the nucleotide and the amine.

Until this time, the Orgel group was trying to find ways in which the nucleotides could have been polymerized in solution under conditions simulating the primordial oceans. For this the template was essential to bring together the monomers for reaction. This approach, however, would require an explanation of the prebiotic appearance of the template. Then Verlander, Lohrmann and Orgel[7] discovered that under certain conditions the template was unnecessary. When the reaction mixture of adenosine 2′, 3′-phosphate with the aliphatic amines at an alkaline pH was allowed to evaporate to dryness and incubate at 85-90°C, a self-polymerization of the cyclic nucleotide occurred. Oligomers up to the hexamer were obtained in good yields and 5 percent of the product was larger than six units long. The length of the primal gene had become extended to six subunits.

The reaction using cyclic nucleotides was not limited to the adenosine derivative. When cytodine 2′,3′-phosphate was heated at 138°C for two days, Tapiere and Nagyvary[8] obtained oligomers up to the hexamer in 50 percent yields. This is a high temperature but just below 140°C where slow decomposition begins. Skoda and his coworkers[9] had also shown uridine 2′, 3′-phosphate underwent a similar polymerization.

While this was going on, Juan Oró and his group in Houston were attempting to polymerize nucleotides another way. As mentioned above, imidazole compounds appeared to be convenient reagents for the condensation of nucleotides. In 1969, O. Pongs and P.O.P. Ts′o,[10] two chemists at Johns Hopkins University, reported the polymerization of thymidine-5′-phosphate (d-TMP) to exclusively the 3′, 5′-linked oligonucleotides in a 40 to 50 percent yield using β-imidazolyl-4(5)-propanoic acid as a catalyst. The reaction conditions, however, called for refluxing 15 minutes in the laboratory solvent, dimethylformamide. Although the conditions were unrelated to a geologic environment, the catalysis and the results were similar to the desired effects of a simulation experiment.

The imidazole ring, as the side chain of histidine, is an important catalytic unit in many enzyme reactions. Since acidic hydrolysis is initiated by a protonation step, enzymes that catalyze substrates by this mechanism have a proton donor and a proton acceptor in their active site. The imidazole structure containing two nitrogens sharing a single hydrogen in a five-member ring with mobile double bonds is capable of acting as both proton donor and acceptor. The two nitrogens are actually equivalent, and with a shift of the double bonds, the hydrogen can reside on one nitrogen or the other. The imidazole's power lies in its ability to donate the hydrogen from one nitrogen and recapture another hydrogen by the second nitrogen, thus regenerating the orginal structure in the process.

It is postulated[11] that when imidazole catalyzes the coupling of the two d-TMP molecules, the exposed electron pair on its one nitrogen captures the hydroxyl hydrogen from the deoxyribose component, starting a chain reaction of shifting electrons. The phosphate of d-TMP loses its acidic proton (H^+) on one side and its anionic oxygen breaks from it as it takes the imidazole hydrogen on the other to form the hydroxyl ion (OH^-). The simultaneous rejection of a proton and hydroxyl ion represents a loss of water molecule and the two d-TMP monomers are joined in the process.

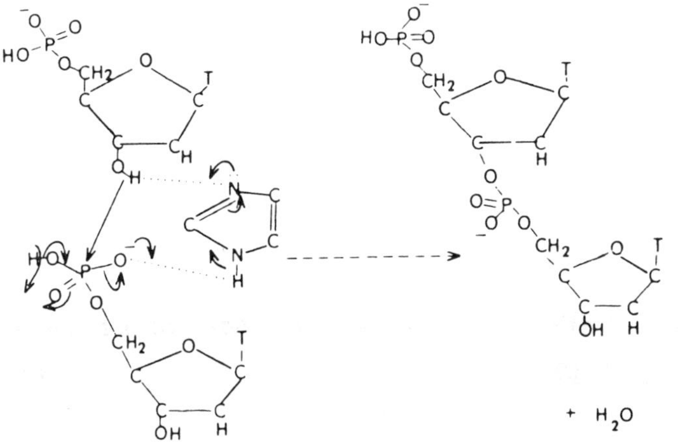

Postulated mechanism of d-TMP polymerization by imidazole. (Ibanez et al., *in* **Chemical Evolution and the Origin of Life**, *North-Holland Publ. Co.,1971)*

In order to adjust the Pongs and Ts'o reaction as a model for abiogenic condensation of mononucleotides, Ibanez, Kimball and Oró[11] attempted the reaction at elevated temperatures with d-TMP and imidazole in water. When the reactants were sealed in a glass tube and incubated at 90°C for 24 hours, the result was oligomers two to seven units long with the natural 3′, 5′-phosphodiester linkage, but the yields were only a few percent at the most.

The problem with attempting the polymerization of nucleotides in water is that removal of a molecule of water from the reactants is unfavored by mass action from the preponderance of the solvent. Nevertheless, there are chemical condensing agents that can extract water from compounds in an aqueous medium and the Houston group investigated these. Carbodiimides, the type of compound reported earlier that Orgel's group used, have been tools of organic chemistry for at least a decade as convenient condensing agents. They were originally used in non-aqueous solvents because of their susceptibility to hydrolysis. But then it was discovered that the salt derivatives of dialkylamino carbodiimides,* which are water-soluble, reacted faster with anions than with water molecules. The mode of action for carbodiimides in condensation reactions is to react first with the anion to form a complex which then hydrolyzes by extracting water from the monomers.** The large amount of free energy liberated by the hydration of the carbodiimides drives the condensation.

---

* 1-Ethyl-3-(3-dimethylaminopropyl)-carbodiimide hydrochloride

**

$$\text{Adenosine-O-}\overset{\text{O}}{\overset{\|}{\underset{\text{OH}}{\underset{|}{\text{P}}}}}\text{-O}^{-} + \text{R-N=C=N-R'} \longrightarrow \text{Adenosine-O-}\overset{\text{O}}{\overset{\|}{\underset{\text{OH}}{\underset{|}{\text{P}}}}}\text{-O-C}(\text{=NHR})(\text{-N-R'})$$

$$\xrightarrow{\text{AMP}} \text{Adenosine-O-}\overset{\text{O}}{\overset{\|}{\underset{\text{OH}}{\underset{|}{\text{P}}}}}\text{-O-Adenosine-O-}\overset{\text{O}}{\overset{\|}{\underset{\text{OH}}{\underset{|}{\text{P}}}}}\text{-O}^{-} + \text{O=C}(\text{NH-R})(\text{NH-R'})$$

Carbodiimides are laboratory chemicals and would not likely to have existed on primordial earth. The tautomer of carbodiimide, on the other hand, is cyanamide,* a chemical that is believed to have been common when the building blocks of life were being formed. Cyanamide, its dimer dicyandiamide which forms in basic solutions, and dicyanamide, another cyanide derivative, are condensing agents simpler than carbodiimides that could have been present and instrumental in prebiotic condensation reactions. Cyanamide is formed by ultraviolet radiation on aqueous solutions of ammonium cyanide. The reaction is not very efficient, but the presence of halide ions improves the yield by a mechanism not well understood. Considering the conditions of the reaction, it is conceivable that large quantities of cyanamide could have been formed and were available on primordial earth to act as a condensing agent.

Because the active species of cyanamide and dicyandiamide is a cation,** the use of them as condensing agents is most effective in acid solution at pH 2. Such a low pH may not have geologic relevance, but the reaction does occur with cyanamide at higher pH's, although much more slowly. When cyanamide was used as a condensing agent along with imidazole as a catalyst, d-TMP could be condensed to oligomers

---

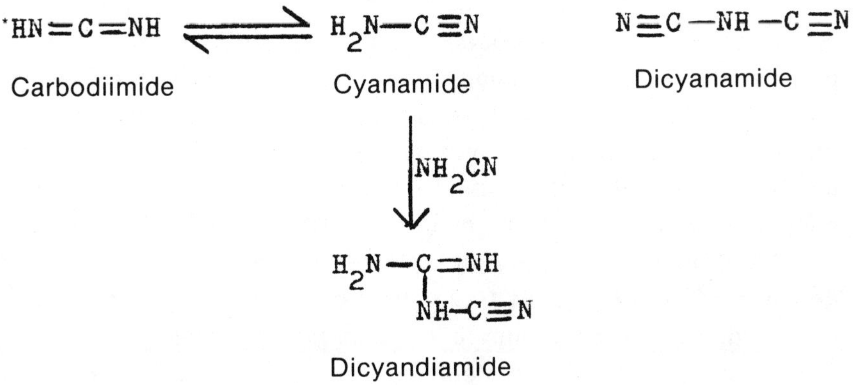

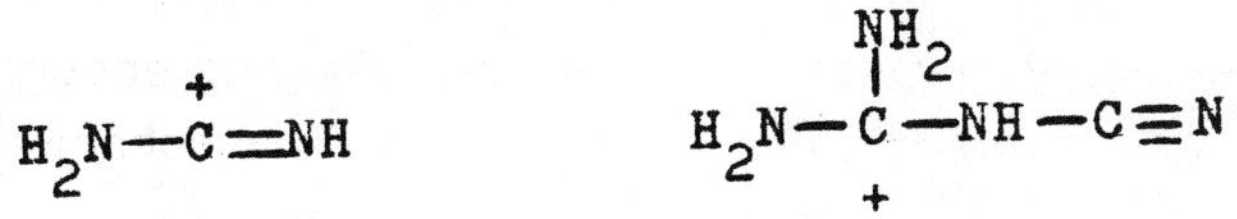

*$HN{=}C{=}NH \rightleftharpoons H_2N{-}C{\equiv}N$ $\qquad N{\equiv}C{-}NH{-}C{\equiv}N$

Carbodiimide — Cyanamide — Dicyanamide

$$H_2N{-}C{\equiv}N \xrightarrow{NH_2CN} H_2N{-}C({=}NH){-}NH{-}C{\equiv}N$$

Dicyandiamide

** $H_2N{-}\overset{+}{C}{=}NH$ $\qquad H_2N{-}\overset{NH_2}{\underset{+}{C}}{-}NH{-}C{\equiv}N$

up to five units in length.[12] But the results from solution reactions, even with elevated temperatures, were not promising. The yields were low and the prospects of extending the condensation reaction beyond a few units seemed dim.

It was at this time it was discovered that one condition seemed to favor polymerization. Whenever the reaction mixture evaporated to dryness, the results were invariably better. This began to give an insight into how the polymerization of the nucleotides could have occurred — not in the primordial ocean itself, but under the drying and baking of solutions of the reactants splashed on rocks or mud flats on the fringes of primeval basins.

E. Stephen-Sherwood and D.G. Odom working with Oró[13] extended the condensation reaction of TMP by adding some of the triphosphate to the reaction. They used cyanamide as the condensing agent and for the catalyst they added AICA, the imidazole derivative that was the intermediate in the synthesis of purines from ammonium cyanide. When the reactants were subjected to drying conditions and incubated at 60-90°C, oligomers up to four units in length were obtained. The advantage of the mixture of nucleotides was that the yield of oligomers was no longer small, but actually 25 to 30 percent, or over ten times greater than with the monophosphate alone.

Yet, despite the success of forming internucleotide bonds under conditions similar to those of primordial earth, the extent of polymerization remained small — too small to imagine assembling to form a functional cell. It were as though Nature was jealously guarding the secret of her great event and had permitted it to happen only after much difficulty. How then could polynucleotides have become large enough to cross the size threshold to perform in a functional cell?

The research on polynucleotides has been directed to find conditions which would have promoted the polymerization of nucleotides into long chains to serve as primal genes. The results to date have indicated oligonucleotides six or eight units in length could have formed under primordial conditions, but no one has succeeded in producing chains much longer. Nevertheless, biological systems succeeded in some way in creating polynucleotides long enough to eventually bring into operation the protein synthesis mechanism.

There is ample reason to believe the chemical procedures used by biological systems were not chance developments, but evolved from the adoption of ordinary chemical interactions. The significance of this concept is that since life processes developed from one step to another in a continuum, it may be possible to retrace the path of evolution to detect what chemical reactions were the precursors to biochemical procedures used by living systems.

It appears nucleotides were not polymerized readily into long chains. There must have been a system that permitted long chains to develop. As pointed out earlier, the condensation seems to be assisted when it is template oriented, although it was found not to be a requirement under drying conditions. But I believe the initial long-chain polynucleotides came about on prebiotic earth in the manner they are still being synthesized by organisms today — as a double-stranded molecule.

When contemporary cells copy DNA, they split the double-stranded molecule and condense nucleotides oriented on a strand of the old DNA. It is unlikely the cell evolved this method of duplicating DNA from its double-stranded molecule without precedence, but rather as a continuation of prebiotic chemistry. In other words, the prebiotic polynucleotides probably did not develop as single condensation products, but as double-stranded molecules.

The problem leading to the first functional cell was similar to that that faced Khorana and his colleagues[14] at Wisconsin and the Massachusetts Institute of Technology when they sought a means of synthesizing a gene. In order to make the gene that codes for tyrosine tRNA, the research group did not attempt to polymerize a single linear molecule by condensing the monomers one on each other. Rather they prepared 39 short fragments, each 10 to 15 nucleotides long. The segments were so chosen that a short piece of one oligomer extended from the other when two complementary fragments were allowed to form a double-stranded complex. The extended section then served as a splint to which an adjoining fragment could be complexed for coupling by the enzyme, DNA ligase. In this way, adding first to one strand, then to the other, the researchers were able to construct a complete double-stranded nucleic acid with an overall length of 207 nucleotides.

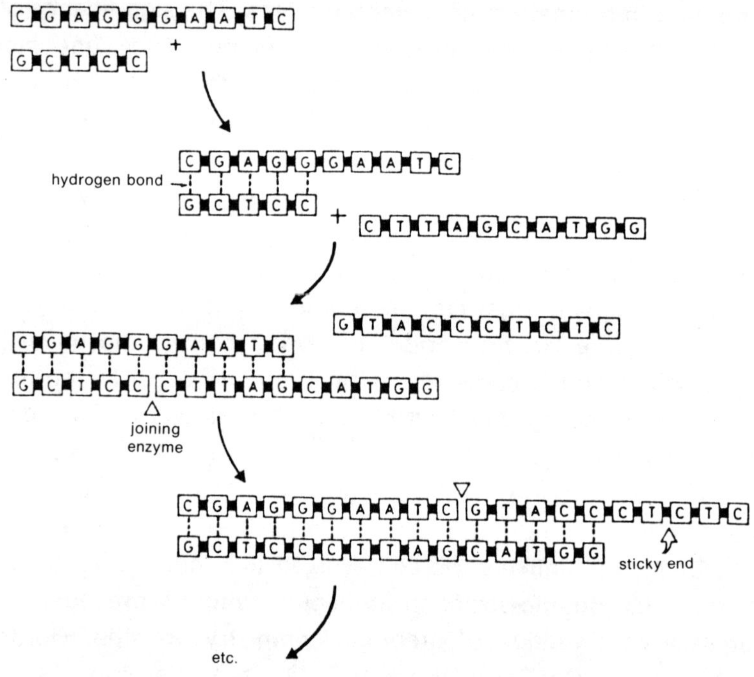

Scheme for synthesizing a gene using splint polynucleotides by the Khorana method

It is in this manner I feel the prebiotic polynucleotides came into being. The results of the experiments simulating drying conditions on primordial earth, particularly in the presence of cyanamide derivatives as condensing agents, indicate that short oligomers formed readily from the nucleotides, but not long ones. With a large variety of oligomers produced when primeval lake beds were flooded and evaporated repeatedly, it seems plausible that oligomers which would form the strongest complexes (that is, those with complementary base pairs) would be selectively retained. Whenever the adjoining segments fitted, they were in position to be coupled by the next drying cycle.

It is a condition that conforms to our present knowledge through simulation experiments that could logically have occurred. It is not an easy experiment to demonstrate in the laboratory, and to my knowledge it has not been attempted, but I believe it is a reasonable explanation of how prebiotic polynucleotides were formed on primordial earth — they grew, segment by segment, in a double-stranded molecule by a reaction repeated over and over again until they crossed over the threshold of functionality for a replicating cell.

References

1. G. Schramm, H. Grotsch and W. Pollmann, Non-enzymatic synthesis of polysaccharides, nucleosides and nucleic acids and the origin of self-reproducing systems, *Angew. Chem. Intl. Ed.* **1**, 1-7 (1962).
2. A.W. Schwartz and S.W. Fox, Condensation of cytidylic acid in the presence of polyphosphoric acid, *Biochim. Biophys. Acta* **134**, 9-16 (1967).
3. A. Kornberg, **Enzymatic Synthesis of Deoxyribonucleic Acid**, Academic Press, New York, 1961.
4. J. Sulston, R. Lohrmann, L.E. Orgel and H.T. Miles, Non-enzymatic synthesis of oligoadenylates on a polyuridylic acid template, *Proc. Nat. Acad. Sci.* **59**, 726-733 (1968).
5. B.J. Weismann, R. Lohrmann, L.E. Orgel, H. Schneider-Bernloehr and J.W. Sulston, Template-directed synthesis with adenosine-5′-phosphorimidazolide, *Science* **161**, 387 (1968).
6. M. Renz, R. Lohrmann, L.E. Orgel, Catalysts for the polymerization of adenosine cyclic 2′, 3′-phosphate on a poly (U) template, *Biochim. Biophys. Acta* **240**, 463-471 (1973).
7. M.S. Verlander, R. Lohrmann and L.E. Orgel, Catalysts for the self-polymerization of adenosine cyclic 2′, 3′-phosphate, *J. Mol. Evol.* **2**, 303-306 (1973).
8. C.M. Tapiero and J. Nagyvary, Prebiotic formation of cytidine nucelotides, *Nature* **231**, 42-43 (1971).
9. J. Skoda, J. Morávek and J. Kopecky, Sixth FEBS Meeting Abstr., 433 (1969).
10. O. Pongs and P.O.P. T'so, Polymerization of 5′-deoxyribonucleotides with **β**-Imidazolyl-4(5)-propanoic acid, *Biochem. Biophys. Res. Comm.* **36**, 475-481 (1971).

11. J. Ibanez, A.P. Kimball and J. Oró, The effect of imidazole, cyanamide, and polyornithine on the condensation of nucleotides in aqueous solutions, in **Chemical Evolution and the Origin of Life**, R. Buvet and C. Ponnamperuma, eds., North-Holland Publ. Co., 1971, pp. 171-179.
12. J.D. Ibanez, A.P. Kimball and J. Oró, Condensation of mononucleotides by imidazole, *J. Mol. Evol.* **1**, 112-114 (1971).
13. E. Stephen-Sherwood, D.G. Odom and J. Oró, The prebiotic synthesis of deoxythymidine oligonucleotides, *J. Mol. Evol.* **3**, 323-330 (1974).
14. K.L. Agarwal, H. Büch, M.H. Caruthers, N. Gupta, H.G. Khorana, K. Kleppe, A. Kumar, E. Ohtsuka, W.L. Rajbhanary, J.H. Van de Sande, V. Sgaramella, H. Weber and T. Yamada, Total synthesis of the gene for an alanine transfer ribonucleic acid from yeast, *Nature* **237**, 27-34 (1970).

25
"Particles of Life"

In the preceding chapters we saw the manner in which prebiological peptides and polynucleotides would have formed on primordial earth. An accumulation of these chemical components set the stage for the final step — the assembling of a cell. Nucleic acids and proteins alone do not possess the character of life. They are static; whereas life is dynamic. A living cell is a working system, and it is the special organization of the macromolecules into a supramolecular structure functioning as an autocatalytic system that represents life. The biological unit then becomes a sequence of events where matter and energy are taken in to become converted to progressively more complex components of a self-sustaining structure.

To this stage, experiments demonstrating the abiotic synthesis of biochemicals have been within the special interests of chemists, but the formation of a cell brings the origin of life to the level where it can be observed by everyone as an entity with the properties of microscopic organisms. In some manner the macromolecules that had condensed from the building blocks managed to associate and pass over the threshold to become life. They assembled into a coordinated arrangement that looked like and functioned as a cell. This was a quantum jump in the events leading to the formation of life and has of course, because of its spectacular feature, received particular attention.

Essentially all substances have structural features that create associative forces with other matter and they aggregate into an unlimited variety of amorphous combinations. But accumulations of organic matter do not just assemble into functional cells; they generally become undistinctive deposits. To form a cell, there had to have been a selection of molecules to fit together in a precise manner for the whole cell to be functional. The problem has been to find the procedure that nature took to assemble the prebiological components into an organized structure that became the living cell.

The most apparent necessity in the formation of the primal cell was containment. A living system cannot exist in free solution, but only with the components confined in close justaposition. An envelope was needed to hold the constituents together while affording access to the surrounding environment for admitting raw materials and to allow a means of dividing during reproduction. Presumably, it had to be a surface that would isolate extremely small volumes of fluid from the surrounding volume of water. To pass from the inanimate to the animate, what substances did the primal cell find available in the earth's early geology to use for its cellular envelope?

A generation after Schwann discovered the cell was the fundamental unit of life, men in the laboratory were attempting to create a living cell from common chemicals. But like the Alchemists and their dream of gold from base metals, their efforts were before an understanding of the underlying chemistry was known. As a result, models were designed primarily to duplicate the outward physical behavior of cells rather than chemical functionality.

In 1867, the German chemist, Moritz Traube,[1] carried out experiments in which he formed semipermeable films of copper ferrocyanide around small crystals of copper sulfate he dropped in solutions of potassium ferrocyanide. These minute encapsulating spheres exhibited some features of growth and Traube believed they could be used to study the physico-chemical properties of cells.

Another generation passed. Then in 1892, Bütschli[2] prepared a model of a live cell by rubbing a drop of olive oil with potash solution. The chemically agitated droplet moved about in an impressive manner engulfing particles in a fashion resembling amoeba. This experiment was carried further by others[3] who created similar models that reenacted the movements, feeding and division of cells.

The culmination of these pseudo-cells around the turn of the century was reached by the experiments of Stèphane Le Duc,[4] professor of l'École de Medicine de Nantes. Le Duc performed an experiment similar to Traube's by adding a piece of fused calcium chloride to a saturated solution of potash and potassium phosphate. A spherical shell of calcium phosphate formed, and as the calcium chloride continued to react, the osmotic pressure created within the sac caused it to expand. By changing the concentrations and adding various substances, Le Duc was able to generate exquisite osmotic forms that bore striking resemblances to algae, mushrooms and other life forms. So enamoured was the professor of his experiments that he believed he had embarked upon a new field of science, and he called it "synthetic biology."

The followers of Le Duc's "synthetic biology" carried the experiments to conclusions even beyond the extravagant claims of the founder. It was an age when radioactivity was not well understood and Madame Curie's radium was hailed as the wonder of science to rid the world of the ravages of disease. By using the mystifying energy of radium, Martin Kuckuck[5] converted a mixture of gelatin, glycerol and salt into a culture of "cells" that were purported to have manifested all the signs of life.

It was to be another generation before a realistic model for a primitive cell was to be devised. During the first half of the century, the chemistry of cells was believed to resemble the properties of colloids. A colloid is a special state of matter where particles are finely dispersed and suspended in a medium of a different phase. It can be solid or liquid particles suspended in a solid, liquid or gas phase. The particles are small enough that their large surface areas can absorb ions and other materials that impart unique properties to the system. Electric charges within the substances or from absorbed ions cause the colloidal particles to repel each other and maintain the suspension. Familiar colloidal systems are smoke, fog, or airborne dust in the atmosphere, as well as muddy water.

Whereas these are colloids that are generally of inorganic substances which lack an affinity for water and the particles remain dispersed by repulsion of their electrical charges, there are colloids of organic compounds that are quite different. These are hydrophilic colloids like gelatin, albumin or starch that appear to dissolve in water but do not diffuse through a membrane.

Large molecules like proteins are water-soluble because water of hydration accumulates in structured masses around the charged or polar groups, holding the protein molecules in their uniform shapes by solvation. If the conditions are altered appreciably by heating, changing the pH or ionic strength, or adding chemicals like urea that break up the water structure, the peptide chain becomes unfolded and adhesive. The protein molecules coagulate by clumping together and are no longer soluble (denaturation). Collagen, the fibrous protein of connective tissue and probably the most abundant animal protein, can be isolated as a crystalline compound, but once denatured, it becomes gelatin, the colloidal base of glue.

Since proteins in the protoplasm were regarded to exist in a colloidal state in the 1920's, it was believed the answer to the origin of life lay in demonstrating the manner in which a colloidal structure could arise from geological conditions. Information for such an experiment came from a phenomenon, first observed in 1927,[6] that was being investigated by Hendrick G. Bungenberg de Jong[7] of the University of Leiden, who later reported on it in 1932.

Bungenberg de Jong had observed that hydrophilic colloids often spontaneously formed two phases. A fluid sediment in colloidal substances separated from and retained equilibrium with an overlying liquid layer free of colloids. He called the phase separation, coacervation, and the colloidal particles, coacervates. In some cases, the colloidal matter did not settle out from the liquid but remained as minute droplets suspended in the water. In effect, they were droplets of fluid separated from the surrounding medium by a thin film of hydrophilic colloids.

The Russian biochemist, A.I. Oparin, in his study of the origin of life, saw a similarity between coacervates and living cells. In his 1936 edition[8] he compared these colloidal droplets to the result when protoplasm is squeezed from plant cells. In spite of its fluid consistency, the protoplasm does not mix with water but remains as little droplets floating in the medium.

Oparin prepared various types of coacervates and studied their physical and chemical properties. Under controlled conditions they formed readily from proteins mixed with other select natural polymers. When a dilute solution of gum arabic, a commercial polysaccharide from the acacia tree, was mixed with a solution of gelatin at a pH under 4.8, coacervation occurred. Below pH 4.8, the isoelectric point* of gelatin, the charge on the protein became positive while the gum arabic remained negative. The two polymers with opposing charges aggregated and formed droplets of the complex gelatin-gum arabic coacervate. By chosing pH levels between the isoelectric points of the polymers, a large number of coacervates with various chemical properties were able to be formed. Coacervates from gelatin and egg lecithin, basic proteins such as histone and a nucleic acid, or other similar combinations were possible.

It was proposed by Oparin that the phenomenon of coacervation could have served as the primitive protocell-forming mechanism. Coacervates do possess a boundary that segregates an environment from the surrounding medium as well as other properties unique to the system; and they show many of the morphological characteristics of cellular inclusions such as vacuoles.

Coacervation can take place in extremely dilute solution — in concentrations as low as 0.001 percent[8] — and coacervates exhibit the property of colloids of being able to absorb substances. Coacervates prepared from gum arabic and protamine sulfate have been shown to absorb from a surrounding medium bacterial lysate that is enriched in

*The pH where anions and cations of a protein are equal.

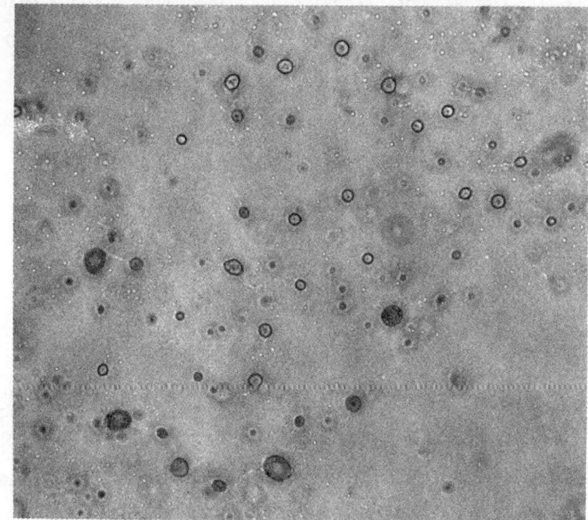

Coacervates prepared from gelatin and gum arabic. (Courtesy of George Hildenbrandt, Pennsylvania State University)

catalase activity.[9] And coacervates of gum arabic and histone or gelatin can concentrate starch from solution 3.5 fold. When β-amylase is present, it too is taken up by the coacervate and the enzyme hydrolyzes the starch.[10] Numerous other experiments have been reported to illustrate that coacervates perform like primitive cells.[10] As an example, adding bacterial oxido-reductase to a coacervate mixture containing NAD_{red} created a simple anaerobic oxidation-reduction system.

Oparin reasoned that there were polymeric substances on prebiological earth that made coacervates that could have served as precursors to the first living cells. But essentially all the simulation experiments to demonstrate the cell-like properties of coacervates are with coacervates prepared from convenient biological polymers. Only if such experiments are performed with valid prebiological constituents are they meaningful simulation tests. And too, because of their colloidal nature, coacervates are easily susceptible to changes in pH and salt concentrations. Nevertheless, Oparin's coacervates were and have remained one of the most scientifically sophisticated hypotheses for the origin of the primal cell.

There have been other models proposed for the origin of the cell. In 1942, A.L. Herrara[11] of Mexico prepared what he called sulphobes by dissolving ammonium thiocyanate in formaldehyde and spreading the solution in a thin film. After several hours, microscopic structures with activities analogous to those of living organisms were reported to have been produced. Herrara saw in these minute shapes the varieties that are formed with amoeba and tissue forms, and believed they may have been significant in simulating the origin of life. He pointed out that the conditions in volcanoes would have produced ammonium thiocyanate by a known reaction from sulfur.

It was not until after the Miller experiment in 1953 that other researchers offered models of cellular and precellular organization. Karl Grossenbacher and C.A. Knight[12] at Berkeley, while carrying out research with the sparking experiment, isolated not only amino acids, but also peptides. Then in examining the solid film and samples of the cloudy liquid from the reaction mixture, they discovered small solid bodies which ranged in size from about 800 Å down to 50 Å or less. These spherules, in the size range of viruses, contained large amounts of minerals, but also amino acids and similar compounds. The authors suggested the spherules were silicates derived from the borosilicate glass of the sparking apparatus and doubted if they played any role in biogenesis.

A research group in Romania investigated the possible formation of organic compounds from a primordial atmosphere under different circumstances. Simionescu, Dénes and Macoveau[13] considered prebiotic components forming by electric discharge in cold plasma conditions adjusted between +20° and -60°C. In simulation experiments under these conditions, a mixture of methane, ammonia and water vapor gave more evolved organic structures. The results were complex polypeptide substances which, when viewed under the microscope, were seen condensed in fibrillar, branched or circular proteid arrangements.

The fact that the Miller experiment made formaldehyde and thiocyanate plausible prebiotic substances gave a new relevance to Herrara's sulphobe structures. Adolph Smith of Sir George Williams University in Montréal with J.J. Silver and Gary Steinman[14] at Pennsylvania State University reinvestigated Herrara's claim of observing life-like forms in his reaction mixture. The researchers discovered when ammonium thiocyanate and formaldehyde were mixed, the colorless solution became slightly red in a few seconds, and finally a golden yellow after one hour. Microscopic examination revealed a high density of spheres 1 to 5 micra in diameter. Additional experiments showed that ultraviolet light promoted the reaction. And when zinc chloride was added to the reaction mixture, the zinc became incorporated into the structures giving rise to localized ATPase-like activity. The chemists felt the experiments clearly indicated how simple chemical substances that are believed to have existed on primordial earth could have been implicated in the formation of cell-like structures before any living cells existed.

Another model for precellular organization that has been much publicized were spheres formed by Sidney Fox and his collaborators using thermal polymers of amino acids. In 1959, Fox, Harada and J. Kendrick[15] reported that hot saturated solutions of their acidic proteinoids, upon cooling, gave large numbers of uniform microscopic spherules. These spherical structures, called proteinoid microspheres, were usually 1.5 to 3 micra in diameter, and were prepared readily from the acidic proteinoid. Basic proteinoids, on the other hand, did not normally make microspheres, but did so when mixed with the acidic proteinoid. Microspheres prepared containing basic proteinoids gave a positive Gram stain; those prepared from acidic proteinoids took up the stain but were negative. It was proposed this observation indicated similarities of surface composition in proteinoid microspheres and bacteria.[16]

As is the case with most of. these physical models of cells, the spheres can coalesce and divide, as well as smaller members adhere to larger ones. This latter featúre, because of its appearance to live microorganisms, has been referred to as "budding." Removing these smaller spheres with mechanical, thermal or electric shock and collecting them by contrifugation, Fox and his group reported they observed them grow in size when placed in a saturated proteinoid solution at 37°C.[17] And by changing the solution conditions these microspheres were induced to undergo various morphological changes simulating replicating cells. In all, five means of "reproduction" have been attributed to these non-biological spheres.

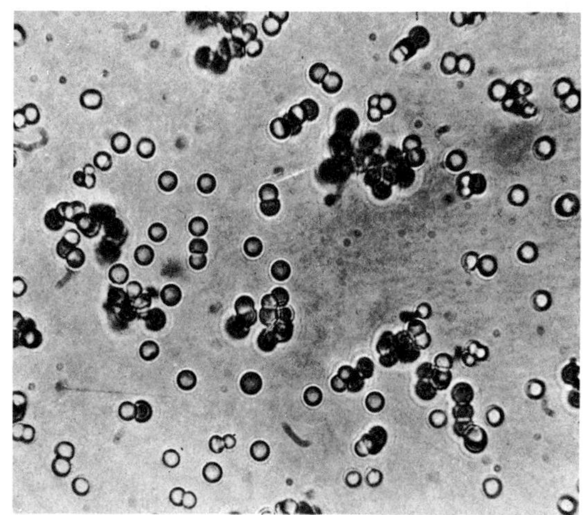

Microspheres formed from the acidic amino acid thermal polymer (proteinoid) boiled in water, (Kenyon and Steinman, **Biochemical Predestination,** *McGraw-Hill, 1969)*

Like Le Duc's osmotic bags of seventy years earlier, Fox has tried to correlate all the bubble physics of proteinoid microspheres to attributes of living cells. By applying a slight pressure to microspheres, they can be made to associate in chains like algae;[18] when spheres fused and there was an exchange of occluded material, it was called communication;[19] and the most recent interpretation of conjugation between microspheres has been declared to be protosexuality.[20]

It is difficult to see that proteinoids or their microspheres have any relevance to the origin of life. As J.D. Bernal has pointed out, "such spherules are quite commonly produced by irregular or branched-chain polymerization, as in starch grains, which cannot effectively lead to a crystal, but forms as assembly of rigid or plastic spheres around nuclei. Any resemblance to organisms, such as the presence of double spheres indicating fission, is probably fortuitous."[21] In effect, Fox's research reflects a retrogression to the older experimental approach to the origin of life which was aimed at producing imitations of primitive life shapes.

Certainly microspheres represent an additional indication that the thermal polymerization of amino acids does not result in copolymerization resembling natural proteins. If one considers the acidic proteinoids as being primarily polyaspartic acid polymers, the intermolecular bonding is not difficult to explain. Carboxylic acids have a strong tendency to dimerize with the carboxyl groups joined together. In the same manner, the aspartic acid side groups in the proteinoid form intermolecular bonds with each other in adjacent molecules. This is consistent with the fact that microspheres dissociate above about pH6 due to ionization of the carboxyl groups.

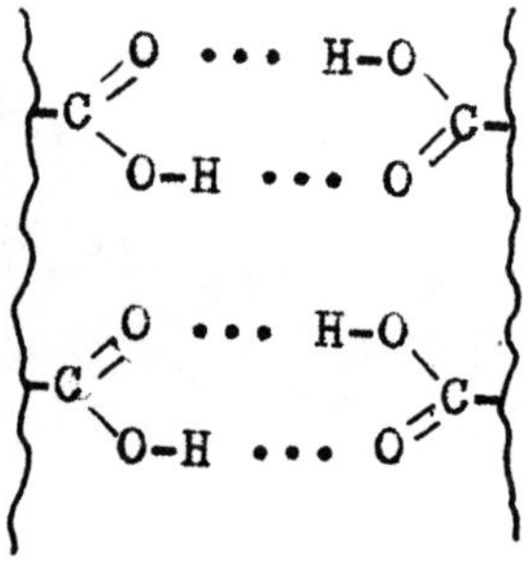

Postulated intermolecular bonding in proteinoid microspheres

By changing the salt concentration, microspheres can be made to swell and shrink, a property that has been suggested to be in the same manner as cells do from a change of osmotic pressure on their semipermeable membrane.[22] Since microspheres have been demonstrated to be too leaky to act as a membrane,[23] the swelling and shrinking cannot be due to osmotic pressure but is obviously from the proteinoid acting like a charged polymer in the manner of Dowex 50.[24] Polymers containing ionizable functional group (e.g., - COOH, -NH-) shrink or swell in varying salt concentrations due to the change in the number of charges on the polymer. High concentrations of salt create shrinking by Coulombic attraction of the charged polymer to the opposing ion. Such polymers are commonly used in the laboratory as ion exchangers.

Approximately two dozen properties of proteins have been assigned to the thermal polymers of amino acids.[25] The "limited heterogeneity" and non-randomness of the composition of proteinoids have been regarded as supporting evidence that amino acids can be thermally copolymerized in sequences resembling proteins. This, however, is inconsistent with the physico-chemical behavior of proteins. Proteins and polypeptides do not form microspheres. Even denatured proteins, as when an egg is boiled, do not aggregate into microspheres, but coagulate in the familiar manner.

There have been similar efforts to create models of the primal cell where a greater regard was given to the gross morphology than chemical functionality. Krishna Bahadur[26] of the University of Allahabad, India, in 1964 prepared microspheres from paraformaldehyde, water and colloidal molybdenum oxide irradiated with visible light. It was claimed these microscopic spheres were capable of growth and division with metabolic activities. Bahadur also prepared microspheres by the thermal polymerization of amino acids and called them Jeewanu, the Sanskrit word for "particles of life."[27]

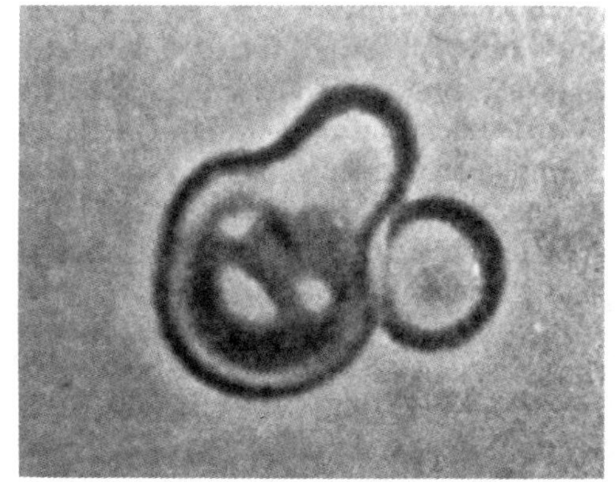

Jeewanu particle showing "budding." (Kenyon and Steinman, **Biochemical Predestination**, *McGraw-Hill, 1969)*

The rationale put forward by Oparin, Fox and others for their models is that the living cell was preceded by a system that had morphological properties resembling cells but was not yet living. Purportedly, Oparin's coacervates became protobionts,[28] and Fox's microspheres, protocells.[29] These structures then supposedly underwent a period of evolution in which they changed until they evolved into the first living cells. No matter how you look at it, this is scientific nonsense. Evolution is a biological process of development through mutation, reproduction and selection. These pseudo-cellular models, like clay, soap bubbles, or any other inanimate objects, have neither the mechanism nor the potential of becoming anything beyond what they are.

Such models for living cells lost their scientific value when the purpose of the cellular membrane was forsaken to emphasize morphological similarities. The hypothesis of coacervates was founded in an age when colloidal chemistry appeared to be the basis of life. Proteinoids arose from an unsuccessful attempt to synthesize an abiotic protein or protein-like material by a simple process. Both hypotheses were overextended to try to encompass the role of prime mover in the origin of life, despite the tremendous strides in molecular biology and membrane chemistry that revealed the chemical principles upon which they were derived had little similarity to the basic chemistry of biological systems.

The question at stake is what forces would have been responsible for the association and assembly of the prebiological polymers. The principal binding force of coacervates is the electrostatic attraction between hydrated biopolymers; the formation of microspheres is dependent basically on the same interaction. Coacervates are generally prepared from biological compounds and microspheres from non-biological compounds; the occurrence of the former on prebiotic earth has had to be justified, and the latter are dead-end substances that would not be synthesized by a functional cell.

But the most serious fault of models from particles held together by ionic forces is that they would have been continually periled with dissolution. Coacervates are notoriously unstable and microspheres exist only in saturated solutions. Their existence in Archean lakes or oceans would have been short-lived.

References

1. M. Traube, Experimente zur Theorie der Zellenbildung und Endosmose, *Arch. für Anat. Physiol. und Wiss. Med.* **87**, 129-165 (1867).
2. O. Bütschli, **Untersuchungen über microscopische Schaume und das Protoplasma**, Leipzig, 1892.
3. L. Rhumbler, Aus dem Lückengebiet zwischen organismischer und anorganismischer Materie, *Ergebn. Anat. Entwichklungsgesch.* **15**, 1-38 (1906).
4. S. Le Duc, **The Mechanism of Life** (transl. by W. Deane Butcher), Rebman Co., New York, 1914.
5. Martin Kuckuck, **L'univers, être vivant. La solution des problèmes de la matière et la vie à l'aide de la biologie universelle**, Librarie Kundig, Geneve, 1911.
6. Wo. Ostwald, und R. Köhler, Ueber die flüssig-flüssige Endmischung von Gelatine durch Sulfosalizylsäure und über die Beziehungen dieses. Systems zur Phasenregel, *Kolloid Z.* **43**, 131-150 (1927).
7. H.G. Bungenberg de Jong, Die Konzervation und ihre Bedeutung für die Biologie, *Protoplasma* **15**, 110-173 (1932).
8. A.I. Oparin, **The Origin of Life** (transl. by S. Morgulis), Dover Publications, Inc., New York, 1953.
9. A.I. Oparin, Biochemical processes in the simplest structures, in **The Origin of Life on the Earth**, English Edition, F. Clark and R.L.M. Synge, eds., Pergamon Press, 1959, pp. 428-436.
10. A.I. Oparin, The pathways of the primary development of metabolism and artificial modeling of this development in coacervate drops, in **The Origins of Prebiological Systems** S.W. Fox, ed., Academic Press, New York, 1965, pp. 331-348.
11. A.L. Herrara, A new theory of the origin and nature of life, *Science* **96**, 14 (1942).
12. K. A. Grossenbacher and C.A. Knight, Amino acids, peptides, and spherules obtained from "primitive earth" gases in a sparking system, in **The Origins of Prebiological Systems**, S.W. Fox, ed., Academic Press, New York, 1965, pp. 173-186.
13. Cr. Dimionescu, F. Dénes and M. Macoveau, Synthesis of some amino acids, sugars and peptides in cold plasma. Electron-microscopic studies on some proteid forms (III), *Biopolymers* **12**, 237-241 (1973).
14. A.E. Smith, J.J. Silver and G. Steinman, Cell-like structures from simple molecules under simulated primitive earth conditions, *Experientia* **24**, 36-38 (1968).
15. S.W. Fox, K. Harada and J. Kendrick, Production of spherules from synthetic proteinoid and hot water, *Science* **129**, 1221-1223 (1959).
16. S.W. Fox and S. Yuyama, Effects of the Gram stain on microspheres from thermal polyamino acids, *J. Bacteriol.* **85**, 279-283 (1963).
17. S.W. Fox, R.J. McCauley and A. Wood, A model of primitive heterotrophic proliferation, *Comp. Biochem. Physiol.* **20**, 773-778 (1967).
18. S.W. Fox and S. Yuyama, Abiotic product of primitive protein and formed microparticles, *Ann. N.Y. Acad. Sci.* **108**, 487-494 (1963).

19. L.L. Hsu, S. Brooke and S.W. Fox, Conjugation of proteinoid microspheres: a model of primordial communication, *Curr. Mod. Biol.* **4**, 12 (1971).
20. L.L. Hsu and S.W. Fox, Interaction between diverse proteinoids and microspheres in simulation of primordial evolution, *Biosystems* **8**, 89-101 (1977).
21. J.D. Bernal, **The Origin of Life**, Weidenfeld and Nicholson, London, 1967, p. 125.
22. S.W. Fox, R.J. McCauley, P. Mongomery, T. Fukushima, K. Harada and C.R. Windsor, Membrane-like properties in microsystems assembled from synthetic protein-like polymers, in **Physical Principles of Biological Membranes**, F. Snell, J. Wolken, G. Iverson and J. Lam, eds.,Gordon and Breach, New York, 1969, pp. 417-432.
23. W. Stillwell, Facilitated diffusion of amino acids across bimolecular lipid membranes as a model for selective accumulation of amino acids in a primordial protocell, *Biosystems* **8**, 111-117 (1976).
24. Lynn Margulis, ed., **Origins of Life**, Gordon and Breach, New York, 1970, p. 157.
25. S.W. Fox, Simulated natural experiments in spontaneous organization of morphological units from proteinoid, in **The Origins of Prebiological Systems**, S.W. Fox, ed., Academic Press, New York, 1965, pp. 361-382.
26. K. Bahadur and S. Ranganayaki, Synthesis of Jeewanu. The units capable of growth, multiplication and metabolic activity. I. Preparation of units capable of growth and division and having metabolic activity, *Zentbl. Bakt. Parasitkde. (II)* **117**, 567-574 (1964).
27. K. Bahadur, Synthesis of Jeewanu. The Units capable of growth, multiplication and metabolic activity. III. Preparation of microspheres capable of growth and division by building and having metabolic activity with peptides prepared thermally, *Zentbl. Bakt. Parasitkde. (II)* **117**, 585-602 (1962).
28. A.I. Oparin, **Genesis and Evolutionary Development of Life**, Academic Press, New York, 1968, pp. 127-151.
29. S.W. Fox, Origin of the cell: experiments and premises, *Naturwis.* **60**, 359-368 (1973).

26

The Vital Envelope

At some point on primordial earth something happened, something that was commonplace and spontaneous in the stages toward a biological system that marked the beginning of life, for it was from that moment on that certain prebiological peptides, polynucleotides and assorted constituents were no longer just chemicals, but became biochemicals associated together in such a way that they became a living cell. What was the nature of that final step? It must have been more than the generation of bizarre spherical particles that are substantively unrelated to biological systems. Rather, it must have been a process that introduced a fundamental property to the organization of matter that distinguishes a living cell. That critical event that became the moment when life began was the encapsulating of a gathering of self-replicating molecules within a semipermeable cellular membrane.

A living cell became a special interaction of matter intermediate between substances firmly bound by covalent bonds and molecules in free solution. In order for the structure of polynucleotides to be expressed through replication and translation, they and their auxillary constituents needed to be confined in close proximity, but still with a degree of freedom to move and interact. For this the cell needed an enclosing sheath that possessed all the physical attributes to segregate the cell from its surrounding environment while still allowing selective access to raw materials and energy.

The confining envelope needed to be impermeable to the cellular components, but able to allow admittance of small molecules; it needed to be elastic for expansion and division, but to be held together spontaneously; it needed to be insoluble in dilute solutions and over a broad pH range; and it needed to be composed of simple chemicals that seal together automatically into the semi-fluid, two-dimensional conformation of the envelope. All these requirements were fulfilled by the bimolecular lipid membrane.

The lipid bilayer membrane is a model of simplicity that forms spontaneously and is a structural feature universal to all living things; every cell, including the smallest free-living microorganism, has it. So fundamental is the lipid bilayer that it, along with the α -helix of proteins and the double-helix of DNA, represent the three basic structures of biological systems. The importance of the lipid membrane is indicated by the fact that the more complex organisms have become, the more extensive has become the number of cellular structures containing membranes.

The composition of lipids in membranes of contemporary cells varies considerably, but generally a membrane consists of approximately half protein and half lipid, with the lipids being mostly phospholipids. These latter compounds represent a series of fatty acid derivatives of glycero-phosphoric acid that vary by the small molecular component joined to the phosphate group.

Because the hydrocarbon chain of fatty acid substituents is repelled by water, whereas, the phosphate end of the molecule is polar and water-soluble, phospholipids are a class of chemicals that align themselves between two physical phases. In water, the phospholipids are driven together by the exclusion of the paraffin chains from water

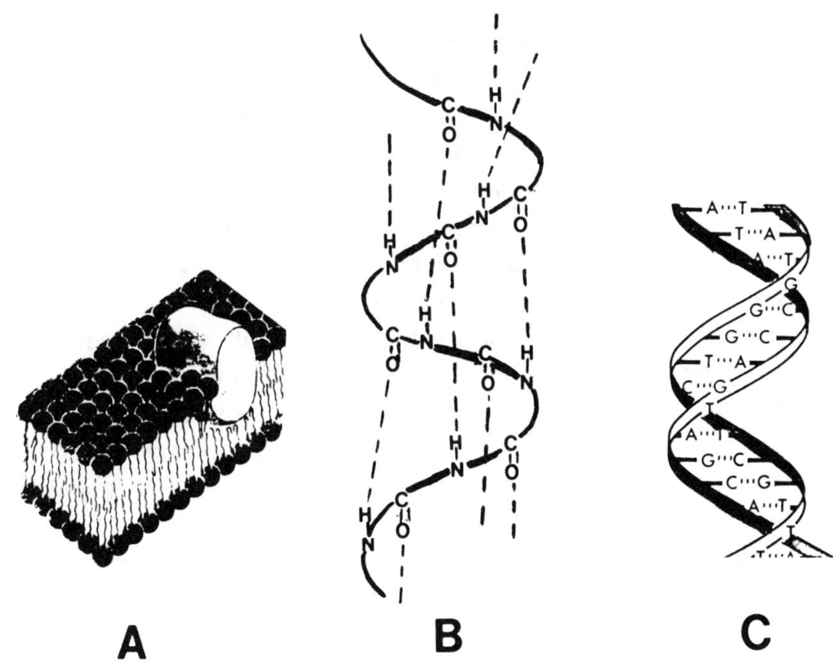

Basic structural units of biological systems. A. Lipid bilayer membrane. B. The helical coil of proteins. C. The double helix of nucleic acids.

into aggregates as sheets of molecules with the polar ends extended into the water. As a surface film, the aggregate is a monomolecular layer at the air-water interface with the hydrocarbon chains directed outward away from the water. Beneath the surface, however, surrounded by water, the phospholipids form spherical shapes with the hydrocarbon chains fused with each other. If a single layer of phospholipid molecules fuse their hydrocarbon chains and form a ball, a micelle results; but if a bimolecular layer creates a spherical enclosure, the particle becomes a liposome, or vesicle, when referring to biological components. It is the vesicle that represents the ubiquitous cellular feature of all life on earth.

A liposome formed of the closed bilayer sheet creates the condition of the living cell where the internal environment can be maintained at a different chemical composition from the surrounding medium. The reproductive and metabolic machinery of a cell could not function unless the substances of low molecular weight that are substrates and precursors for biosynthesis were retained within a membrane. These double-lipid membranes with their hydrophilic ends outward are intrinsically stable barriers to prevent the loss of valuable cellular constituents and to maintain the concentration gradient essential for a biological system.

The membrane must isolate the cell from its environment — but not completely. Nutrients must enter the cell and waste products must be expelled. Generally, a cellular membrane is pervious to lipid-soluble substances and water, but admits only soluble organic compounds containing no more than three to five carbon atoms. The penetration of ions depends on the number of electric charges per ion: polyvalent species such as calcium and sulfate ions appear to be very slow to penetrate cells. And there is a barrier to the positive charge; small anions like chloride and bicarbonate penetrate the membrane of red blood cells about a million times faster than cations of similar size. This selectivity of ionic charge, characteristic of the cellular membrane, is also demonstrated by liposomes of phospholipids by several orders of magnitude.[1]

The protein portion of contemporary cellular membranes contains enzymes and other specific molecules that perform functions for

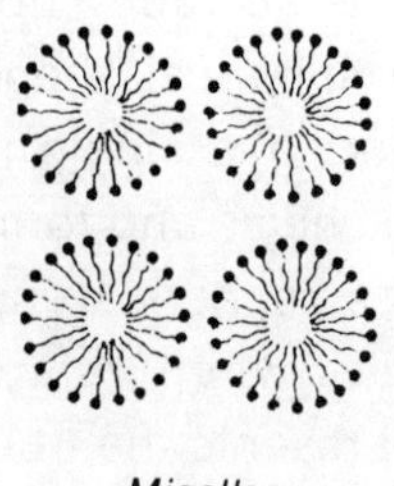

Micelles

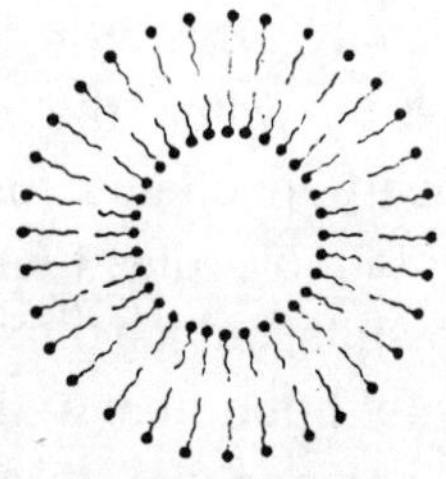

Liposome (vesicle)

today's organisms that would have been too advanced for the unsophisticated encapsulating envelope the primitive cells possessed. There are, however, some processes, because of their fundamental character, that would have been shared by the primal cells and their more evolved descendants alike. Primarily, all would have had to bring into the cell across the lipid barrier nutrients from the outside medium to to fuel their growth.

Many substances of importance — sugars, amino acids, nucleotides — are not soluble in lipid, exceed the size limit of permeability, and yet penetrate cellular membranes easily. It is believed contemporary cells possess a special transport mechanism to take these essential materials across the lipid barrier. Since this active transport system appears to be constructed of special proteins in the membrane, it is too developed to have been available to the primal cells. How then would vital components have crossed the lipid layer to supply the primitive cell from the outside medium?

William Stillwell[2] of Michigan State University has proposed a mechanism that could have served as a rudimentary transport system for the diffusion of amino acids across the lipid membrane of primal cells. When amino acids are condensed with simple water-soluble aldehydes, the resulting imines are capable of diffusing across the lipid barrier. Once inside the cell, dissociation of the imine would liberate the amino acid which would be retained by the membrane while the aldehyde, capable of diffusing across the membrane, would pass out again from the cell. This type of diffusion is known as carrier mediated or facilitated diffusion. Since it does not involve complex transport proteins, it could have been an important transport system with the primitive cells.

The lipid bilayer membrane possesses an additional property, both unique and indispensable, for the developing cell. It gave the cell its insulating capacity to electric charge. All membranes of living cells manifest a difference of electrical potential between the two sides of the membrane. In order to absorb photons of sunlight and pass the energy along the electron transfer system to synthesize ATP, the chain of electron carriers has to be insulated to prevent short circuiting. Only the lipid membrane possesses the thin, insulating features necessary

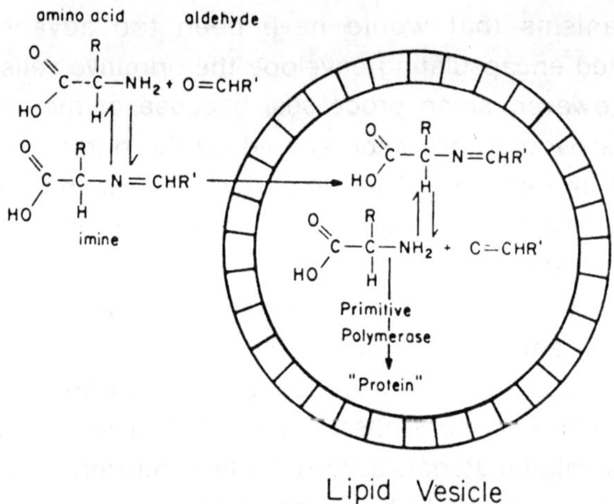

Scheme indicating the adehyde mediated uptake of amino acids into a lipid vesicle. (Stillwell, Biosystems **8**, 111, 1976)

to perform as a biochemical capacitor.

The lipid vesicle appears to be the sole model for the envelope of a primordial cell that fulfills all the biological requirements. Neither coacervates, proteinoid microspheres, Jeewanu particles or inorganic spherules have all the vital properties of a lipid bilayer membrane. They are too leaky to retain small molecular weight substances, too thick and conducting to serve as insulators, and they all fail to comply with the *Principle of Continuity,* that generalization that requires that each stage of evolution develop as a continuation from the previous one. There have been efforts to incorporate essential features of the lipid membrane into coacervates and microspheres, but the purpose becomes suspect. Neither coacervates nor proteinoids have any role in biological systems, nor is there evidence that they have ever had. On the other hand, the lipid bilayer appears to have been the vital envelope from the beginning of life.

The creation of a biological system was the result of natural substances responding to spontaneous reactions. The building blocks of life were found to be energetically favored structures produced from the interaction of intense energy with matter. Their polymerizations followed set chemical reactions under common terrestrial conditions; the nucleotides form pairing through hydrogen bonding for replication; and polypeptides wrap themselves into the helical coil. So too, then, do lipids assemble spontaneously in an aqueous environment to form the basis of the cellular membrane.

The familiar condition of oil forming a film on water is the characteristic spontaneity of lipids to structure formation. It illustrates how even a minute amount of lipid will automatically spread into sheets of aligned molecules. Surface films are monomolecular layers formed at the interface of water and air; whereas, within the aqueous volume without the interface, the lipids in a sense create their own interface by keeping their polar ends toward water while orienting their nonpolar tails together. If a sphere is formed encapsulating water, the result is a bilayer membrane enclosure — a vesicle.

This is an ordinary feature of nature whose significance to the origin of life was first pointed out by Reg Goldacre[3] of the Chester Beatty Research Institute of London. In 1958, Goldacre published a paper on surface films he observed to be common for all lakes, rivers and streams. Rarely noticed unless dust-ladened or examined carefully, there is a monolayer of elastic film on the surface of all bodies of water that appears to be a part of the natural environment. Tadpoles eat it, fresh-water snails crawl upside down along the under surface, and small arthopods can be seen supported by it as they hop across the surface. It is a molecular film, not of oil, but presumably of lipoproteins from leaves, pollen and other material that fall in the water.

When the film is compressed by a reduction in the surface area, as occurs when a stream changes abruptly from shallow to deep, or by the flow of water under a floating barrier, or even by surface pressure from the wind, the film wrinkles in a series of folds. The buckling film, in cases where the hydrophobic surface folds back upon itself, fuses, entrapping air and water in alternating loops. As the air gradually escapes, the bubbles collapse, bringing together adjacent sections of the film to form a double lipoprotein membrane which severs from the surface film in little cylinders that roll away freely in the water. These elongated structures quickly give rise to spherical cell-like particles, each consisting of the lipid bilayer membrane with an enclosed aqueous environment. Goldacre found the properties of collapsed lipoprotein films — surface tension, adhesiveness, osmotic expansion-concentration — resemble closely the properties of biological membranes.

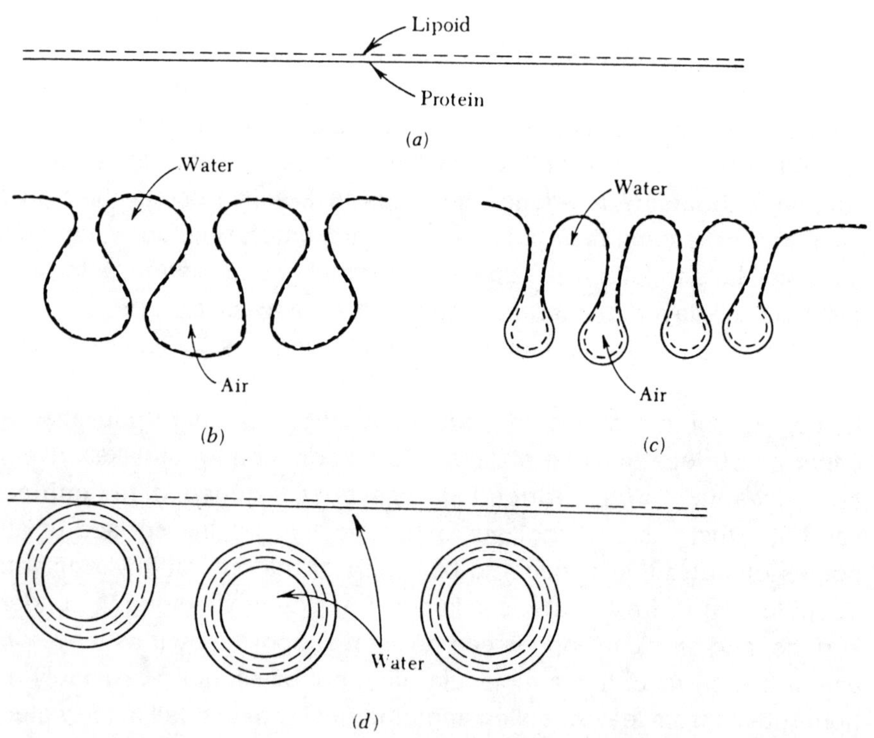

Proposed model for the formation of biphasic vesicles by wave action on surface films. (Goldacre, in **Surface Phenomena in Chemistry and Biology**, *Pergamon Press, 1958)*

Lipoproteins forming the surface films are complexes between proteins and lipids that are principally phospholipids. It is the hydrophobic paraffin chain of the fatty acid components of the phospholipids, being excluded from water, that orients the lipid molecules in a monomolecular layer at the air-water interface. The binding between protein and phospholipid is generally believed to be predominantly ionic occurring at the interface, although hydrophobic side groups of the protein can interact with the lipid layer. When a bilayer results from the collapse of the film, the hydrophobic chains of the two layers of lipids are fused and the pinched off unit becomes a vesicle with the proteins attached to both sides of the membrane.

The surface film is of biological origin. Would its counterpart have existed on prebiological earth? It seems probable that it would have been a common feature then, as it is now. Phospholipids are compounds that result from the condensation of fatty acids, glycerol, phosphoric acid and an additional small component. It has been reported that cyanamide, the condensing agent implicated in the abiotic formation of polynucleotides and polypeptides, also catalyzes glycerol phosphorylation in acid solutions. In experiments studying the abiotic synthesis of phospholipids on primordial earth, Will Hargreaves, Sean Mulvhill and Dave Deamer[4] of the University of California at Davis found fatty acids and fatty aldehydes reacted with glycerol when mixtures were dried together and incubated at 65°C for one week. Then in experiments simulating tidal pools, they prepared dilute solutions containing glycerol, phosphate, cyanamide, and added various hydrocarbon derivatives for the surface films. When they evaporated the mixtures to dryness and baked the residue at 65°C on sand or clay, they were able to detect in the resulting material the presence of phospholipids similar to phosphatidic acid, phosphatidyl glycerophosphate and some residual neutral lipids. Moreover, when water was added to the products and the mixture was agitated, a heterogeneous suspension of vesicles with the lipid bilayer membrane formed readily. A particular significance was attached to the phosphatidyl glycerol because this lipid and its aminoacyl derivatives are prominant in membranes of procaryotes.

As Hargreaves and Deamer[5] continued their study, they found the tendency to form cell-like structures was exhibited, not only by lipids simpler than the phospholipids, but also spontaneously without wave action or other forms of turbulence. Single-chain charged molecules

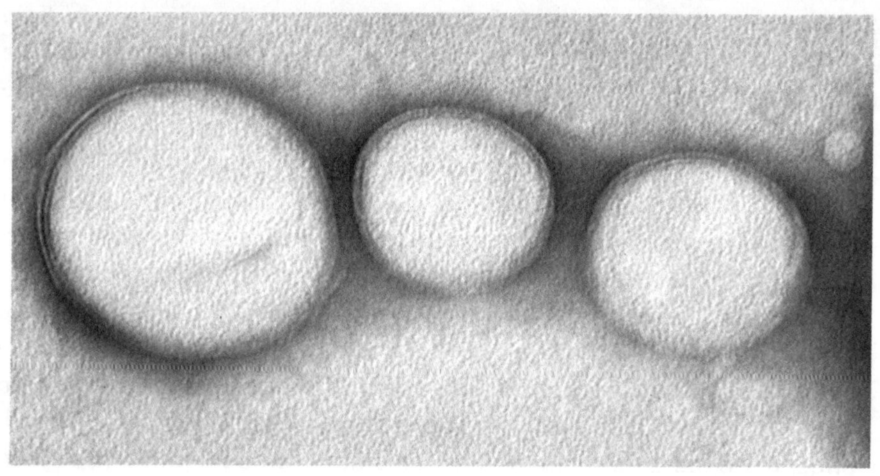

Vesicles produced in an extract of an experiment simulating the prebiotic synthesis of lipids. (Hargreaves et al., Nature **226,** 78, *1977)*

formed stable lipid vesicles, and even the uncharged monoacylglycerols coalesced into liposomes when dispersed in water. Furthermore, saturated fatty acids of 8 to 16 carbons formed lipid vesicles when the conditions were slightly alkaline.

The critical parameters for the formation of vesicles were pH, temperature and the hydrocarbon chain-length. The minimum chain lengths from which membranes could form in pure dispersions appeared to be 8 carbons for both fatty acids and monoacylglycerides. The required temperature range was between 20 and 55^{0}C, and the pH, 7 to 9, conditions that exist within most terrestrial environments.

The simple glycerolipids were presumably more prevalent than phospholipids on the primordial scene. Sand or clay in dry mudflats or catchbasins could have provided the circumstances for condensation-dehydration reactions where the hydrophilic and hydrophobic molecules combined to form glycerolipids. In addition to surface catalysts such as silica and clay, the chemical condensing agents, cyanamide and dicyanamide, may have assisted in the prebiotic synthesis of these membranogenic compounds.

Deamer and Hargreaves believe the initial membranes on primordial earth were partly or largely lipid. Even before biosynthesis became a reality, there could have been selective forces favoring stability that concentrated available phospholipids into particular cells. The ionic and hydrophobic interactions between the membrane lipids and peptides would have allowed the latter to become intercalated in the membrane structure, perhaps injecting selective permeability. And

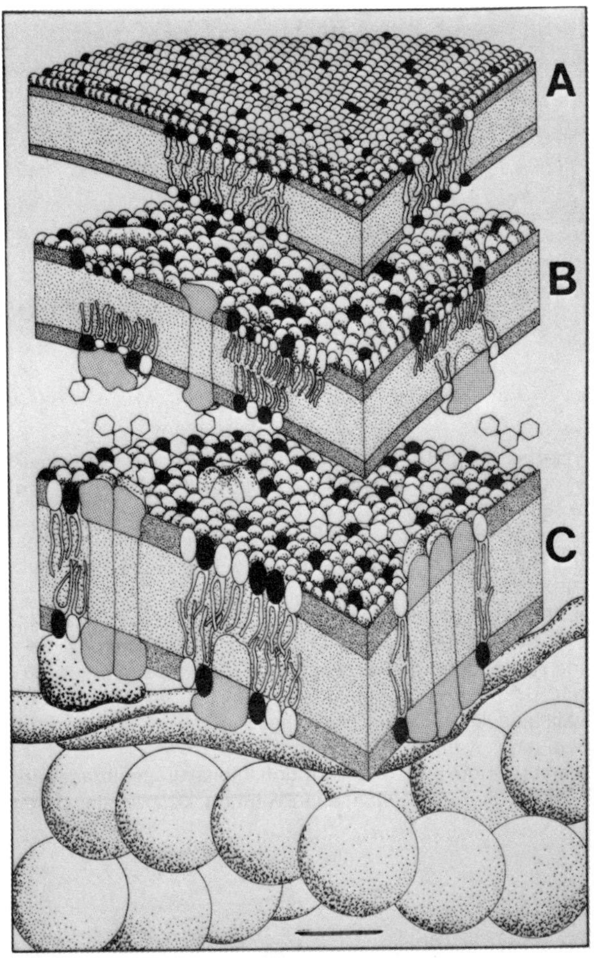

Hypothetical steps in biomembrane evolution. The bar represents 50 nm. A. Simplest bilayer membrane containing single-chain lipids with C_8-C_{12} hydrocarbons. B. Membrane containing both monoalkyl and dialkyl lipids (C_{10}-C_{16}) with adsorbed and intercalated polypeptides. C. Advanced membrane of C_{16} - C_{18} dialkyl lipids containing proteins and carbohydrates, and associated with peripheral protein systems. (Hargreaves and Deamer, in **Light Transducing Membranes: Structure, Function, and Evolution,** *Academic Press, 1978*

eventually, the synthesis of proteins would have evolved proteins incorporated into the membrane for specific functions as enzymes or as agents for the transport of substances into and out of the cell.

The development of the envelope to create the primitive cells was an act that must have occurred readily on primordial earth. The lipid vesicles generated spontaneously when the lipid concentration reached the critical level where they form. Since the natural forces leading to cellular structure existed, they inevitably led to the self-assembly of primitive cells without the directing influence of pre-existing biological systems.

References

1. A.D. Bangham and R.W. Horne, Negative staining of phospholipids and their structural modification by surface active agents as observed in the electron microscope, *J. Mol. Biol.* **8**, 660-668 (1964).
2. W. Stillwell, Facilitated diffusion of amino acids across bimolecular lipid membranes as a model for selective accumulation of amino acids in a primordial protocell, Biosystems **8**, 111-117 (1976).
3. R.J. Goldacre, Surface films, their collapse on compression, the shapes and sizes of cells and the origin of life, in **Surface Phenomena in Chemistry and Biology**, J.F. Danielli, K.G.A. Pankhurst and A.C. Riddiford, eds., Pergamon Press, New York, 1958, pp. 278-298.
4. W.R. Hargreaves, S.J. Mulvhill and D.W. Deamer, Synthesis of phospholipids and membranes in prebiotic conditions, *Nature* **266**, 78-80 (1977).
5. W.R. Hargreaves and D.W. Deamer, Origin and early evolution of bilayer membranes, in **Light Transducing Membranes: Structure, Function, and Evolution**, D.W. Deamer, ed., Academic Press, 1978.

27
A Cell is Born

The primordial scene no longer exists. The prebiotic substances that gave birth to the first living cells are long gone, consumed and transformed in countless recycling processes by the very organisms they created. Nothing remains as witness to that event over three and a half eons ago on Archean Earth when matter and energy came together to create a living entity that eventually was to spread over every niche in the thin watery and gaseous film that sheaths the globe and then reach with tentacles outward toward the immense universe.

To reconstruct what happened between three and four billion years ago, we are required to study the patterns of life processes, establish recognizable trends of behavior, and attempt to retrace the steps that life has taken. Only then can we tread back into time, back beyond the beginning of the metazoae, coelenterates, the sponges, beyond when eucaryotes appeared, back when oxygen was no longer a sustenance of life, back to the hot, strange world of the Archean where shallow oceans skimmed around juvenile continents, scarred and blackened by the volcanic convulsions that gave them birth.

The prebiotic substances that formed on primordial earth washed into low-lying basins and collected. There they interacted with each other through a multitude of possible chemical combinations, some hydrolyzing quickly to recombine again another way; others more stable, accumulating. Life resulted from combinations that survived. But survival of chemical substances, normally regarded in the sense of resistance to decomposition, in this case was accomplished by a vastly superior assurance of survival. The manner in which particular combinations succeeded in perpetuating their existence was by making copies of themselves.

It began with the nucleotides. These chemicals could combine with each other in various weak associations through hydrogen bonding, some combinations stronger than others, but all dissociating in solution rather easily. When converted to activated derivatives such as poly-phosphates, phosphoramidates or cyclic 2′, 3′-phosphates, the nucleotides condensed into short chains. More often than not, the monomers became joined through 2′, 5′-linkages, as well as the 3′, 5′-bonding found in biological systems.

In order to carry out effective replication, the polynucleotides of an organism would have needed to be exclusively one type of linkage. By what means did the primeval cells have access to polynucleotides of a uniform bonding?

David Usher[1] of Cornell University has demonstrated that oligonucleotides containing both 2′, 5′- and 3′, 5′-linkages would gradually have become the normal 3′, 5′-polynucleotides from the effect of a cyclical pattern in nature. When the 3′, 5′-bonded oligonucleotides twist into a double helix, they have a greater resistance to hydrolysis than the 2′, 5′-bonded nucleotides that disrupt the helical configuration. By exposing mixed polymers to the conditions of a natural cycle, Usher showed that preferential hydrolysis of the 2′, 5′-bond favored the accumulation of the biological polynucleotides.

In the experiment the nucleotides (nucleoside 2′, 3′-phosphates) were warmed and baked in the presence of imidazole and other abiotic catalysts, followed by cooling and the addition of a small amount of water. When the cycle was repeated over and over, Usher observed a progressive accumulation of oligonucleotides with the 3′, 5′-linkage. It would have been a process that occurred frequently on primordial earth.

Each morning as the sun rose high over the Archean landscape, the heat of the sun condensed the nucleotides into mixed oligomers. With the passing of the day, the temperature dropped, bringing the dew and dampening of the polymers. During the noctural interval, some 3′, 5′-bonded oligomers in solution found complementary partners to form short helices. As the sun rose again to repeat the cycle, those nucleotides wrapped in helices were slightly protected against hydrolysis, while the unprotected 2′, 5′-bound nucleotides were subjected to preferential hydrolysis. Day after day the cycle went on, each time more polynucleotide than before survived with the 3′, 5′-linkage into longer and longer chains.

The nucleotides with their purine and pyrimidine bases were mere chemical substances. Nevertheless, they had the ability to form hydrogen bonding, not with other nucleotides like themselves, but with a nucleotide of the other base type. In so doing, the polynucleotides were making chains of complementary nucleotides that formed the most stable associations. Only by separating the double-stranded structure and making a copy of the "negative" did replication of molecules on earth begin. When this occurred, it became the basis of perpetuating molecular species.

For the polynucleotides to continue to form, they needed an applicable activation procedure and shielding from the intense ultraviolet rays that wreak destruction on the nucleotide structure. Sediments protected those polynucleotides that were covered, but allowed little opportunity for further interactions. Only when they were carried into depths beneath a thick cover of water were the polynucleotides free to move in solution while spared from the fierce radiation.* Those replicating molecules that were washed into catchbasins eventually found themselves encased in vesicles formed from the elastic lipid film that covered primordial waters.

In such an arrangement, they were held in close association while having the advantage of movement that they had with the concentrated solution where there was a small amount of water; but to survive in water they needed to be supplied with free energy, which is to say, phosphorylation. It appears it was at this stage that the nascent cells developed a rudimentary form of photosynthesis.

In his paper on the origin of photophosphorylation, Stillwell[2] suggests that, under the reducing conditions and intense ultraviolet light of primordial earth, the early forms of cells could have used photophosphorylation based on quinol phosphates to produce their ATP and other activated nucleotides. In contemporary cells quinones are present in the photophosphorylation chain, but chlorophyll and carotenoids are the initial collectors of visible light. Stillwell reasons the series of reactants originally began with quinones and was extended to more effective absorbers of visible light as the ultraviolet rays lost their intensity when the ozone layer began to form.

Ultraviolet light was destructive in large amounts, but it was also the most available energy source to be captured by simple substances. When hydroquinones are exposed to ultraviolet light in the presence of

---

*Ultraviolet light of 1800 Å penetrates less than 1 cm; whereas, the 2800 Å wavelength penetrates 10 meters of water before reaching extinction.

inorganic phosphates, quinol phosphates are formed. Quinol phosphates are strong phosphorylating agents, and together with a water-soluble iron sulfide complex (the forerunner of ferredoxin), they phosphorylate ADP to ATP. Presumably, the other nucleotides were capable of being activated in the same manner.

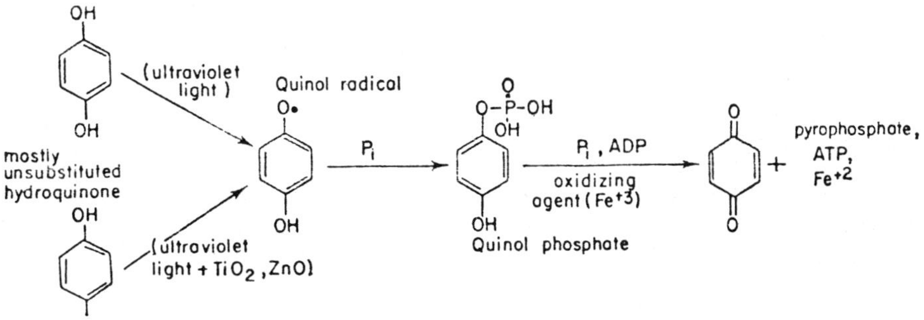

Proposed model for photophosphorylation using ultraviolet light to produce ATP (Stillwell, J. Theor. Biol. **65**, *479, 1977)*

The advantage of this model is that it shows that photophosphorylation could have developed early in the formation of life from simple substances without the complex membrane structuring that has been found with the later photosynthetic mechanism. As the genetic apparatus or organisms became larger and more susceptible to damage by ultraviolet light, the cells could thrive in depths or areas with optimal light for photophosphorylation and survival.

Eventually, when organisms evolved to the point of greater synthesis capability, they were able to develop photosynthesis based entirely on visible light activation using porphyrins, the class of chemicals that included chlorophyll. Stillwell points out that even after porphyrins were being used and H_2S, H_2 and reduced organic compounds became adopted as electron donors, phosphorylation may still have been through quinol phosphates. Only after the porphyrin-quinone-iron sulfide complex became lipophilic and attached to an elaborate membrane structure did quinones lose their role as phosphorylating agents and become only electron and proton shuttles in the photosynthesis mechanism, a role they currently perform.

These primitive cells with their rudimentary form of photophosphorylation and replicating polynucleotides could have been numerous, but life was at an extremely retarded pace. The reactions were slow — sometimes taking days, months, even years — for there were no enzymes. The lipid membranes were not generated by biosynthesis, but still relied upon the accumulated prebiotic lipid deposition. A crude form of exchange of material probably existed between vesicles when two coalesced, then redivided, or when an existing cell would come in contact with and absorb more lipid and separate into two different cells. During this period the cells were probably in confined environments such as volcanic lakes or catchment areas where encounters would be favored.

The primeval cells may have existed at this stage for millions, or conceivably, hundreds of millions of years. There were amino acids and other organic substances in the aquatic environment, but they would have been of no particular significance. Amino acids that passed into the cells may have, while they were still as the imines or by the amino group being complexed on some inner cellular component, occasionally formed adenylates and, subsequently, short peptides. But these probably had no consequences on the cells at the time except to represent clutter.

The polynucleotides would have been subjected to mutational change during this period, but the greatest variety could have resulted from exchange of short polynucleotides between the population of cells. Coupling of these units into longer ones over a long time span would have produced a tremendously large number of combinations. It seems reasonable to assume it was one of these polynucleotides, after it was transcribed to a complementary chain, that gave a molecule that folded back on itself and assumed a three-dimensional shape held together by opposing complementary bases. This polynucleotide became the first transfer RNA; the nucleotide chain from which it was transcribed, the first gene.

The gene for the first tRNA, because transcription is a one-on-one nucleotide relationship, needed to have been no longer than the tRNA itself. Margaret Dayhoff and her colleagues[3] at the Georgetown University Medical Center in Washington have studied the molecular evolution of the tRNA's and feel the evidence strongly indicates that the tRNA's are all derived from a single gene. All tRNA's are synthesized from C, G, A and U, each contain an identical tetramer sequence in one lobe, all end in CCA, and all have about the same length. They point out that the probability of even two such similar molecules occurring independently and simultaneously in the same cell would have been extremely small. On the other hand, duplication of the tRNA gene followed by independent mutational changes in the separate genes would have given closely similar products. Subsequent doublings expanded the number of tRNA's to accommodate a variety of amino acids.

The ancestral tRNA either accepted amino acids from amino acid adenylates or the terminal CCA end of the tRNA could have been activated and coupled with amino acids directly. In any event, the tRNA apparently began as a non-specific intermediary in condensing amino acids when the tRNA-amino acid complex aligned on a polynucleotide chain serving like a contemporary messenger nucleic acid. In what manner tRNA's evolved their specificity is not yet understood, although the specificity linking each tRNA to a particular amino acid resides in the enzyme that promotes the attachment. But eventually the tRNA's managed to bring into operation the mechanism for condensing the amino acids into peptides correlating to the nucleotide sequence on the messenger molecule.

Ribosomes are subcellular particles that play an essential role in the synthesis of polypeptides. Without ribosomes the tRNA-amino acid complex does not remain attached to the mRNA long enough to react. For the primitive cell to begin the mechanism, it needed something to participate as a ribosome or to have carried out the step in some manner without the aid of these particles.

Crick and others[4] have speculated that the initial protein synthesis may have occurred with tRNA's that bound to five base-pairs instead of three on the mRNA as with contemporary organisms. In this way the binding would have been sufficiently strong to hold the tRNA-amino acid complex in place long enough for the condensation to occur without a ribosome. They further propose that, because of the resulting restrictions this placed on the number of codons, only four amino acids — glycine, serine, aspartic acid and asparagine — were coded for in the original mechanism.

On the other hand, contemporary ribosomes are approximately one-half nucleic acid, with the remainder a variety of proteins. This chemist is inclined to believe the protein synthesis mechanism used primitive ribosomes that were complexes of polynucleotides, and the triplet served as the codon from the beginning.

All amino acids used by later organisms may not have existed prebiologically. Aspartic acid, glycine, serine and alanine, the four most common α-amino acids generated from cyanides and found prevalent in ferredoxin, most certainly were prebiotic. But arginine and histidine, which have not been produced in simulated experiments, presumably originated only through biosynthesis as organisms evolved.

There are two categories of amino acids: structural amino acids and those with functional groups on the side-chain. Some of the latter, notably those with an attached basic group, play vital roles in enzymes, but are not readily formed by simulation experiments. As a result, other prebiotic compounds may have acted as substitutes until the biogenic synthesis of these amino acids developed. As an example, 4-amino-imidazole-5-carboxamide, the imidazole derivative from ammonium cyanide, may have served in the capacity of histidine for the emerging cell. Tryptophan, phenylalanine, tyrosine and methionine are other possible candidates for a biosynthetic origin.

Once the primeval cell established a degree of specificity to the messenger polynucleotide, any useful peptides would no longer be a chance happening, but would be able to be produced as needed, giving the cell a selective advantage. One of the first such peptides was the ancestral ferredoxin whose origin Eck and Dayhoff[5] have traced back to a tetrapeptide.

Ferredoxin, now an iron sulfide protein of 55 amino acids in advanced forms of life, evolved to a progressively larger molecule because each change introduced a protein that was more efficient as an electron carrier than the predecessor. There remains little doubt that this is the manner in which enzymes originated.

The primitive cell was probably already using iron sulfide as a catalyst, either alone, attached to cysteine, or with some abiotic peptide. The evolutionary development of ferredoxin seems to have begun with the peptide, ala-asp-ser-gly. The peptide's gene, 12 nucleotides long, eventually doubled; and as the synthesizing abilities of organisms became more versatile and efficient, the genetic mechanism was able to incorporate other amino acids. Cysteine was among these amino acids and the sulfide bond became attached to the iron sulfide. Mutations which modified and complicated the amino acid sequence created a series of changes that ultimately led to an intricate protein-iron sulfide complex of greatly enhanced efficiency.

Enzymes are not singular substances, but seem so only because their extreme efficiency pales any other catalysts by comparison. This is misleading and has created the impression that no kind of biological system could exist without them. Certainly no organism comparable to contemporary life could, but possibly for several hundred million years there may have been primitive cells existing before enzymes evolved. Once enzymes developed, however, their selective advantage to the cells was so immense that cells with enzymes spread rapidly, sweeping away all primitive life in their swath.

Enzymes evolved from simpler, less efficient substances that performed the same function. Histidine, pyridoxine, iron sulfide and others are all substances that catalyze chemical reactions. They are also components that became part of or complexed with peptide chains in combinations that promoted the reactions faster than they alone. Eventually, enzymes evolved out of the developing protein synthesis that had these catalytic chemicals incorporated as a part of their structure to be biocatalysts.

The first enzymes to have evolved would have been those that would facilitate the propagation mechanism. Any advantage to reproduction sent the innovation spreading with the faster-breeding cells throughout the population. In this way, ferredoxin, by accelerating photophosphorylation, gave an advantage to the primitive cell. The structural detail of the enzymes associated with polymerization and translation processes are not yet elucidated to the point that their origins can be defined, but presumably these enzymes would have been among the earliest to appear in biological systems.

The oldest fossils of organisms ever found on earth have been discovered in the Fig Tree and Onverwacht formations in the Barberton Mountain Land of the eastern Transvaal of South Africa. The fossils are in chert that occurs, sometimes in horizontal layers, but more often in pockets that had been in the surface of some ancient lava. There, in the mineral-rich waters of volcanic lakes, the earliest forms of life on earth thrived, died and were buried in sediments to become entombed for three and a half billion years.

Were these the primitive cells that first formed from an assemblage of prebiotic substances to form life, or were these life after several hundred million years of perfecting the genetic and metabolic mechanisms? In a comparative study of the evolution of cytochromes and transfer RNA's, McLaughlin and Dayhoff[6] have computed the appearance of procaryotes to be 2.6 times more remote than that of eucaryotes. If the eucaryotes evolved 1.3 billion years ago as suggested by Cloud's microfossils, the primitive cells may have existed as long ago as 3.9 billion years.

This is quite remarkable. Considering that the earth was formed 4.6 billion years ago followed by the *T. Tauri* stage of the sun, this allowed less than a billion years for the atmosphere and waters to form from volcanism, the prebiological organic compounds to be produced and accumulated, and the primitive cells to arise and evolve into fully functional organisms. It represented approximately the time span of the first orogeny where the heat from radioactivity in the earth built up and went through the cycle of mountain building. So early did the primitive cells occur, that the processes that led to their formation must have been highly probable. So probable, in fact, was the event that it must be regarded as having been inevitable.

References

1. D.A. Usher, Early chemical evolution of nucleic acids: A theoretical model, *Science* **196,** 311-313 (1977).
2. W. Stillwell, On the origin of photophosphorylation, *J. Theor. Biol.* **65,** 479-497 (1977.)
3. **Altas of Protein Sequence and Structure,** M.O. Dayhoff, ed., vol. 5, National Biomedical Research Foundation, Silver Spring, Md., 1972, pp. 111-117.
4. F. H. C. Crick, S. Brenner, A. Klug and G. Pieczenik, A speculation on the origin of protein synthesis, *Origins of Life* **7,** 389-397 (1976).
5. R. V. Eck and M. O. Dayhoff, Evolution of the structure of ferredoxin based on living relics of primitive amino acid sequences, *Science* **152,** 363-366 (1966).
6. P. J. McLaughlin and M. O. Dayhoff, Eukaryotes versus prokaryotes: An estimate of evolutionary distance, *Science* **168,** 1469-1471 (1970).
7. **Atlas of Protein Sequence and Structure,** M. O. Dayhoff, ed., vol. 5, National Biomedical Research Foundation, Silver Springs, Md., 1972, p. 116.

28
The Phenomenal Cell

The primitive cells that floated and rolled languidly in the warm waters of Archean volcanic lakes nearly 4 billion years ago were the beginning. They were genetically alive. They had crossed the threshold and no longer were merely inanimate molecules; they were an association of components that formed a unit in which nucleotides were activated, condensed to polynucleotides on other polynucleotides, and in the process, performed molecular reproduction. But still, it may have ended there except for one critical feature — these primitive cells had the capacity for change. In this way the door was left ajar.

The cells existed as a collection of chemical reactions, and any improvement on the efficiency of these reactions made the cell more competitive for the substances in the medium. Cells with access to components that were most effective in reproduction and whose alteration in chemical structures that accelerated rates of reaction became prevalent. It was this ability to change, with the advantage being bestowed upon the most efficient, that carried the primitive cells from being just genetically alive to organisms as we know them today with their impressive powers of metabolism.

The path leading to metabolically alive cells meandered through thickets of changes, each improving upon the cells' capacity to catalyze their biochemical reactions. These were to culminate eventually in the most impressive catalysts ever to exist — the enzymes. But before the enzymes were to become a part of cellular mechanics, there must have been a long interval for laying the basis of their emergence.

The amino acids, purines, pyrimidines and lipids entered the biological systems fully formed. These were the building blocks for the condensed polymeric components and cellular structure. The proteins, however, are composed of a greater variety of amino acids than seemingly would have been available in the reservoir of prebiotic substances. Nevertheless, few new amino acids could have been introduced after the beginnng of protein synthesis. Once proteins became the mainstay of cellular function, any change in a single amino acid would have affected, not one, but a large number of proteins. For that reason, it appears the amino acid series existed before the advent of enzymes.

Amino acids are usually thought of in terms of subunits of proteins, but they also serve as precursors to other biochemicals, including amino acids. Those amino acids produced most readily from cyanides, viz., alanine, serine, aspartic acid and glycine, would have been in the environment in the greatest amounts. It is from these same few amino acids that contemporary cells synthesize a large variety of their basic components, presumably by chemical pathways passed down from the early primitive cells. Even before enzymes then, the amino acids of biogenic origin must have been synthesized in primitive cells by simple chemical transformations that were the precursors of today's biochemical reactions.

The synthesis of the amino acids generally involved the transfer of functional groups — amino, methyl, $-CO_3$, CH_2OH, -CHO — from one component or amino acid to another. By group transfer reactions a few amino acids can be converted to a wide variety of other amino acids and essential biological constituents. It is by these reactions and others that aspartic acid serves as the precursor to purines, pyrimidines, alanine, threonine, lysine, methionine and arginine. Serine, another amino acid from HCN, can degrade to pyruvate; the decarboxylation of pyruvic acid can, in turn, lead to acetate; and acetate in the activated form as acetyl coenzyme A is directly involved in the synthesis of lipids for the cellular membrane.

It is impressive how few substances can serve as precursors to other vital constituents. In some organisms, pyruvate, acetate and carbonate — substances that would have been common on primordial earth — can furnish all the carbon to serine, glycine, cysteine, alanine, valine, leucine, isoleucine, lysinc, aspartic acid, threonine, methionine, glutamic acid, proline and arginine.[1]

All the chemical reactions used by biological systems already existed before life. The developing cells, therefore, did not create new chemical reactions to synthesize their constituents, but merely adopted means of exercising control over the many possible combinations. They accomplished this by accelerating select reactions with catalysts; and of the catalysts used that became permanently incorporated in the cellular metabolic machinery, some of the most important were the coenzymes.

Enzymes are proteins with catalytic properties. They can be simple polypeptide chains or they can be conjugated proteins with a nonprotein moiety attached for a specific function. A coenzyme, therefore, is the nonprotein portion of an enzyme whose presence is required for the activity. It may be regarded as the dissociable portion of conjugated proteins. Many coenzymes contain vitamins as part of their structure, and generally they function as acceptors of electrons or functional groups.

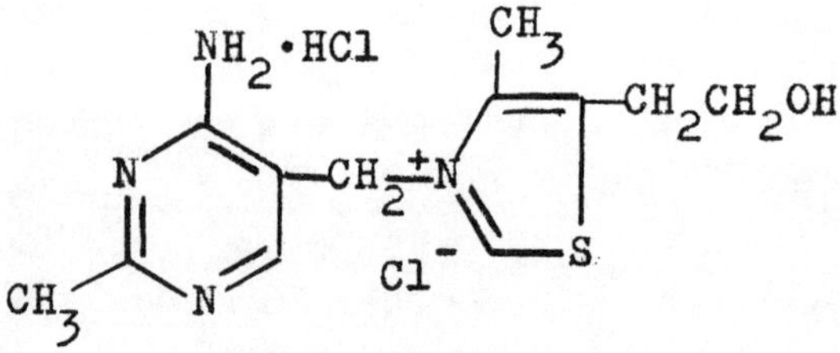

$NH_2 \cdot HCl$ CH_3 CH_2CH_2OH N CH_2 $\overset{+}{N}$ S Cl^- CH_3 N

Thiamine

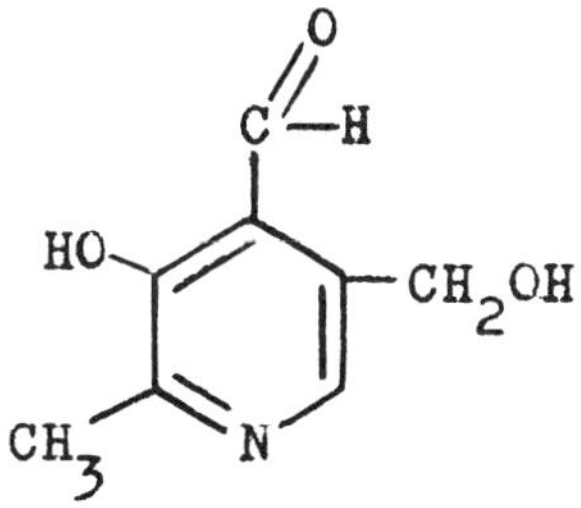

Pyridoxal

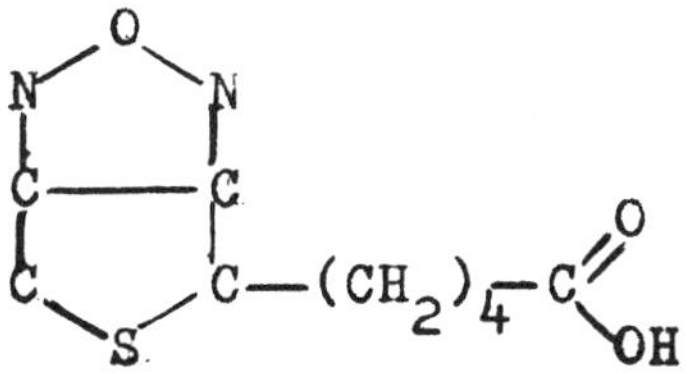

Biotin

Like other fundamental components, most of the coenzymes appear to be of ancient origin and probably they or their immediate antecedents became a part of biological systems fully formed. The pyridine nucleotides, NAD and NADP, became hydrogen acceptors for oxidation-reduction reactions, and coenzyme A became the instrument for acyl transfer. These are nucleotide derivatives of relatively simple composition that could have arisen abiotically. Of coenzymes used in group transfer, there were thiamine, pyridoxal and biotin.

Thiamine, as thiamine pyrophosphate, in an alkaline medium catalyzes the cleavage of $-\overset{O}{\overset{\|}{C}}-\overset{O}{\overset{\|}{C}}-$ with the formation of an "active aldehyde." In this way, thiamine or its primordial counterpart accelerated the breakdown of pyruvate to acetate to be available in forming acetyl-S-Co A. Thus acetyl and other acyl groups were converted to the activated state for glyceride synthesis in order that the primitive cells could commense preparing their own lipid membrane.

Pyridoxal phosphate participates in several types of reactions. It is able to catalyze decarboxylations, deaminations and transaminations of amino acids; and it also can transfer sulfur from methionine to serine to form cysteine.

Biotin functions as a coenzyme in CO_2 fixation and decarboxylation enzymes. A number of other enzyme reactions are reportedly affected by biotin. These include succinic dehydrogenase and decarboxylase, as well as the deaminase of aspartic acid, serine and threonine. Biotin is also involved in the synthesis of carbamyl phosphate,

$H_2N-\overset{O}{\overset{\|}{C}}-O-PO_3H$, a compound required in pyrimidine synthesis.

The biosynthesis of purines and pyrimidines, the bases of nucleic acids, is found in all organisms and probably was one of the earliest synthesis that was necessary for survival. In contemporary organisms, pyrimidines are synthesized by a scheme that must be original because of its universality and simplicity. In this procedure carbamyl phosphate reacts with aspartic acid to give ureidosuccinic acid, a compound that cyclizes to orotic acid, the precursor of the pyrimidines.

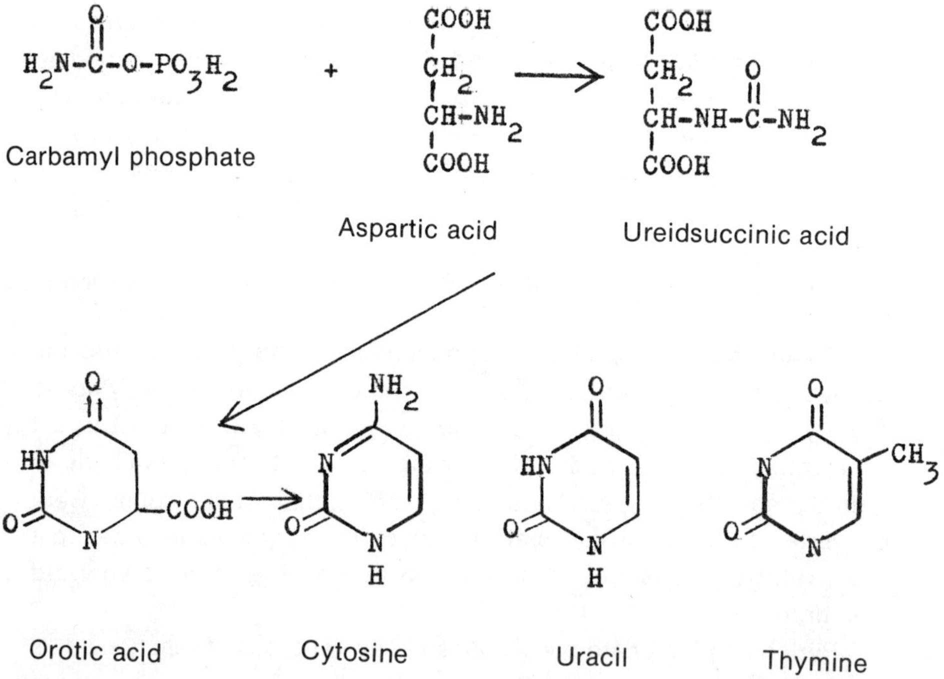

Both aspartic acid and glycine, as well as formate and CO_2 are utilized for purine biosynthesis, while two of the nitrogen atoms of the purine come from glutamine.

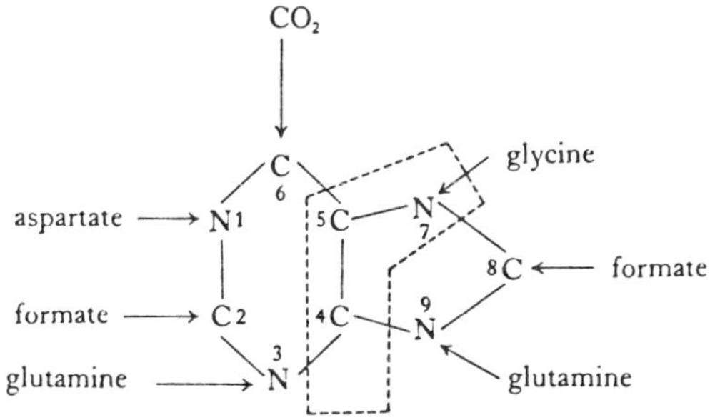

Thus, within the primitive cells that began as being genetically alive, there was a sizable collection of spontaneous chemical reactions going on at varying rates that was eventually to create a metabolically active organism. From these reactions the primitive cells received an assortment of amino acids that became incorporated into the early biogenic peptides. And the cells that contained catalysts such as imidazole derivatives and coenzymes began generating other biochemicals that were serving as useful components. Most reactions were at a slow rate and those primitive cells without substances to accelerate useful transformations would eventually have been lost by being dissociated or absorbed by more successful cells.

The ascending road to survival was open to cells in which reactions were faster and ever more specific, for efficiency was the path away from uncontrolled interactions and toward specific reactions synthesizing specific products. The coenzymes are general catalysts for a type of chemical reaction. When they became attached to polypeptide chains, however, their movement became restricted and closely associated with the peptide's interaction with the reactant. Rudimentary enzymes came into being. Slowly, step by step, as enzymes improved by amino acid substitution and enlargement, they narrowed the catalytic role of the coenzymes to reactions that are specific for only those molecules that can act as a substrate by fitting into the shape of the protein. By producing catalysts for specific reactions, the chaos of having many reactive species together in the cellular medium became organized into regulated series. And as the control of the cellular reactions was shifted to the synthesis of enzymes, biosynthesis became genetically programmed.

The synthesis of its own catalysts created one of life's most dynamic features. It became autocatalytic. Those cells that evolved enzymes that accelerated the synthesis of enzymes to accelerate the reactions ever faster quickly outpaced all other primitive cells. It was a cyclical process that placed the development of life on an escalator. The use of cycles eventually became a dominant theme in the formation of self-sustaining life forms.[2]

Like all the fundamental reactions of biological systems, the breakdown of glucose to lactic acid existed before enzymes. Ch. Degani and M. Halmann[3] have shown that the alkaline degradation of glucose 6-phosphate proceeds without enzyme action by parallel and consecutive reactions.

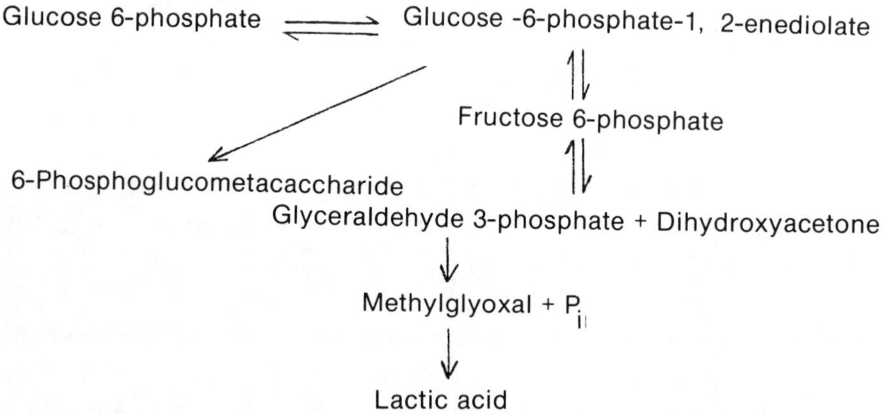

The cell capitalized on the existing glycolysis by directing the series of spontaneous reactions through pyruvic acid, and with the assistance of the coenzyme, NAD, tapped some of the chemical energy released in the degradation to produce two molecules of ATP.

Here then, became a means of extracting energy from the chemical structure of substances in the environment. Glucose was elevated to a central role as a source of chemical energy when organisms completed the cycle by generating glucose from pyruvic acid. In addition to glucose, the clostridia, some of the most ancient anaerobes, were able to use for substrates in fermentation, alcohols, carboxylic acids and amino acids — substances that would have existed in the prebiotic reserve.[4]

It has also been discovered that clostridia, as well as the photosynthetic bacteria, *Chromatium* and *C. thiosulfatophilium*, are capable of enzymic CO_2 fixation in a reaction driven by reduced ferredoxin.[5] The CO_2 assimilation carboxylates acetyl coenzyme A to pyruvate, which leads to the formation of the amino acids: aspartic and glutamic acids, and alanine.

Until recently it has generally been believed the earth's aboriginal organisms were heterotrophs that extracted chemical energy through fermentation of the reserve of prebiological organic substances. It now appears there is another phenotype of bacterium that represents a life form that may prove to be as ancient as the clostridia and photosynthetic bacteria.

Carl Woese and his group[6] at the University of Illinois have been investigating the evolutionary diversification of the bacteria through comparative characterization of their ribosomal RNA's. The oligonucleotides produced by enzymic hydrolysis of rRNA's from two species of methanogenic bacteria were compared to similar fractions from the *Bacillus*, the blue-green alga and the *Enteric-Vibrio* species. The methanogens are characterized by their ability to reduce CO_2 to methane and water. The similarity of the results from the methanogens was considered sufficient for them to belong to the same genus, but they bore so slight a resemblance to the other bacterial species that they must have arisen from a phylogenetic event antedating the divergence of the others from the main bacterial line. It appears the most ancient divergence from the line of bacterial descent may have been by the methanogenic bacteria.

If the primordial atmosphere had been formed by the outgassing of volcanoes as now believed, it would have consisted principally of CO_2, water, nitrogen and hydrogen. The reduction of CO_2 by H_2 to methane and water is a spontaneous reaction, but the rate is slow enough that it could have been harnessed by a biological system. The methanogens apparently derived their chemical energy from this particular reaction. Some contemporary methanogens can use other sources that are convertible to CO_2, such as formic acid, but none can metabolize typical organic carbon sources like more advanced

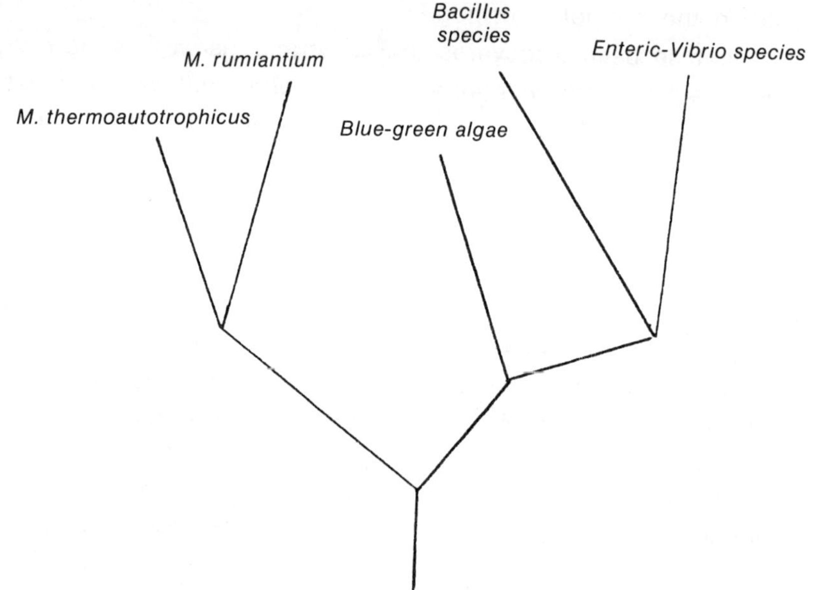

A dendrogram showing the divergence of methanogenic bacteria from three groups of procaryotic organisms. (Adapted from Batch et al.,J. Mol. Evol. **9,** *305, 1977)*

bacteria can.[7]

The primitive cells began as genetic replicating systems drawing their components from the prebiotic reserve. the number of amino acids was expanded through transformations and eventually the synthesis of enzymes brought into bloom the metabolic processes of fully functional organisms. These were all extremely early adaptations which established life patterns for all forms of life on earth. Proteins have increased in number and composition ever since, but the amino acids became unchangeable, for any further change of a basic building block would affect the efficacy of thousands of proteins in an organism with devastating results.

While the fundamental nature of life was being established, a peculiar thing was happening. Some cells began to use selectively more of one optical isomer of amino acids and ribose than another.

The differentiation probably began slowly but accelerated exponentially as cells consumed the debris of other cells until within a relatively short time, all cells were using exclusively L- α -amino acids and D-sugars.

Compounds with an asymmetrical carbon (carbon with four different substituents) have two stereoisomers for each of these carbons. The isomers are nonsuperimposable mirror images of each other, and as a consequence, one form rotates polarized light to the left (-), the other rotates it to the right (+). The configurations of the optical isomers are designated D and L to indicate, not the direction of rotation, but an arbitrary assignment of the substituents at the α -carbon of amino acids, the 4-carbon of pentoses (e.g., ribose) and the 5-carbon of hexoses (e.g., glucose).

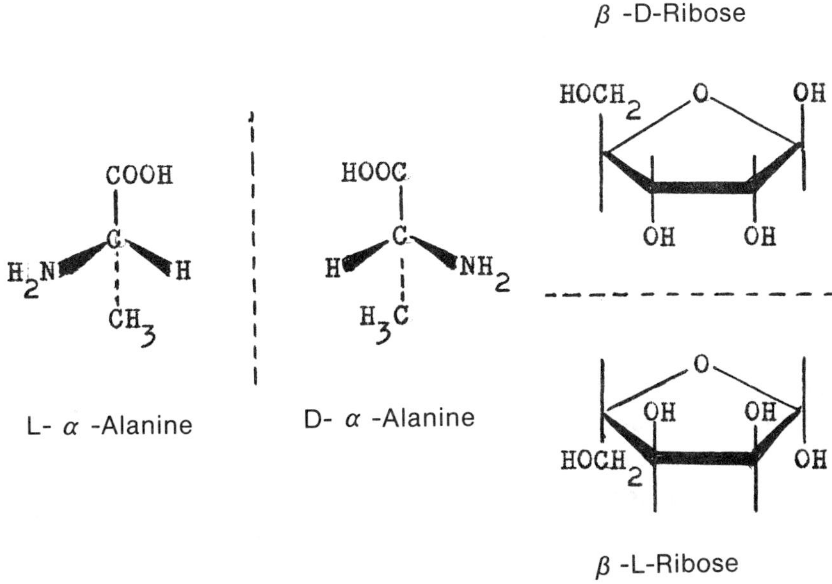

The stereoselectivity by the primitive cells was a giant step in the direction of organizing matter into the functional system we call life. Since the free energies of optical isomers in an optically inactive environment are identical, the synthesis of amino acids, sugars and other asymmetrical substances, except by organisms, gives an equal number of the possible stereoisomers. Such racemic mixtures fail to exhibit any optical activity. So unusual then is this property of biological molecules that it has been regarded as a characteristic of living systems and has been a principal property tested in organic substances of meteorites, geological deposits and planetary explorations to determine whether or not they are of biogenic origin.

Ever since 1815, when Biot discovered that sugars, tartaric acid, camphor and terpentine oil rotated plane polarized light in the liquid state or solution, the riddle of the origin of optical activity has intrigued scientists. Pasteur learned it was a feature intrinsic to the asymmetry of individual molecules. Thinking the earth's magnetic field might be the dissymmetrical factor that induces asymmetric synthesis, he tried unsuccessfully to prepare optical isomers by using powerful magnetic fields. One reason for his lack of success was because his premise was wrong. The magnetic field and rotation of the earth are actually symmetrical forces.

In the laboratory optical isomers can be separated only with great difficulty, and then usually with the assistance of another purified isomer. For years stereospecific synthesis remained an elusive goal. So frustrated were chemists in their attempts to synthesize stereoisomers that F.R. Japp[8] in 1898 resurrected Vitalism by declaring that the primary synthesis of asymmetrical molecules could be derived only from asymmetrical molecules.

Japp was not completely correct in his conclusion, but he did emphasize the question: How could the optical activity of biological systems have originated if only living cells are able to produce it? Theories to explain the way biological systems became stereohomogeneous fall into two categories: the before life, and the after the origin of life theories. The before life advocates try to find a physical means that could have produced stereospecific synthesis of the prebiotic compounds; the other contend that stereohomogeneity is of biological origin.

Van't Hoff[9] in 1894 considered polarized light as a possible factor that could have caused asymmetrical synthesis under natural conditions. Since then it has been suggested that partially plane polarized light from the sky that has been converted into partially right-handed circularly polarized light when reflected on the earth's surface under the influence of its magnetic field could have resolved optical isomers. This hypothesis has been tested experimentally by the stereoselective photodestruction of isomers with circularized polarized light.[10] The percent resolution achieved, however, was extremely small, even after half of the starting material had been decomposed. The significance of the results was further diminished by the fact that natural light is not as polarized as that used in the experiments. As an origin of stereoisomerism, the tests were unconvincing.

There are many optically active crystals in nature, an example being the right- and left-handed crystals of quartz. Upon melting or dissolution, quartz crystals lose their activity since it is due, not to asymmetrical molecules, but to the helical arrangement of the -Si-O-Si-O-chains in the crystal. Harada[11] used optically active quartz powder to orient the formation of amino acid crystals, but the activities were so small as to be near the limit of accuracy.

Under carefully controlled conditions it is possible to induce preferential crystallization of optical isomers from supersaturated solutions of racemic mixtures through seeding or spontaneously. Tartaric acid, malic acid, lactic acid, threonine, histidine, glutamic acid and many others have been resolved by this procedure. The seeding technique is used in this way to prepare monosodium L-glutamate industrially in Japan. As appealing as this technique may appear, it is difficult to envision this as the origin of biological optical activity. It does not exhibit a selective preference of one isomer over the other and the laboratory conditions are too idealized for a natural setting.

It has also been postulated that natural radioactivity may have been a contributing factor in the stereoselectivity of early organisms.[12] Goldhaber and others showed that beta-decay electrons emitted from ^{60}Co are polarized by spinning in one direction. Conceivably the dissymmetry of these elementary particles could affect molecules with an asymmetrical physical force. In a recent article in *Origins of Life*, Noyes, Bonner and Tomlin[14] of Stanford University suggested that beta-decay electrons from ^{14}C in amino acids could have exhibited some selective destruction of the D-isomer. The reaction, however, appears to work only on leucine and it is questionable whether the rate of conversion would be fast enough to exceed racemization.

Optical isomerism in amino acids and sugars is not an absolutely stable configuration. Optical isomers racemize and lose their activity by equilibrating toward an equal number of both isomers; optically active amino acids racemize through ionization of the α-hydrogen by a rate that is independent of pH between 3 and 8 but is affected by temperature. The respective half-lives for isoleucine, alanine and phenylalanine are 35,000, 11,000 and 2,000 years at 25°C.[15]

The difficulty with the attempts to find a pre-life explanation of optical activity is that all the conditions believed to have been present in the primordial environment favor racemization and not the accumulation of optical isomers. Stereoselectivity must therefore have been a procedure adopted by early organisms in some manner, and because of an associated advantage, spread throughout all of life on earth.

One does not have to look far in molecular biology to see the answer. A replicating double-stranded nucleic acid can be constructed of either all D-ribotides or all L-ribotides, but it is not possible to build a regular structure with a mixture of the two.[16] To change from D- to L-β-uridine requires inversion of each substituent in the plane of the ribose ring. If an attempt were made to insert L-β-uridine into a double-stranded nucleic acid helix, the 3′- and 5′-hydroxyls would not join up correctly with the adjacent nucleotides.

Activated D-adenylic acid will condense with D-adenosine, but not with L-adenosine, on a poly-D-uridylic acid template. The polynucleotides of the primitive organisms were optically active, not from some intriguing natural formation of particular isomers, but because only stereospecific polynucleotides would have worked in the genetic mechanism.

Similarly, it is the helical configuration that gives protein its specific shape. And it is upon the specific shape that depend solubility, the capacity to crystallize, and the ability to enter into specific chemical reactions with other molecules. Limited helical conformation is possible with amino acids that are not optically pure, but the structure is severely hindered by steric effects. A random assortment of L- and D-amino acid residues, however, seems to make the α-helix

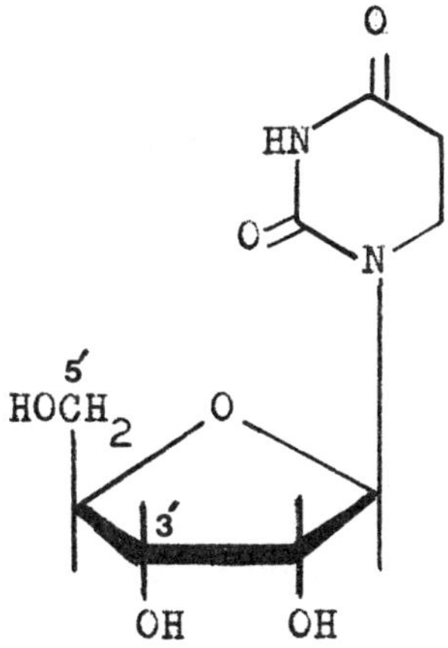

D- β -Uridine

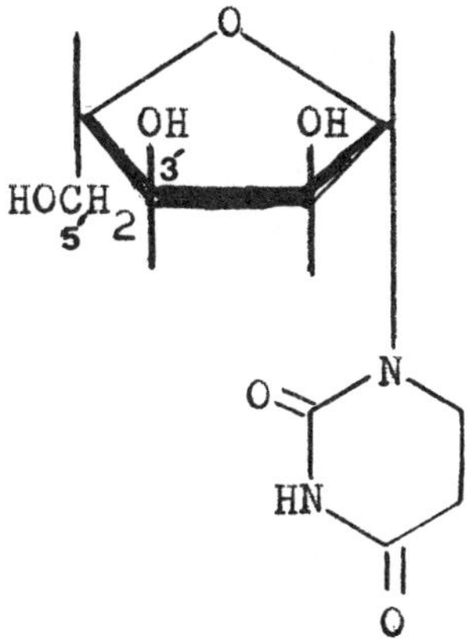

L- β -Uridine

impossible. The incorporation of only L-amino acids by the emerging cells probably occurred when peptide synthesis took place by translation of the stereohomogeneous polynucleotides and only amino acids of the same spatial orientation would align properly for condensing.*

All biological systems on earth use the same optical isomers.

---

*There are exceptions to the stereohomogeneity of natural products. Antibiotics, gramicidin, tyrocidine and others are peptides with D-amino acids included in their chains.

Presumably, an organism using exclusively L-ribose and D-amino acids would function equally effectively as their counterpart that evolved. If the prebiotic substances were racemic, why did not both types of organisms arise? We can only surmise that the primitive cells that used D-ribose occurred first and were efficient enough to be synthesizing many of their components before any of their opposites appeared.

There have been attempts to dramatize the emergence of the first cell as a "war" between optical antipodes for the hoard of prebiotic substances. This seems odd considering that neither would be using the isomer of the other. Rather, it seems more plausible that the one form of primitive cell developed and the amino acids and sugars synthesized by its optically active enzymes quickly overwhelmed all biological substances with its form of optical activity.

If, therefore, essentially all organic matter on earth is of biogenic origin, the amount of prebiotic organic matter that existed on primordial earth has probably been greatly exaggerated. Blum[17] has pointed out that if all the oxygen on earth corresponds to the amount of CO_2 that was assimilated into carbohydrates, this amounts to 4×10^{19} moles. At the present rate of metabolism, without being replenished through further photosynthesis, the organic material would last as a food supply only about 3,000 years. Since the present rate of use is considerably faster than in primeval times, a rough estimate of how long primitive life could have developed before evolving photosynthesis could not have been more than a few tens of thousands of years.

This estimate suggests that photosynthesis appeared very near the beginning of life. But it also indicates that there was no vast accumulation of prebiotic organic matter on primordial earth to sustain life for any length of time. There was no mythical primordial soup, except on a localized scale. Life began in a fairly sparce accumulation of precursors and survived only by becoming self-sustaining.

Oldest microfossils
Enzymic metabolism
Evolution of enzymes
Biosynthesis of peptides
Series of tRNA's evolve
Transfer RNA appears
Rudimentary photosynthesis develops
Liposomes engulf polynucleotides
Polynucleotides and peptides form
Building blocks of life produced
Secondary atmosphere forms
Origin of the Earth

4.6 Billions of Years 3.4

Sequence of events postulated to have led to the formation of a biological cell. Only the origin of the earth and the age of the oldest microfossil have been dated experimentally.

References

1. Phillip H. Abelson, Chemical events on the primitive earth, *Proc. Nat. Acad. Sci.* **55**, 1365-1372 (1966).
2. H.J. Morowitz, Physical background of cycles in biological systems, *J. Theor. Biol.* **13**, 60-62 (1966).
3. Ch. Degani and M. Halmann, Chemical evolution of carbohydrate metabolism, *Nature* **216**, 1207 (1967).
4. K. Decker, K. Jungermann and R.K. Thauer, Wege der Energiegewinnung in Anaerobiern, *Angew. Chem.* **82**, 153-173 (1970).
5. R. Bachofen, B.B. Buchanan and D.I. Arnon, Ferredoxin as a reductant in pyruvate synthesis by a bacterial extract, *Proc. Nat. Acad. Sci.* **51**, 690-694 (1964).

6. R. Batch, L. Magrum, G. Fox, R. Wolfe and C. Woese, An ancient divergence among the bacteria, *J. Mol. Evol.* **9**, 305-311 (1977).
7. Carl R. Woese, A comment on methanogenic bacteria and the primitive ecology, *J. Mol. Evol.* **9**, 369-371 (1977).
8. F.R. Japp, Stereochemistry and vitalism, *Nature* **58**, 452 (1898).
9. J.H. Van't Hoff, **The Arrangement of Atoms in Space**, 2nd ed., Longmans, London, 1898.
10. W. Kuhn and E. Braun, Photochemische Erzeugung optisch aktiver Stoffe,*Naturwiss,* **17**, 227-228 (1929).
11. K. Harada, Origin and development of optical activity of organic compounds on primordial earth, *Naturwiss.* **57**, 114-119 (1970).
12. F. Vester, T.I.V. Ulbricht and H. Krauch, Optische Aktivität und die Paritätsverletzung im **β**-Zerfall, *Naturwiss.* **46**, 68 (1957).
14. M. Goldhaber, L. Grodzins and A.W. Sunyar, Evidence for circular polarization of Bremsstrahlung produced by beta rays, *Phys. Rev.* **106**, 826-828 (1957).
14. H.P. Noyes, W.A. Bonner and J.A. Tomlin, On the origin of biological chirality via natural beta-decay, *Origins of Life* **8**, 21-23 (1977).
15. S.L. Miller and L.E. Orgel, **The Origins of Life on the Earth**, Prentice-Hall, Inc., Englewood Cliffs, N.J., 1974, p. 171.
16. G. Wald, Origin of optical activity, *Ann. N.Y. Acad. Sci.* **69**, 352-368 (1957).
17. Harold F. Blum, **Time's Arrow and Evolution**, 2nd ed., Harper and Bros., New York, N.Y., 1962, p. 172.

Martian sunset over Chryse Planitia taken on August 20, 1976, by Viking 1. The camera began scanning the scene about 4 minutes after the sun had dipped below the horizon. The sun had set nearly 3 degrees below the horizon by the time this computer enhanced picture was completed. (Courtesy, NASA)

29

Other Ways, Other Places

The greatest obstacle to reconstructing how life began has been the success of its evolution. The efficiency and complexity of any living thing, even the simplest microorganism, is so awe-inspiring that it has created the impression that life cannot exist except as it exists now. The image of thousands of gigantic molecules orchestrated in precise harmony in a packet too small to be seen evolving unaided from simple substances and becoming life challenges the imagination. Yet, because of the enormous length of time life has existed on earth, evolution required progressive changes in individual proteins to occur no more often than every few million years. One difficulty is that our impressions are locked in our world of size and time. A lifetime, the age of civilization, the interval since man has been a species, are moments compared to the 3 billion years it took the primitive cell to evolve to the level of the jellyfish. For 85 percent of the time life has been on earth, it existed solely as single-celled microorganisms.

Locked in step with the earth's own evolution, life passes only once. The prebiotic substances that led to life's beginning could have formed only under the reducing conditions of the primordial atmosphere; eucaryotes arose only after a long evolution of procaryotes and in response to the oxygenation of the environment; multicellular organisms were possible only after the Pasteur point of free oxygen was reached; and colonization of land came after the ozone layer developed as a protective screen to the ultraviolet rays.

Once it had come into being, life could go only in one direction — from the simple to the complex.* It is under the forces of selection favoring perpetuation of those variations that can best assure their survival and reproduction. The result of that selection has been toward greater efficiency and complexity. As organisms passed beyond the primitive cell stage of complexity, their assembly ceased being intrinsic in their chemical structure and became interlocked with specific components whose syntheses are genetically programmed into the cells' composition. When organisms reached this stage there was no turning back — they could only go forward. Life had become

*Viruses and rickettsiae seem to have evolved contrary to this principle, but they apparently are degenerate forms instead of more evolved types.

committted to the treadmill where a cell can arise only from a pre-existing cell.

As organisms attained the level of complexity where self-assembly was no longer possible, the specter of death became a part of life. The growth of complexity required perfect union. With each step of evolution, whenever the assembly of cellular constituents became dissociated, the chances of it coming together again into a functional unit became ever more improbable. Life lost became life irrecoverable. It was to be preserved only by passing it on to new generations.

The building blocks of biological systems are the nucleotides, amino acids, carbohydrates and lipids; the architecture consists of the chain-like polymers of these units fitted together into a concerted cellular entity. The blocks have remained the same; it is their polymers that have grown and varied, molded by mutational change and the pressures of natural selection. The enzymes, whose nature determine the complete physical and chemical character of an organism, have continued to be subjected to evolutionary change, marching to the *Principle of Continuity*, each step in evolution following the preceding step in an uninterrupted advance for nearly 4 billion years.

The result has been that organisms have retained their fundamental nature, but have divided and evolved into immense varieties to capture all available chemical and energy sources. The incredibly diverse and bizarre morphology of the insects and microscopic life attests to the many forms life can assume to this end. And the conditions under which organisms can survive to eke out an existence in an ecological niche is astonishing. The alga, *Cyandium calidarium*, can grow in concentrated solutions of hot sulfuric acid, sulfate-producing bacteria are reported to grow and reproduce at 104°C (219°F) under very high pressures, and many organisms use organic and inorganic antifreezes to lower the freezing point of their internal liquids so they can live several tens of degrees below 0°C. Some insects use dimethyl sulfoxide for antifreeze.

The environments, therefore, under which life can exist are extreme and varied. The many examples illustrate the adaptability of the biological system through selection from variation in the enzymes and the processes derived from them. But still, all different forms of life are basically the same. They use nucleic acids for their reservoir of information and enzymes to catalyze their chemical conversions. The building blocks are identical; organisms differ only in the structures assembled from them. In effect, when it comes to examples of life, we have only one.

The question is whether there is only one example of life because it can exist in only one form, and therefore is unique, or whether it is simply the surviving one of a number of possible ways it could have occurred. We have already entertained the idea that organisms use L-α-amino acids and D-sugars, but there appears to be no reason why we could not have become composed of D-α-amino acids and L-sugars. Also, the genetic code could probably have been other combinations without any sacrifice of efficacy. These are cases where the selection was not based on some advantage, but because only one antipode and one code could be used and the incidental circumstances at the time dictated the choice. Once the living cells assembled, however, all living things from that time on became committed to one type of biological system for the remainder of life's existence.

Could the primitive cells have begun differently? Mary Ellen Jones of Brandeis University and Fritz Lipmann[1] of the Rockefeller Institute have suggested that early living organisms may have used inorganic polyphosphate instead of ATP for energy transformation. If pyrophosphate preceded ATP as the early energy-rich phosphate compound, it is possible there are metabolic remnants of this among the primitive types of microorganisms alive today. This was, indeed, found to be the case. I.S. Kulaev[2] discovered there are bacteria and fungi containing enzymes that catalyze the synthesis of inorganic polyphosphates instead of ATP, and Baltscheffsky[3] found eight reactions involving inorganic pyrophosphates in chromatophores of *Rhodospirillum rubrum*, a photosynthetic bacterium. If pyrophosphate was used before ATP in cellular metabolism, it was probably superseded because of the nucleotide's ability to make finer and more specific contacts with cellular metabolites, as well as ATP's capacity to perform other functions that are inaccessible to inorganic polyphosphates.

There is also a consideration that early peptides may have been synthesized by a procedure preceding ribosomal protein synthesis where the amino acid sequence is coded in the base sequence of a nucleic acid. Glutathione* and polyglutamic acid are uncoded peptides,[4] as are gramicidin S and tyrocidine, the microbial antibiotics.[5]

Gramicidin S is a cyclic decapeptide containing a repeated chain of five different amino acids, including D-phenylalanine and ornithine, neither of which are found in proteins. Fritz Lipmann and coworkers[5] found that two combined enzyme fractions from *Bacillus brevis*, when supplied with ATP, Mg^{++} and the five amino acids, synthesized the decapeptide.

The structure of gramicidin S

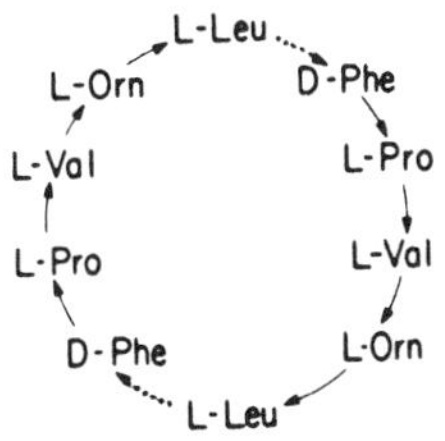

L-Leu
L-Orn D-Phe
L-Val L-Pro
L-Pro L-Val
D-Phe L-Orn
L-Leu

Apparently the pentapeptide is formed by a mechanism analogous to the manner fatty acids are synthesized. To synthesize fatty acids, the acetyl-S-Co A complexes are condensed and reduced while remaining bound to a multienzyme system. Lipmann's findings are that the pentapeptide of gramicidin is synthesized in a similar manner beginning with D-phenylalanine and followed by the sequential addition of proline, valine, ornithine and leucine. The synthesis of gramicidin is completed by coupling of two chains into the cyclic decapeptide molecule. Bacteria produce tyrocidine in the same manner.[6] The length of polypeptides synthesized by this method is limited, the longest being antibiotics that are straight chains of 15 amino acids.

Fatty acid synthesis, being essential for the cellular membrane, must have been one of the earliest biosyntheses of the primitive cells. Lipmann[7] suggests that the similarity between the synthesis of fatty acids and the antibiotics could indicate that this procedure is more ancient than the ribosome-linked protein synthesis.

---

*γ-L-Glutamyl-L-cysteinylglycine.

$$
\begin{array}{l}
\boxed{CO_2} \\
CH_2 \cdot COSCoA \\
\downarrow \\
CH_3 \cdot CO \cdot SCoA \longrightarrow CH_3 \cdot CO + HS \cdot CoA \quad (CH_2 \cdot COSCoA + CO_2)
\end{array}
$$

$$
\begin{array}{l}
NH_2 \cdot CHR \cdot COOsRNA \\
\downarrow \\
NH \cdot CHR \cdot CO \cdot O \cdot sRNA \longrightarrow NH\ CHR \cdot CO + HO \cdot sRNA \quad (NH \cdot CHR\ COOsRNA)
\end{array}
$$

Comparison of fatty acid synthesis with non-coded peptide synthesis

The sulfhydryl enzymes, however, are a common group and there is no indication the enzyme specificity in attaching amino acids to small peptides is any different than the coupling of a chemical group in the synthesis of other compounds. The reaction is mediated by complex protein catalysts, and if it occurred before the development of enzymes, it would have been non-specific. I suspect this non-ribosomal synthesis does not antedate enzymes, but bacteria evolved it because it imparted some advantage by having the antibiotic synthesized *in situ* in the cell wall or similar location by enzymes.

Extending back a step earlier, could life have been assembled from building blocks other than the nucleotides and amino acids? In order for the primitive cells to arise, they needed primarily a mode of molecular replication to be genetically alive. The basis had to be some chemical structure that would adhere to other chemical units in a uniform way while they condensed, thus creating a copy. The bonding had to be strong enough to be functional, but weak enough that the copies could be separated after the replication. And too, for the genetic material to become the informational center for the construction of all cellular components in a metabolically alive organism, it had to have many units, which is to say, many information bits, within a large molecule.

The basis of the genetic material of life on earth are the purines and pyrimidines with their hydrogen bonding. These chemicals alone fail to fulfill all the requirements because they cannot condense with one another to make polymers. They can, however, condense with sugars, the sugars can be phosphorylated, and the nucleotide units can unite through diester linkages. Interestingly, even after this involved process to make polymers containing the heterocyclic bases, the polynucleotides do not make copies directly, but make "negatives" that act as the template for the copy.

It seems like a complicated procedure, but it survived and was adopted by the primitive cells for one reason: not only could the structure of a polynucleotide be transcribed into another polynucleotide, it could be translated into chemicals of a different nature and different function — the peptides — which developed into powerful catalysts.

At first glance, amino acids seem to be the logical choice for forming informational molecules. They are varied and have a carboxyl and amino group that allow the units to link with each other. Despite being able to form polymers more directly than the purines and pyrimidines, however, the amino acids fail as informational molecules because the information cannot be retrieved. The amino acid side chains do not form precise interactions in the manner that characterizes the bases, and as a result, transcribing and translating polypeptides never became feasible for biological systems.*

Life arose with its particular biological nature of purines, pyrimidines and amino acids because these were the chemical substances available on prebiotic earth. Energy acting on the volcanic gases of primordial earth generated cyanides, and ammonium cyanide condensed principally to the purines and a select number of α-amino acids. The pyrimidines apparently formed less readily, but would have been selectively adsorbed to become incorporated into functional systems. What is most impressive is the relatively small number of chemicals formed from condensation, and yet these were sufficient basis to assemble cells that became self-sustaining forms of life.

Only four elements — carbon, hydrogen, nitrogen and oxygen — make up 98 percent of the composition of protoplasm. Except for helium,

---

*The agent responsible for scrapie, a disease aflicting sheep, appears to be a virus-size replicating form that contains a protein but no nucleic acid.[8] Its mode of reproduction is speculative, but one suggestion by J.S. Griffith[9] is that the protein acts as an antigen to stimulate the production of an antibody that is identical to itself.

these are the four most abundant elements in the universe. The occurrence of life cannot, therefore, be attributed to some rare element. Nor are the building blocks unusual chemical compounds, for they form readily from the condensation of cyanide. Of the 36 elements used by organisms, McClendon[10] found nine — C, H, N, O, P, S, Mg, K and Fe — to be essential. The remaining 27 elements appear to have become incorporated, not because they are essential for life, but because they were useful and were available in the environment in sufficient quantity.

Of the nine essential elements, only C, H, N and O are so unique as to be indispensable for the structuring of a biological system. The other five — P, S, Mg, K and Fe — are elements whose chemical properties under conditions of earth make them essential for our developed biochemistry. These properties, however, are not restricted exclusively to these elements, but are also exhibited to some extent in closely related elements. Conceivably, under different chemical environments, a biological system could evolve where arsenic substitutes for phosphorus, selenium for sulfur, manganese for magnesium, rubidium for potassium, and cobalt, nickel or vanadium for iron.

Carbon is the backbone of life. With its remarkable capability for linking with many elements including other carbon atoms into an enormous variety of combinations, this element above all stands responsible for the architecture of biological systems. It is so indispensable and common, it is easy to assume that any life form must be based on carbon. And yet, there is another element, also common on earth, that can link with itself and other elements into long chains and different combinations much like carbon. That element is silicon.

Silicon can form Si-Si chain compounds, but their stability is less than that of their carbon counterparts. The carbon-carbon bond is about twice as strong thermodynamically as the silicon-silicon bond. On the other hand, silicon has a strong affinity for oxygen and the highly stable Si-O-Si-O chains form the crystalline arrays of quartz and many other minerals. Carbon also combines with oxygen readily, but the result is quite different. Whereas silicon dioxide is the component of sand, carbon dioxide is a gas, and it is the volatility of carbon compounds that led to this element being concentrated in the earth's hydrosphere and atmosphere.

Silicon may never be a proper basis for a biological system, but there is a hypothesis that silicon minerals could have played a role in the origin of life. A.G. Cairns-Smith[11] of the University of Glasgow believes a functional cell would have had to have been too complex to assemble from the prebiotic building blocks within a reasonable time and under ordinary circumstances. Instead, he proposes that life evolved through natural selection from inorganic crystals.

When crystals form, often imperfections in the lattice appear that are replicated in further crystallization. Since the replication of these imperfections is self-selective, it represents reproduction not unlike that of nucleic acids. In fact, many kinds of crystals could, in principle, hold a large amount of information, and the information density of a colloidal clay crystalite could be comparable to that of DNA.

Cairns-Smith contends that a crystal as a primitive gene could have controlled the development of organic macromolecules through the adsorption or organic molecules to it. Evolution of the primitive genographs proceeded through selective elaboration that had survival value for the clay crystalites that held them. Eventually, the first organisms emerged by a genetic metamorphosis as the organic macromolecules gradually took over the control mechanism and the crystalites were discarded.

Although the chemicals from which life arose are common, the circumstances of the earth's evolution may be more extraordinary. The earth's size and distance from the sun were critical, for it was the heat generated from the disintegration of radioactive elements, unable to be dissipated into space, that carried the earth through a thermal evolution, liberating volatiles from the interior and creating the hydrosphere and atmosphere. Of all the planets, asteroids and satellites in our solar system, the earth alone has liquid water in abundance.

Venus, closer to the earth in size and space than any other, became trapped in a runaway "greenhouse effect" and lost its water and all opportunity to Cytherean life as its surface temperature soared. Mars, with evidence of past volcanism, appears to be a planet in an Ice Age with water that once flowed on its surface remaining sealed in polar ice caps. And beyond Mars and the asteroids revolve the planetary giants: Jupiter, Saturn, Uranus and Neptune. Although these four outer planets are much larger, they differ from the terrestrial planets more significantly in chemical composition. They are composed almost entirely of gases. Jupiter is 80 percent hydrogen,[12] Saturn, 60 percent, with the balance almost certainly helium; and although Uranus and Neptune contain quantities of carbon, nitrogen and oxygen, they too are globes of partly frozen, partly liquified, gases.

It is difficult to conceive of biological systems developing in the absence of water. Nevertheless, there may be parts of the solar system containing an aqueous environment with little resemblance to the earth that may have fostered the early stages of life formation. The atmosphere of Jupiter consists of methane, ammonia and hydrogen — the primordial gases that can lead to prebiotic substances. This atmosphere, however, is not uniformly distributed, but is stratified through a temperature gradient. Calculations by Gallet[13] suggest that below clouds of frozen ammonia droplets, gaseous ammonia forms a layer; and a few kilometers beneath the ammonia clouds lie successive tiers of ice, liquid water and water vapor. Carl Sagen[13] suggested that organic compounds derived from the ammonia and methane could interact in this zone to yield the larger molecules necessary for life.

To test this hypothesis, Fritz Woeller and Cyril Ponnamperuma[14] at the Ames Research Center carried out reactions on simulated Jovian atmospheres with an electric dischange. The volatile fraction from the experiment did, in fact, contain precursors of many biological compounds. But in addition to the volatiles, the reaction also yielded a non-volatile fraction consisting of orange-red polymers. Woeller and Ponnamperuma speculated that this polymeric substance may be responsible for the color of the Great Red Spot of Jupiter.

The majority of large worlds in our solar system are not planets — they are satellites. Thirty moons orbit Jupiter, Saturn, Uranus and Neptune, some of them extremely large. Three of Jupiter's four Galilean satellites, Europa, Ganymede and Calisto, are approximately the size of the planet Mercury, as is the Saturnian satellite, Titan, and Neptune's Triton. These are not hunks of debris like Phobos and Deimos that circle Mars; these are large bodies the size of our own moon or larger, each a different kind of world, some with thin atmospheres, some ice-covered. In this far region of the solar system there are entire moons with the density of ice, hundreds of miles across, circling planets like enormous snowballs in space.

The larger moons have low densities indicative of composites of rocky and icy material. It is speculated that within these large bodies the heat from radioactive decay produced melting, causing the silicates to settle to the core as compacted mud and a thin ice crust to form, floating on a thick mantle of ammonia in water. Some surfaces seem to consist exclusively of ice, while others may be mixtures of ice with hydrates of ammonia, methane and various substances. These moons represent a whole new class of worlds with different compositions and structures, and they promise a whole new class of phenomena.

Titan, the largest moon of Saturn, appears to have a relatively dense atmosphere — several times denser than that of Mars — with red clouds that usually obscure the satellite's surface. Methane has been detected, ammonia is probably present, and it appears there is also an appreciable amount of hydrogen. The effect of the hydrogen is that it creates a "greenhouse effect" that elevates the temperature to approximately that of earth. If Mars proves to be lifeless, the next place within our family of planets that may have spawned life lies 1 billion miles out on a Saturnian moon called Titan.

We have deeply ingrained impressions of what life is and should be — all from our one example. As we explore other worlds we are probably open for many surprises. Life arose on earth and in its particular nature because it was possible from the prebiotic substances and there was sufficient time for them to organize into a biological system. With enough time, what was possible became inevitable. Time is the parameter that allows it to happen and is analogous to a computer that scans all possible combinations until the solution is found.

Nevertheless, with other substances and other chemical environments, the chances of radically different biological systems evolving remains a possibility. Liquid ammonia may be a more common solvent in our solar system and throughout the universe than liquid water. If all the possibilities of life forming in the universe are explored, its occurrence in liquid ammonia may be prevalent.

Whereas water is liquid between 0 and 100°C, ammonia is liquid between -78 and -33°C. Water has a high surface tension that makes

Saturn seen from its largest moon. Titan, 760,000 miles away, as envisioned by the artist, Chesley Bonestell. (Courtesy, Griffith Observatory)

spontaneous formation of cells with lipid-water interfaces ideal. Liquid ammonia is much less viscous, and polar substances are more soluble in water than ammonia. Chlorides, sulfates, hydroxides and oxides, for example, are insoluble in liquid ammonia.

But since our single known example of life evolved as a biological system adapted to an aqueous environment, the properties of water should naturally appear to us as the most ideal. A form of fish swimming in its sea of liquid ammonia would doubtless find our world intolerably hot and the chemical properties of water just as alien and distasteful.

Our life form arose from prebiotic compounds that formed out of the gasses from volcanic activity. If other worlds of different composition underwent volcanism, their atmospheres could differ significantly from that of primordial earth. Would they then have evolved a different biological system?

The answer is probably no. The Miller experiment does not depend so much on the chemical composition of the gases as the elements present. A reduced atmosphere containing carbon, hydrogen, nitrogen and oxygen, regardless of the chemical form, when exposed to high energy, will produce the same building blocks of life that formed on primordial earth.

Life probably occurs throughout the universe in many different forms and in environmental extremes, but it seems the basis for it is likely to be the same. In this respect it is unique. Life is just something that happens. It is like the thermonuclear reactions in stellar evolution. It is a relationship between matter and energy that occurs spontaneously when the conditions are within narrow limits and it evolves through stages. There are many varieties of both, but their fundamental chemistry and physics follow the same pattern and it is universal.

References

1. M.E. Jones and F. Lipmann, Chemical and enzymatic synthesis of carbamyl phosphate, *Proc. Nat. Acad. Sci.* **46**, 1194-1205 (1960).
2. I.S. Kulaev, Inorganic polyphosphates in evolution of phosphorus metabolism, in **Chemical Evolution and the Origin of Life**, R. Buvet and C. Ponnamperuma, eds., North-Holland Publ. Co., Amsterdam, 1971, pp. 458-465.
3. H. Baltscheffsky, Inorganic pyrophosphate and the origin and evolution of biological energy transformation, ibid., pp. 466-473.
4. **Atlas of Protein Sequence and Structure**, vol. 5, M.O. Dayhoff, ed., National Biomedical Research Foundation, Silver Spring, Md., 1972, p. 117.
5. W. Gevers, H. Kleinkauf and F. Lipmann, The activation of amino acids for biosynthesis of gramicidin S, *Proc. Nat. Acad. Sci.* **60**, 269-276 (1968); ———, Interrelation between activation and polymerization of gramicidin S biosynthesis, Proc. Nat. Acad. Sci. **62**, 226-233 (1969).
6. R. Roskoski, Jr., H. Kleinkauf, W. Gevers and F. Lipmann, Non-ribosomal polypeptide synthesis: Activation and condensation of amino acids in tyrocidin formation, *Fed. Proc.* **29**, 468 (1970).
7. W. Gevers, H. Kleinkauf and F. Lipmann, Peptidyl transfers in gramicidin S biosynthesis from enzyme-bound thioester intermediates, *Proc. Nat. Acad. Sci.* **63**, 1335-1342 (1969).
8. R.A. Gibbons and G.D. Hunter, Nature of the scrapie agent, *Nature* **215**, 1041-1043 (1967).
9. J.S. Griffith, Self-replication and scrapie, *Nature* **215**, 1043-1044 (1967).
10. J.B. McClendon, Elemental abundances as a factor in the origins of mineral nutrient requirements, *J. Mol. Evol.* **8**, 175-195 (1976).
11. A.G. Cairns-Smith, The origin of life and the nature of the primitive gene, *J. Theoret. Biol.* **10**, 53-88 (1965).
12. P.J.E. Peebles, The structure and composition of Jupiter and Saturn, *Astrophys. J.* **140**, 328-347 (1964).
13. Cited in R. Wildt, H.J. Smith, E.E. Salpeter and A.G.W. Cameron, The planet Jupiter, *Physics Today* **16**, (May), 19-23 (1963).
14. F. Woeller and C. Ponnamperuma, Organic synthesis in a simulated Jovian atmosphere, *Icarus* **10**, 386-392 (1969).

30
Where is Evolution Headed?

Life has been on earth for nearly 4 billion years. During that incredibly long time, the earth has reeled from cataclysmic explosions, rocked with countless volcanic upheavals, and moaned repeatedly under the grinding upthrust of mountains. Continents have wandered, collided and buckled; oceans have appeared, disappeared and reappeared; sea floors have risen to become dry land, and land has submerged to become covered by seas. Great regions have blown hot and dry; and whole continents have been locked in the frigid grip of vast layers of ice. Through it all the perpetual, slow, relentless erosion by wind and rain has eaten, shaped and reshaped the earth's surface. Yet, life has endured.

Life has endured, generation after generation, producing more than can live, sacrificing many that the most fit may survive. Species have followed species, rung after rung, in a continuous climb of the ladder called evolution. And in that long ascent, life has retained rapport with its surroundings by evolving its window to the universe — intelligence.

The molecular basis of the microbes' response to light, gravity, temperature and food substances became the nerve tissue of multicellular organisms. The bacterium's ability to "know" what is good for him, elicited in ionic and conformational changes, evolved into intelligence of higher life forms. Nerve tissue became sense organs, the nerve cord developed to coordinate motor behavior, and an enlargement at one end became the brain. Mobility to gather food and to respond to the environment led to choice of action, decision making, and the thought process.

The trend of increasing intelligence is discernible in evolutionary history; the brain increases relative to size and the forebrain increases most of all. When fish appeared 450 million years ago, the forebrain developed to serve essentially the olfactory sense. The coming of the reptiles saw a larger, more complex forebrain. By the time mammals evolved, the forebrain had become not only the largest portion of the brain, its surface had acquired several layers of nerve cells called the cortex. In the primates, folding and convolutions of the cortex greatly expanded the number of nerve cells, and with them, intelligence.

The primates appeared as squirrel-size creatures at the beginning of the Tertiary Period 65 million years ago. They evolved slowly at first, but then in the second half of the period, particularly with the pongid ape stock, rapid evolutionary development and diversification began to occur. By the time the Pleistocene Epoch began 2.5 to 3 million years ago, an offshoot of the primate line walked erect and had teeth that were more manlike than apelike. He still had a brain only slightly larger than his primate cousins, but he did something that was carrying him across animality to humanity — he used tools.

This was Australopithecus. Fossils of this early stage of man began to be discovered in the southern half of Africa in 1924 by Broom, Dart, Robinson, Leaky and others. By 1954, the remains of at least 65 and possibly 100 individuals had been found. Not only did Australopithecus use tools, but from primitive stone artifacts found by Oakley, Leaky and others in Tanganyika, there is evidence he was making them 1,750,000 years ago.

Australopithecus was not quite human, but behind him stretched 4 million years of slow evolution after deviating from the main primate group. Slowly, he began the ascent that was to accelerate until his descendants emerged as modern man.

Like the primates, Australopithecus lived in the tropics. His diet consisted of nuts, roots, fruit and berries, but on occasion he was a scavenger of the kill of predators. There is no evidence he used fire. Africa was the cradle of humanity, but China was to become the place of Prometheus.

During the middle of the Pleistocene, 1,000,000 to 250,000 years ago, there appeared *Homo erectus*, the first species of true man. *Homo erectus* had a long flat skull cap with a frontal bone forming a continuous ridge over the eyes, his dentition had a mixture of human and ape characteristics, and his lower jaw had no chin. Nevertheless, Erectus had a brain capacity nearly twice as large as Australopithecus. Two races of *Home erectus* have been found: Java man of the southern race, and Peking man to the north. No implements have yet been located with Java man, but Peking man made crude stone choppers and rough flakes for tools, and remains of hearths are abundant in caves where he lived.

It was Erectus who begat *Homo sapiens*. There was a rise of intelligence during the era of *Homo erectus* as man fanned out from the tropics into cool regions where ingenuity and flexible behavior were more necessary for survival. Sapiens was in Europe 250,000 years ago when the continent was gripped in the throes of the Ris glaciation. By 125,000 years ago, the long climatic agony of the Ris tapered off and a period of interglacial warmth came on the land for 50,000 years. By the mid-point of this warm interval, 100,000 years ago, Europe was inhabited by the Neanderthal people.

Neanderthal man, first discovered in 1856 at Neanderthal near Düsseldorf, Germany, was a well-muscled hunter about five and a half feet tall, with heavy bones, a strong, chinless jaw, and a large head. He used fire and rough stone tools, lived in caves, but also constructed shelters of animal skins he prepared, and probably wore skins as clothing. The Neanderthals were superb hunters and they expanded over a large area and into different climatic zones.

Neanderthal had a brain as large as modern man, and with his endowed intelligence he brought into the world a higher level of being. In 1960, at the Shanidar cave in the rugged Zarros Mountains of northern

Iraq, Ralph Solecki of Columbia University unearthed a grave of a Neanderthal buried 60,000 years ago. He carefully collected soil samples from the grave and sent them to his colleague, Arlette Leroi-Gourhan, at the Musée de l'Homme in France for analysis. As Leroi-Gourhan examined the samples, she discovered clusters of pollen and preserved parts of species related to grape hyacinth, bachelor's button, hollyhock and groundsel. These are all species of brightly colored flowers. The pollen was in clusters of unprecendented abundance and the implication was unmistakable. Sixty thousand years ago the deceased had been laid to rest on a woven bed of pine boughs amid flowers gathered and placed with him by his companions. Six hundred centuries ago in people living in caves there had been a stirring of the human spirit.

As more is discovered of the Neanderthal people, we learn they cared for the aged and the handicapped, attempted to control destiny through magical rites, conceived of life after death, and may have moved toward art and symbol making. They buried their dead, sometimes in select places as cemeteries, and left with the dead flint flakes, bone splinters and other artifacts as either mementos or as implements needed for the life hereafter.

The interglacial period drew to a close 75,000 years ago and glaciers began to grow in Europe. The change in climate brought snowy winters and cool, rainy summers. Grasslands spread and wooded portions of Germany and northern France gave way to tundra and forest-tundra mixture as the last glaciation (Würm) descended on Europe. Herds of reindeer, woolly rhinos and mammoths grazed on the grasslands and ate the moss and lichens of the subarctic landscape. It was a climate to tax the will, but the Neanderthal remained and hunted.

Then between 35,000 and 40,000 years ago, while the Würm glaciation was still at its height, a tall athletic hunter of large game came from out of the East. This hunter had bones structurally like our own; some individuals were nearly six feet tall. Nor did he differ significantly from ourselves in mental capacity. This was Cro-Magnon man: *Homo sapiens sapiens*. Early precursors of Sapiens lived in Europe before the Neanderthals only to disappear. When he returned, he replaced Neanderthal man rather suddenly. The fate of the latter has not been established; only that he did not survive. Nonetheless, it appears probable our ancestor did not regard the Neanderthals as human and killed them.

The peculiarity of the human species is its large brain. Its rapid development is a wonder of evolution. Within less than one million years man evolved a brain triple the size of the other primates. He became much more intelligent than necessary to occupy an ecological niche in the animal world. The selective pressure among land animals to develop intelligence accelerated rapidly with mammals, and by the time man appeared, it propelled him far in advance of the other animals.

	Cranial capacity (Cubic centimeters)
Chimpanzee and gorilla	325-650
Australopithecus	450-650
Java man	770-1,000
Peking man	900-1,200
Neanderthal man	1,300-1,425
Cro-Magnon man (Modern)	1,200-1,500

Mankind evolved and is evolving. It seems extremely improbable that after billions of years, evolution will come to a halt because we are on top of the column. The same basic driving forces behind evolution have not ceased and apparently will go on as long as life exists. Where then, are we headed? To answer this question we need to establish what has brought us to where we are.

Evolution does not advance on a linear course. The procaryotes, beginning between 3.5 and 3.9 billion years ago, were the sole form of life until eucaryotes appeared 1.3 billion years ago, or after a time span of approximately 2.5 billion years. Within another 700 to 800 million years, the metazoae began to appear. There then followed a succession through fish and reptiles to mammals, 180 million years ago. Sixty-five million years ago the primates began, and man appeared as a separate species within the last 5 million years.

Each major development in evolution appears to take less and less time to occur. And each development, as shown by the emergence of man, begins slowly, but fed by its own momentum, begins to accelerate until it races to its developed state. When it reaches its final form — a new step in evolution — the new life form begins to repeat the cycle, evolving some feature that ultimately leads to the succeeding step.

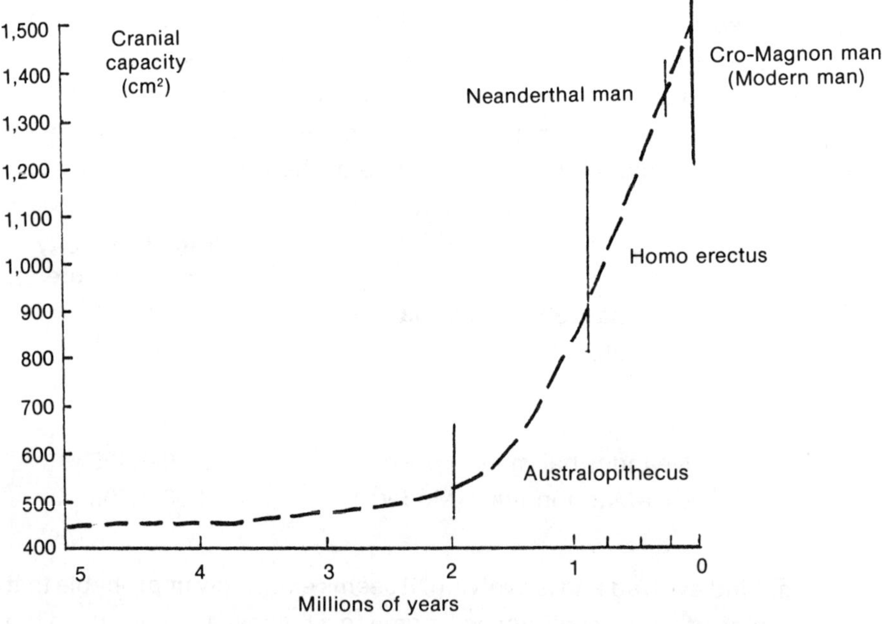

The evolution of man's brain size

After each ascent, the new life form diversifies and spreads widely. Most of the species remain at that level of life and evolve slowly or remain so unchanged as to become "living fossils." From the many, only a few, often only one, begin the slow ascent that is to carry them eventually to the next level of life. The intermediate types along the way are usually doomed to extinction, being succeeded by their more advanced offspring.

The ascending diagram of looping patterns is based on broad generalizations, but nevertheless, serves as a useful guide to gauge evolution. It covers only the sequence of steps that have led through the animal kingdom to man. Plants, of course, represent a different development. Still, the graph shows some interesting, yet disturbing, implications. The first two steps, the formation of eucaryotes and metazoae, were so large that they have been regarded as breakthroughs in evolution. The succeeding steps became progressively smaller, but at the same time appeared more quickly. The pattern forms converging curves that are so close when man evolved that one wonders if there is sufficient time for a succeeding step to evolve. Furthermore, do the converging lines represent an end to this sucession of evolution, or is it

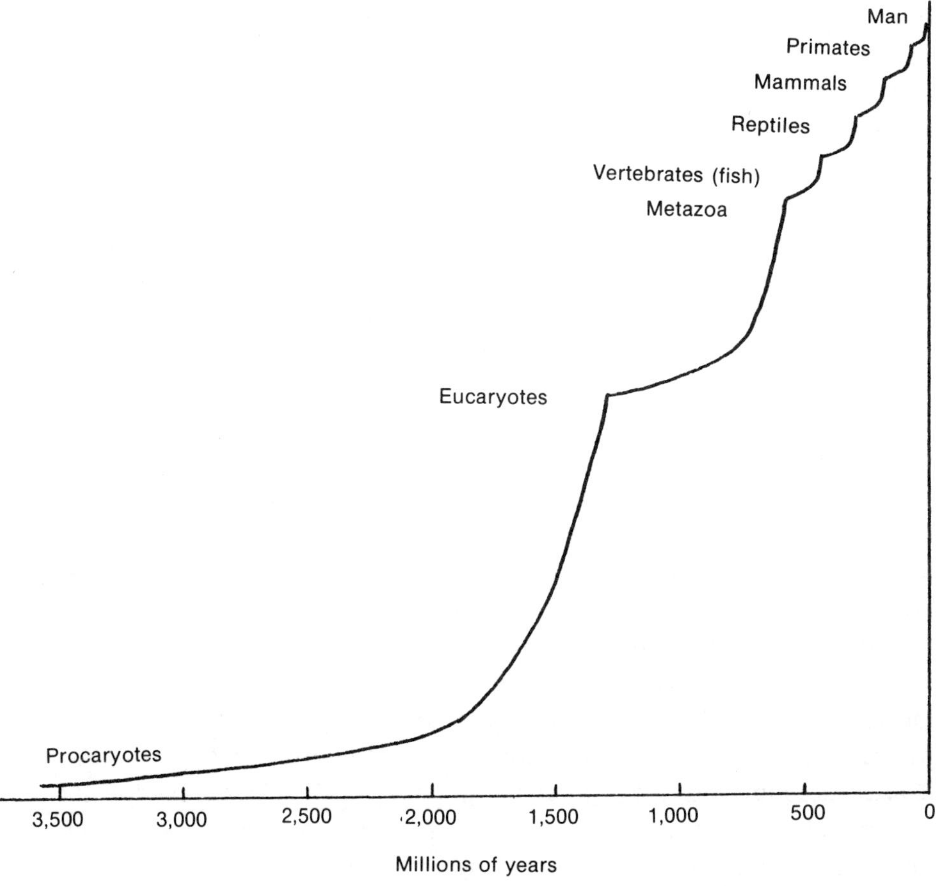

Diagram tracing the principal stages of evolution leading to man. The shape of each curve is assumed to approximate the graph depicting the development of man.

followed by some major breakthrough to begin a completely new system of development?

Man's biological development seems to have reached its final form 50,000 to 100,000 years ago. We have not changed substantially, either physically or in intelligence, since that time. Instead, man has extended his biological development by using tools and weapons. Weapons extend might, machines extend power, writing extends memory and computers extend intelligence.

Man's use of implements to extend his biological powers beyond physical development seems to be a new phase of evolution. Here is advancement no longer restricted to the rate of mutational change and limitations of physical nature that has catapulted man far in advance of other life on earth. Man has used his newly acquired superiority, at the peril of many other animals, to expand his ecological niche until it includes every climate and region of the globe.

But before becoming complacent with the idea, we should bear in mind that all new life forms seem to have expanded rapidly and widely when they first developed. They then diversified, becoming more specialized and confining themselves to narrow divisions of the ancestral niche. Eventually, some lost out to succeeding species, some found refuge in isolated crannies, and a select few evolved further to a new form of life.

This, I venture to suggest, is the fate of man. It is a pattern of nature that appears so inevitable that to believe it will cease being repeated seems unreasonable. The less certain aspect of the evaluation is establishing at what stage of the evolutionary step we are at the present, and in what manner change will occur, and when.

There is one certainty — life is expansionist. The heritage of everything living that has been passed down to us from the primordial replicating molecules is the drive to perpetuate one's existence. Darwin recognized that variation among individuals coupled with overpopulation created the perpetual struggle for survival with the fittest the ultimate winner. What the victor wins is a place in the ecological niche, that slice of the environment that contains the necessities of life.

The trend of evolution through the vertebrates from fish to man has been in the development of the mental faculties. Animals can think systematically in varying degrees by recognizing cyclical processes and anticipating a repeat of the action. They can store experiences as memory; they transfer thoughts by communication through specific stimuli coded as gestures, sound, smell and touch; and they form bonds between individuals through emotional attachment. Man, however, has evolved a capability of thought that cannot be more than at the elementary level in other animals. He can think abstractly.

As intelligence increases among species, there are fewer bits of information or repetitions needed to recognize a series. It is man's abstract thinking that sets him in advance of the animals. He is able to establish a real situation from information that is so distant from the conclusion that it appears to be unconnected, and in this way, he uses imagination to extend reality far beyond the horizon of other beings. Only in this way has he been able to perceive the electron and the multitude of objects either so small or so distant to be beyond detection by his senses.

Reality, then, is the universe within the range of perception. To a microbe it is the limitless molasses-thick medium of a drop of water; to animals it is the world between sky and earth bound by the horizon; but to man it extends to the unseen and the unreachable, beyond the senses to a world unreal to all other life on earth.

It is into all reality that life, led by man, is expanding. Reality is no longer restricted to the horizons of the senses, but extends to the far reaches conceived by the mind. Physical reality may or may not be finite, for what exists is what we perceive, or identify as reality, and how far we can extend reality is uncertain.

Man has remained a single, although highly polymorphic, sexual species. When the environment is widely diversified, as is the case with modern society, there are suitable opportunities for all genotypes so there exists no stimulus for natural selection. If, however, a type of individual with particular mental faculties were to be more fit, then reproductive isolation and the subsequent breaking up of the single species into derived ones can and will occur. This, I conjecture, is the evolutionary fate of man.

Man himself, will not change appreciably or advance beyond his technological society, simply because technology has replaced biological evolution. Nevertheless, he will splinter into types of humans with differing mental faculties that will lead to diversification and separate species. From among these types, a new species, Omega man, will emerge either alone, in union with others, or with mechanical amplification to transcend to new dimensions of time and space beyond our comprehension — as much beyond our imagination as our world was to the emerging eucaryotes.

Man is a part of nature and all that he thinks, builds or destroys has to be considered as part of life's pattern. Presumably, he will expand his niche until expansion under his way of life is no longer possible. It appears that man has the capability to spread into space to occupy the solar system. But then, beyond, stretch expanses of time and space so enormous that we find ourselves as isolated as microbes in drops of water. Our level of biological development throughout the universe remains isolated — limited by our dimensions and the laws of nature we have formulated.

Every period of history believes it is the enlightened age. Yet, there seems to be no end in sight of scientific progress. Will the evolution from man to Omega man be a gradual transition, one step fusing into another, as man continues to add to Nature's laws?

It is conceivable, perhaps even probable, that there is one or even many dimensions beyond our perception, analogous to the way we inhabit time and space in dimensions beyond those of our microbial ancestors. They are real dimensions of time and space, beyond our reach in size and perception. But still, life continues to expand and each stage has within it the basis to develop the succeeding tier. If evolution is to proceed through the line of man to a next higher form, there must exist within man's nature the making of Omega man.

Man's brain differs from the primates, not only in size, but structurally. The grunts and shrieks of the anthropoid ape blossomed into the full bloom of language, not because of a modified larynx or palate, but because of an evolved cortex that permitted vocalization. The advanced intelligence carried man over into a realm of perception and creativity beyond the comprehension of the primate level. Man senses the infinite and the infinitesimal, the transcendence of time through precognition and déjà vu, the onmipotent and the omnipresent. His intelligence has evolved where, unlike any other form of life, he is touching on a new dimension. It is man's spirituality, psyche and superego, and that part of man that makes him the forerunner of Omega man. It is also this human craving of the supernatural that made the gods the extension of man's superego.

Omega man's comprehension and participation in the dimensions of the supernatural is what man yearns for himself, but cannot have. It is reasonable to assume that man's intellect is not the ultimate, but merely represents a stage intermediate between the primates and Omega man. A type of intelligence more evolved than man's could conceive of a reality and exercise control over it in a manner beyond our ability to comprehend. What comprehension and powers over Nature Omega man will be able to command can only be suggested by man's image of the supernatural.

But is there time? The convergence of curves of evolutionary advancement and the shortening of time between stages is ominous. It takes time to evolve biological adaptations, even when selective pressure is high. From the first mammals to the first primates took about 125 million years; the primates evolved to an anthropoid ape in 60 million years; and within 5 million years, man ascended to his biological development. The intervals are not regular, but the pace is quickening decidedly. If man has changed little in the last 50,000 to 100,000 years, this suggests we are at the stage of development of the next tier where the feature leading to the succeeding life form is moving slowly, but building up momentum. On such a shortened curve, conceivably Omega man could succeed man in fewer than 10,000 years.

The question remains: How is it biologically possible? We must consider that everything that we do is as much a part of the design of nature as the actions of plants and animals. Even with man, the advancement through mutational change and adaptation was too slow. Man exceeded his biological evolution by developing the use of tools and weapons that led to his technology. How then can Omega man arise in so short a time?

The answer is unavoidable.

Man will make him.

SUGGESTED BOOKS ON THE ORIGIN OF LIFE

Bernal, J. D., **The Origin of Life,** Weidenfeld and Nicholson, London, 1967.

Blum, H. F., **Time's Arrow and Evolution,** Harper and Row, Publishers, Inc., New York, 1962.

Brooks, J. and G. Shaw, **Origin and Development of Living Systems,** Academic Press, New York, 1973.

Calvin, M., **Chemical Evolution,** Oxford University Press, New York and Oxford, 1969.

Fox, S. W. and K. Dose, **Molecular Evolution and the Origins of Life,** W. H. Freeman & Co., San Francisco, 1972.

Kenyon, D. H. and G. Steinman, **Biochemical Predestination,** McGraw-Hill Co., New York, 1969.

Miller, S. L. and L. Orgel, **The Origins of Life on Earth,** Prentice-Hall, Inc., Englewood Cliffs, New Jersey, 1974.

Oparin, A. I., **Genesis and Evolutionary Development of Life,** Academic Press, New York, 1968.

--------------, **The Chemical Origin of Life,** Chas. C. Thomas Springfield, Ill., 1964.

Rutten, M. G., **The Origin of Life,** Elsevier Publishing Co., Amsterdam, 1971.

BOOKS OF SELECT PAPERS

Geochemistry and the Origin of Life, Keith A. Kvenvolden, ed., Dowden, Hutchinson and Ross, Inc., 1974.

The Origins of Prebiological Systems, S. W. Fox, ed., Academic Press, New York, 1965.

JOURNALS ON THE ORIGIN OF LIFE

Origins of Life
Biosystems
J. Molecular Evolution
J. Precambrian Research

Author Index

S

T

U

V

W

Subject Index